# Succulent SEX Craft

YOUR HANDS-ON GUIDE TO

EROTIC PLAY & PRACTICE

*For Men and Women, Singles and Partners*

---

ILLUSTRATED BY THE AUTHOR
AND OTHER ARTISTS LIVING AND DEAD

---

SHERI WINSTON CNM, RN, BSN, LMT
*with* CARL FRANKEL

MANGO GARDEN

KINGSTON, NEW YORK

## About The Center for the Intimate Arts

The mission of Sheri Winston's Center for the Intimate Arts is to provide empowering, enlightening, entertaining erotic education for everyone!

We envision a world where sex is understood, honored and free from shame, where our bodies' ecstatic potential is explored and celebrated, and relationships are based on integrity, compassion and love.

Our products and services include:

In-person and online classes, workshops and presentations for lay people and professionals.

Individual and couples coaching and counseling (in-person and via phone/skype).

Books in digital and hard-copy format, which we publish via our imprint, Mango Garden Press. For more information, visit **MangoGardenPress.com**.

Articles, written blogs and video 'vlogs' by Sheri Winston and Carl Frankel. These can be found on our website as well in articles by Carl Frankel at YourTango.com.

For more information or to sign up for our newsletter, please visit us at **IntimateArtsCenter.com**.

©2014 Sheri Winston / Mango Garden Press

Cover and Interior Design: Tilman Reitzle
ISBN 978-0-9898138-0-8
Library of Congress #: 2013948687

Mango Garden Press
PO Box 3184
Kingston, NY 12402
www.MangoGardenPress.com

*Printed on Forest Stewardship Council-certified,
30% post-consumer recycled paper.*

# CONTENTS

# SECTION ONE

# Old Stories, New Stories

*There is only one way to see things, until someone
shows us how to look at them with different eyes.*

PABLO PICASSO

Franz von Bayros, *Book Plate*

# CHAPTER ONE

# WELCOME TO EROTIC U.

*Sex is…the engine, the driven inner*
*workings of all that shines and breathes.*

LOUISE ERDRICH

## A Journey Into Conscious Sexuality

D EAR READER, I HAVE TWO VERY IMPORTANT QUESTIONS FOR YOU:
Do you feel great about sex? Is it all you wish it to be? If either answer is
"no," then this book is for you. If both answers are "yes," this book is for you, too.

Maybe you're reading this book because you'd like to be more sexually
responsive, share more pleasure with your lover, make your solo sex hotter or
rekindle the excitement in your intimate relationship.

Perhaps you already have pretty great sex, but want it to be fabulous. Maybe
it's already fabulous, but you want it to be transcendent. Possibly you're already
an erotic virtuoso, in which case you're here because you know there's always
more to learn.

Maybe you have sexual challenges. There may be sex-negative voices re-
sounding in your head with their 'no's' and 'should's' and 'can't's.' Perhaps
you've had life experiences that caused you to enfold your sexuality behind
armor or numbness. You may have spent much of your life feeling sexually
inadequate, broken or damaged. Perchance you've decided it's time to change
that and find your path to wholeness, joy and ecstatic pleasure.

Over the years, two things have become clear to me: We're on a lifelong
learning journey, and our sexuality is a vital part of our lives and all life. I know
from both personal and professional experience that we all have enormous
sexual potential, although for many it remains untapped. For most people, their
sexuality is like a huge pleasure trove that has never been fully explored. Yet it's
right there inside us!

Since 1999, I've been teaching people how to transform their sexuality into a reliable wellspring of energy and ecstasy. I'm here to help you connect to your wonderful sexy self and to facilitate your erotic empowerment and integration.

I do these things, and more, through The Center for the Intimate Arts, which I founded and where I teach what we lightheartedly call 'sex ed for grown-ups.' Our classes and workshops are drawn from our extensive (and, like the universe, constantly expanding) Wholistic Sexuality™ curriculum.

Why Wholistic Sexuality? Because:

- The approach integrates modern science, ancient wisdom traditions, contemporary holistic perspectives, biology, sociology, anthropology, zoology, anatomy, physiology, evolutionary theory, philosophy and spirituality.

- It encompasses the complex and elegant connections of your mind, body, emotions, spirit and energy.

- It includes the connections between you and your own self, other people, the communities you participate in, and the wide and juicy world.

William Blake, *The Reunion of the Soul and the Body*

SUCCULENT SEX CRAFT

My life's purpose is to be an agent of transformation and empowerment, especially in the area of sexuality. That's why I developed the Wholistic Sexuality paradigm and based it on conscious connection and an integral view of sexuality.

I envision a world where sex is viewed as normal and sacred, pleasure is celebrated, and intimate connection is honored and supported. My mission is to help catalyze a personal, cultural and planetary attitude adjustment so that sexuality is seen as a revered and glorious aspect of being human. This is my spiritual path, my joy and my work.

Philosophically, this book is ambitious. It lays out a vision of sexual potential, a paradigm of authentic connection, and a pathway to erotic empowerment through an integrated web of ideas and images.

*Everybody is a genius. But if you judge a fish by its ability to climb a tree, it will live its whole life believing that it is stupid.*

ALBERT EINSTEIN

But it's also very practical. It's a hands-on handbook with multiple maps and models and a heaping helping of games and practices. It's your guide to leading a life that's rich with pleasure, erotic fulfillment and sexual wholeness. I hope you're as excited as I am to go on this learning journey.

## What On Earth Is A Wholistic Sexuality Teacher? And Why Might You Want One?

When I tell people I'm a Wholistic Sexuality teacher, they typically respond in one of four ways. Some are keenly interested and ask all sorts of questions. (*All* sorts!) Others act like they didn't hear me and instantly change the subject. (Eek, sex!) A third group says something along the lines of, "I don't need any help. I don't have any sexual problems." Or, "I already know what I'm doing." And some respond dismissively with comments like, "That's silly, sex is natural, why would anyone need to take a class about that?"

If people are curious and interested, great! Let's talk. If people don't want to converse about sex, I can't make them, nor would I want to. But I do have answers for the latter two groups. First, Wholistic Sexuality isn't only for people with 'sexual problems.' It's for anyone who aspires to more connection, intimacy and ecstasy.

As for the people who believe that sex is just something you do, no instruction required, what they don't understand is that we've been learning about sex our whole lives. From how your genitals were handled during diaper changes to your first back-seat fumbles, from adolescent jokes to TV sitcoms, from textbooks to the plethora of porn—you've been learning about sex your whole life. You've absorbed innumerable lessons about your body, pleasure, relationships, power dynamics, what is and isn't okay to talk about, suitable language, gender roles, what's sexually appropriate, what's hot and not, and much more. Your teachers have been your families of origin, schools (and playgrounds), places of worship, peers and our ubiquitous entertainment and advertising culture. This is your real sex ed and it's immensely powerful. You don't choose to take this class; it just happens. Much of our sexuality education has been unconscious and, for the most part, unquestioned.

A lot of people believe that when it comes to your capacity for sexual pleasure, you have to play the cards you were dealt, good, bad or indifferent—there's not much room for improvement. People typically believe that learning sexual skills is only about improving your ability to please your partners (like learning to give great oral sex). However, many of your own sexual abilities, including your sexual responses, turn-ons, pleasure pathways and desires, are learned—and therefore amenable to conscious learning. You can learn how to get turned on more easily and in more ways, how to deepen your arousal, and how to become orgasmic (or more orgasmic, or crazy-orgasmic). More broadly, you can learn to become an expert at optimizing your own pleasure.

> *I am always doing that which I cannot do, in order that I may learn how to do it.*
>
> PABLO PICASSO

Whether your sex life is problematic, okay, good or great . . . you can make it better. First, though, you need to replace the false "sex is natural, not learned" story with a new (and true) one. Sex is both natural and learned. In fact, great sexual and relationship skills not only can be learned, they *need to be* learned if you want to excel at intimacy and develop mastery of your own pleasure.

You also need to understand that everyone is capable of becoming more erotically adept—and that includes you. Not only can you get better at sex, you can get *much* better at sex. You can vastly expand your repertoire of what's sexually possible. You can even become a sexual virtuoso (or something close to it).

And: It helps to have a teacher.

Welcome to Erotic U!

## A Note on Language

Writing this book, like my last one, posed a conundrum for me. I wanted it to be liberating and empowering, and I also didn't want to offend. Words have enormous power. They can empower or shame; they can normalize and create inclusivity or marginalize and create separation.

We don't even have a comfortable, sexy and safe set of words for talking about sex. We can stick to language that's scientific and safe, but these words often lack heart and are the opposite of sexy. Another option is to use euphemisms whose vagueness and imprecision often reflects the speaker's discomfort. We

SUCCULENT SEX CRAFT

also have profanity, the slang terms that are too naughty to say on the radio, the so-called 'dirty' words.

How can we talk about sexuality in a way that empowers and legitimizes the erotic when all our choices have such limitations? I've dealt with this issue by being consciously inclusive in my use of language. I have two goals in doing this. First, to make the point that there are no bad words, no dirty words, no language that is taboo. Second, to model liberation. When we don't allow shame to limit how we use sexual language, we free ourselves from the shackles of sexual disgrace and degradation.

Words are only sounds that mean what we make them mean. Whether you say 'intercourse,' 'boink,' 'make the beast with two backs,' or 'fuck'— it all means the same thing. Whether

> *What do you make of a society that is so primitive that it clings to the belief that certain words in its language are so powerful that they could corrupt you the moment you hear them?*
>
> FRANK ZAPPA

we're being insulting, wicked, sexy, or respectfully and deliciously loving depends on the intent and the context. It's not the words themselves but the meaning we attach to them that matters.

In these pages, you'll find the scientific next to the silly and the sacred alongside the supposedly profane. For female genitalia, I use anatomical terms next to 'pussy' and 'yoni' (the sacred Sanskrit). Male genitalia might be 'cock' or the Sanskrit 'lingam.' If any of these words shocks or offends you, I invite you to remind yourself that they're just sounds and syllables and allow the deeper intention of communication and liberation to arise. My use of sexual language is a conscious strategy intended to support you on your journey towards sexual freedom and empowerment.

I also invite you, the reader, to use whatever words work best for you. Find your own comfortable, sacred, sexy words. Claim your own language of liberation!

## WORD NERD: THE F-WORD

THE WORD "FUCK" was outlawed in print in England (by the Obscene Publications Act, 1857) and the U.S. (by the Comstock Act, 1873).

Fuck wasn't in a single English language dictionary from 1795 to 1965.

In 1948, publishers convinced Norman Mailer to use the euphemism fug instead of fuck in his book "The Naked and the Dead." When Mailer later was introduced to Dorothy Parker, she greeted him with, "So you're the man who can't spell 'fuck.'"

FOOD FOR THOUGHT

### The Language Problem

MAKE A LIST of the euphemisms and terms for sex that you know. Include different sexual activities.

Look over your list. Note the positive and negative connotations of the words and phrases:

How many were insulting, derogatory?

How many were about getting something from someone or giving something up?

How many were loving? Caring? Connected? Respectful?

Were any sacred?

(This also makes a fun game to play with partners and friends!)

## Something Old, Something New

Many of the ideas in these pages were introduced in my first book, *Women's Anatomy of Arousal: Secret Maps to Buried Pleasure*. This book takes some of that material and delves deeper. A few topics such as female genital anatomy are only briefly covered here since they were dealt with so thoroughly in the previous book. (In fact, if you want more in-depth information about things like female ejaculation, women's connected network of erectile structures, and how to make all her parts very happy, that's the place to go!) Other topics, particularly the yin-yang

Gustave Courbet, *La Bacchante*

model, are repeated in these pages because they're essential to the Wholistic Sexuality model. Since not everyone reading *Succulent Sexcraft* will have read my first book, I felt the need to include this information.

For the most part, though, this book expands dramatically on topics that were touched on lightly in *Women's Anatomy of Arousal* while adding a practical dimension with its many games and exercises.

## What Makes This Book Special

### 1. IT'S ALIVE!

This book is web-interactive. That right—there's more on a special website for sexcrafty folks like you! As a purchaser of this book, you can join the Succulent SexCraft community for  free. You can then peruse the community web pages for more information, additional exercises, video segments and use interactive pages where you can share with other readers. These pages will be continually updated, creating a living community of information, support and education.

Go to GETSEXCRAFTY.COM and join now for free!

### 2. SUCCULENT SEXCRAFT SIDEBARS

In order to simplify the material, this book contains a multitude of sidebars that fall into five general categories:

---

**PLAY & PRACTICE**

YOUR HANDS-ON GUIDES to practices, exercises, and games along with suggestions for play. They're divided into the following categories:

SOLO PLAY, PARTNER PLAY, OR BOTH

HOT AND JUICY TIPS

DIVINE PLEASURE

FOOD FOR THOUGHT

---

*Succulent Summary*

---

Science Geek Goodies

---

**WORD NERD**

---

Fascinating Facts

Anna Di Scala, *Love Me Forver*

### 3. ART AND IMAGES

The book is lavishly illustrated with art from three sources: contemporary artists who have generously shared their work, my own art, and vintage and classical art from the public domain. We're grateful for the art contributed by our community members. We invite you to check out these wonderful artists via the contact info listed in the back of the book.

## Your Hands-On Guide

This is a hands-on guide to erotic play and practice, with a wealth of options for solo and partnered experiences. I call the activities by different names—games, exercises, practices, rituals. I also refer to your homework assignments as 'homeplay.' None of these words is right or wrong: each highlights an aspect of what's involved. Use whichever linguistic and conceptual frameworks work best for you.

Similarly, approach the activities in the way that's likeliest to get you actually to do them. These ideas are a smorgasbord. Take what appeals and leave the rest.

*Whatever you can do or dream you can, begin it. Boldness has genius, power, and magic in it.*

JOHANN WOLFGANG VON GOETHE

That said, I also encourage you to take some chances. You have to stretch to become more flexible—that's how you learn. If you're not comfortable doing something in the way I suggest, try doing it differently, in a way that works for you. Play with the exercises in your own way and at your own pace. Feel free to skip what doesn't appeal to you, to repeat what you like and to devise variations.

As for the hands-on part, I mean that literally. That's right: I'm telling you, in no uncertain terms, to go play with yourself. And with your partners, too, if you have them. It's important to embody the precepts I put forth here, so don't just read, do!

If you're partnered, I strongly encourage you to start with solo play before embarking on duets. Or at least, do solo play as well as duets. Your solo practice is for you, so sharing your experiences is encouraged but entirely optional. You don't have to do the exercises in a particular sequence, although there is a logic to how they're laid out—the exercises build on each other. Do what sounds appealing, easy and fun. At some point, you may want to go back and do some of the practices and games you skipped. Maybe then they won't seem so challenging and you'll feel ready to tackle them.

It's also interesting to repeat games at a later date and see what may have changed for you. There is no limit to how many times you can play with these ideas. Do what works for you—you're the cook and I'm just laying out ingredients and possible recipes.

If you find that you aren't inclined to actually do the exercises, that's okay too. Just read them over and imagine yourself doing what's suggested. At a minimum, do it in your mind! What happens in your imagination is still powerful and effective, although doing it with your whole body is more so.

Hopefully, you'll continue to play with these ideas—and yourself!—for the rest of your days.

### YOUR HOMEPLAY JOURNAL

Franz von Bayros

I gently encourage you to create a dedicated notebook for your journey, especially for the *Food For Thought* exercises. Keeping a special journal to write in (and, if you're inclined, to draw in) will help you get more from your thought experiments. Take notes; be free-associative. Writing can bring out information from your depths that you didn't know was there. It will also give you something to review later for additional understanding, which can further your journey.

If you do decide to journal your experience, I encourage you to spread your wings creatively. If making art is fun for you, create whatever images and pictures you're inspired to make. Note that I did not say, "If you are an artist"—talent and a pedigree aren't required. Illustrate and doodle away if it delights you to do so! This is for you and you alone. No one else will see or judge your images or responses.

## Play and Practice

I love the word 'practice' because of its double connotation. It means repeating an action in order to gain proficiency (like practicing the guitar), and it's also something you do to cultivate inner development (like meditating as a spiritual practice). What a great word to apply to your erotic learning journey! Repeating an action lays down a neural groove, a mind-body pattern that literally forms an embedded trail. The more you travel down that path, the easier it becomes as your skills become ingrained. That's why practice takes you to mastery. And, contrary to what many of us grew up believing, this

> *It is, after all, the dab of grit that seeps into an oyster's shell that makes the pearl, not pearl-making seminars with other oysters.*
>
> STEPHEN KING

is especially true about sex. So practice, lots and lots! It may not get you to Carnegie Hall, but it will get you to all the wonderfully ecstatic places you want to be. (And you'll have all kinds of fun doing those finger exercises.)

I encourage you to practice on a regular or semi-regular basis. If you do, you'll get better faster. If you only play these games occasionally, that's okay, too—you'll still get something out of them. Something is better than nothing—and more is better.

Finding time to practice in our busy lives may seem challenging. Let me reassure you on this count: You don't have to dedicate your entire life to developing sexual mastery. The best way to make progress is with a multi-faceted approach. First, find ways to incorporate these suggestions into your current sex life (and non-sex life). Add them to what you're already doing. Next, find little bits of time for practice. Many of these suggestions can be done in a few minutes or in ten-minute chunks. Finally, at least occasionally, consciously carve out an hour or two (or more) dedicated to special training in pleasure. It's the gift that keeps on giving … to yourself.

> *We all have a better guide in ourselves if we would attend to it than any other person can be.*
>
> JANE AUSTEN

You can play with your skills at any time, both when you're being sexual and when you're not. Use them non-sexually by adding them to your regular exercise or meditation practice. Play with them when you're washing your dishes or during a break from work. For your erotic playtime, experiment with using your skills before you're aroused. Then try them in early-, mid- and high-level arousal. Add them in as you have orgasms.

Just as important as practice is play—spontaneous, pleasure-filled, unstructured erotic play. Be original, be inspired, be imaginative. Be child-like and invent your own games for exploring and expanding your sexuality. Give yourself permission to be creative and have fun!

Set aside time for each—structured practice and spontaneous play.

Notice what happens when you play and practice. Whatever we call it, it's really play, so . . . play with it! Remember how you played 'pretend' games as a child? Treat these exercises similarly. Make them an innocent exploration, a creative fun journey, a spontaneous inventive game. Take what looks tempting, play with it and enjoy!

Adriaen van der Werff, *Amorous Couple Spied upon by Children*, 1694

## No Right Way

If there's one thing I want to stress ere above all, it's that there is no one right way to do any of this. You are utterly unique and there is only what works for you and what expands your experience. Don't get stuck in the headspace of thinking, "Am I doing this right?" There is no 'right' and there is no 'wrong.'

Life is like being in a fabulous laboratory where we get to try successive experiments to see what happens. That's your only real job—run experiments inside the laboratory of yourself and discover what happens. Be in inquiry. Research what connects you to your pleasure. Ask, "What happens when I do it *this* way?" And then: "What happens when I try it *that* way?" Keep running your delicious experiments. Observe what happens when you take one approach, then another. Combine skills and notice how they enhance each other. Try everything at least once or, better yet, several times and notice the results. As you pursue your studies at Erotic U., your goal is to discover the pathways that connect you to your erotic energy. When you discover a practice that really resonates for you, play with it!

> *There is no one right way, there is only what works for you.*
>
> YOURS TRULY

Don't try to do everything at once. Take it one step or skill at a time. If you're working with breath, just focus on that. When you feel like you've got the breathing part down, add a second skill like using sounds. When you have a nice breathing and sounding pattern going, add movement. If at any time it feels like there are too many things to keep track of, let something go. If something doesn't work, try it in a different way or at another time. The key is to be patient, self-loving and just do it.

## Conscious Learning

In many ways, learning to expand your sexual pleasure is like learning to play a musical instrument. It's about acquiring a set of complex skills, albeit more intimate ones. There's one important difference, though. If you don't know how to play the piano, you don't feel weird, ashamed or somehow broken. Nor do you believe that everyone except you already knows how to play really well. We all understand that playing an instrument requires conscious learning and practice over time. No one is born knowing how to tickle the ivories, yet somehow we're supposed to know how to have great sex without the benefit of lessons or teachers.

> *The most exciting phrase to hear in science, the one that heralds new discoveries, is not 'Eureka!' but 'That's funny.'*
>
> ISAAC ASIMOV

In one way, learning sex is unlike learning to play the piano. With sex, you aren't only the musician, you're also the instrument. In this sense, it's more like learning to dance. Whether it's the piano or the instrument of yourself that you're studying, learning is required to become a skilled artist—and anyone who wants to learn, can.

### THE LEARNING PROCESS

Whether you're learning to speak a new language, play the piano or develop your sexual skills, the basic process is the same.

There may be some groundwork to do before you reach the starting gate. You might have some unlearning to do. Since you don't know what you don't know, you may not know there's something *to* learn or what's possible. That's why it's essential to have a vision of your true sexual potential—so you know where you can go.

You may also need to call on your courage. It can seem scary to break out of old molds, to try new things, to push your edges and grow. This is especially true when sex is involved. Take heart and remember—this is a fun and rewarding trip!

It's not easy to be at the start of a journey when the destination seems far away. Let me reassure you—you'll get there, one step at a time.

At the beginning, you have to be okay with feeling like, well, a beginner. For many, that's an uncomfortable, even shameful place to be, especially

Thomas Rowlandson, *Love on a Bicycle*

with sex, which our culture tells us is supposed to come naturally. Don't make your beginner's status mean you're clueless, incompetent or an embarrassment. Let go of those negative stories! There's nothing wrong with not-knowing. Wherever you are in your learning journey, it's okay.

At the start, what you're doing may not feel fluid or easy. When learning new skills, it's common to have to think about what you're doing. Don't let this get you down—it's normal at this stage. With practice, your actions will become more automatic and natural.

If you feel awkward, don't worry about that, either. This, too, is normal and disappears with practice. Get comfortable with feeling uncomfortable. Discomfort is a sign that you're stretching out of your familiar comfort zone into something new. It's a good sign. It means you're learning.

You will make mistakes—and that's great! Mistakes are an important part of learning. They don't mean you screwed up or failed—they're merely an experiment that didn't pan out. Don't let mistakes keep you from continuing. This is your learning lab and, like those folks in the white coats, you progress through trial and error—and the 'error' part is as important as the 'trial.'

If you maintain a positive attitude and don't get discouraged by the normal fumbling and bumbling phase, you'll keep practicing and playing, and over time what was difficult will become easier. As your learning becomes embodied, you'll become more adept and your actions will come more naturally. You'll become fluent.

Once you've developed a solid foundation of basic skills, you can go on to learn more advanced ones. As this happens, take a moment occasionally to note your progress and congratulate yourself. You set out to master a new language and you're succeeding. You're learning to speak Eros.

If you persevere, eventually you'll become facile and accomplished (no thinking required!). At some point, everything you've learned will become integrated and you'll find yourself moving effortlessly and magically in the flow. You will have developed mastery. Bravo!

And then . . . you can keep on learning!

---

*In school we learn that mistakes are bad, and we are punished for making them. Yet, if you look at the way humans are designed to learn, we learn by making mistakes. We learn to walk by falling down. If we never fell down, we would never walk.*

ROBERT T. KIYOSAKI

---

SUCCULENT SEX CRAFT

### LAB VERSUS LIFE

It's important to distinguish between your erotic *life* and your erotic *learning*. I'm not suggesting that you shouldn't play with lovers until you've achieved a certain level of mastery with yourself, or that you need to be a virtuoso at playing erotic duets in

Paul-Émile Bécat

order to commit to a conscious, loving relationship. That would be silly. Lead your life normally. Play with yourself, play with others and enter into relationships (or not) as your heart moves you.

Yet it's also true that in order to develop erotic mastery, whether you're partnered or not, your solo sex sessions are your foundational learning laboratory and practice hall. Remember, the better you know your own instrument and the more skilled you are at making it sing, the more skills you'll have to bring to your erotic couplings.

### SOME NOTES ON EROTIC MASTERY

Don't expect to become a virtuoso overnight. Mastery takes time, energy, attention and practice. Lots of it. This is true for playing the piano and it's true for sex, too. It's been estimated that becoming expert at anything takes at least 10,000 hours. Luckily, since we're talking about sex here, you've probably already put in quite a few hours! In addition, you have some

very deep, hardwired sexual circuits that make developing your erotic proficiency much easier than mastering Mozart. This is one area of your life where you can make pretty quick progress on your learning journey once you have a guide, maps and the desire to excel.

*The more technique you have the less you have to worry about it. The more technique there is the less there is.*

PABLO PICASSO

Also bear in mind that while technique is an indispensable means to an end, erotic mastery isn't solely about technique. Great sex isn't about performance or 'doing it right'—it's a magical improvisational dance. Technique provides a foundation of embodied learning that you then use to play freely and imaginatively—it's the underlying skill set that allows you to be fully in the moment and open to the flow. So learn your moves, practice your techniques, train your mind and body to excel—then forget all that and let passion and energy be your guide.

## Partner Play

When you have sex with someone else, it's like going on a journey together. You may have been to Sex Land many times already, but you still don't know the entire geography (and never will, which is one reason it can be so much fun). It's a landscape you create anew every time.

You co-create this unique erotic adventure with your partner. The more you master your abilities—and the more skilled your partner is—the easier it will be to make each trip a voyage into ecstasy.

### Playing and Learning in the Playpen

Just as you devote sessions to play and practice with yourself, I encourage you to do the same with your ongoing erotic partners. It's important and useful to set aside time for structured exercises, games and learning. When you're having improvisational, unstructured sex, it can break (and brake) the flow if you pause for extended discussions, explanations and critiques. So when and how do we practice skills with our partners? The answer is by creating 'playpens'—sessions that are separate from your regular sex and are specifically dedicated to learning and communicating in a fun way. Playpens are when you dive into instructive games that you invented or found in this book. They're when you carve out the time and space to work on technique, practice set pieces and give each other feedback. They're where you can discuss, critique, exchange feedback and learn—and have it be okay.

---

PLAY & PRACTICE

PARTNER PLAY

### Playpen Design

A playpen has three elements: a game, a set amount of time, and a place to play in. Design yours by first, devising a specific idea for a game and then, creating your container of time and space.

What will you play? That's entirely up to you. Figure out what you want to learn and make a game of it. Feedback skills, touch techniques, pleasuring specific parts, show-and-tell . . . the list is limited only by your imagination. Focus on learning, communicating and having fun.

Use your imagination to create the setting for your game—it doesn't always need to be your bedroom.

Allocate a set amount of time. While you can just use a clock, you can also set a timer or go with a playlist of songs.

After you're done, check in with each other about how it went, discuss possible changes and share thoughts about future playpens.

---

SUCCULENT SEX CRAFT

## Positions

JUST AS THERE IS NO ONE right position for solo play, intercourse or any other sexual activity, there is no 'correct' or 'incorrect' position for playing with partners. However, some positions can especially enhance your experience of connection, such as having your bodies aligned, eye-to-eye and crotch-to-crotch.

To play with direct alignment, one option is the Tantric position of yab-yum, where one partner (in traditional Tantra, the woman) sits on the cross-legged lap of the other partner (traditionally the man) with her legs wrapped around him. A firm pillow under her rear and two under his knees can make this position more comfortable.

If your size, weight or joints won't accommodate yab-yum, you can try a variation I call yum-yum. You sit facing each other, crotch to crotch, each with one leg over the other's thigh and one under.

Another option is to sit in facing chairs or stools. Straddling a backless bench is also good. While these don't create the same groin-to-groin connection as yab-yum and yum-yum, they do align your bodies and energy systems, and this can enhance your connection.

You can also do many play and practice exercises while lying on your sides, face-to-face, with your heads on pillows.

You needn't limit yourself to eye-to-eye postures. Go head-to-toe and see how that feels. You can make like a pair of scissors and just have your crotches connecting. You can sit on the floor with your legs spread apart and only the soles of your feet touching. You can lie on your sides and spoon front to back.

Here, too, there are no rules, so experiment and discover what works best for you and your partner. Firm pillows, meditation cushions, back supports and sex furniture can make things easier and more fun. The key is to be comfortable and able to relax while playing and practicing.

Salvador Viniegra, *The First Kiss of Adam and Eve*

## Learning to Be a Human Being

A Native American teacher of mine once told me that we're born as human *animals* and spend our lives learning to be human *beings*. It's my fervent hope that this book will help you learn to be more loving, to access the sacredness that is inside and around you, and to become a more vibrant, sexually empowered human being. That's what Erotic U. is really about—learning to celebrate the extraordinary gift of being human through the pathway of the erotic.

This book is designed to be a springboard from which you can run your own experiments. I hope you make this offering a part of your grand experiment in leading a juicy, fulfilling life. Developing erotic mastery is about learning to play the instrument of yourself so you can make extraordinary erotic music alone and create magical improvisations of pleasure with others. Learning requires four

*You only live once, but if you do it right, once is enough.*

MAE WEST

things: desire, dedication, time and practice. With these ingredients, anyone can learn to achieve proficiency, go on to become adept, and ultimately develop mastery. This is true for anything you want to excel at, including your sexuality.

Now let the games begin!

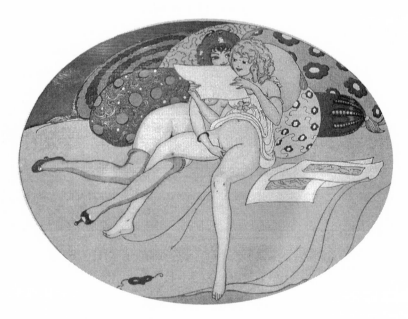

Gerda Wegener, *Les Delassements de Eros*

CHAPTER TWO

# THE GHOSTS OF SEX
# PAST AND PRESENT

*The erotic has often been misnamed by men and used against women.*
*It has been made into the confused, the trivial, the psychotic, the plasticized*
*sensation. For this reason, we have often turned away from the exploration*
*and consideration of the erotic as a source of power and information.*

AUDRE LORDE

## In the Beginning Was…Sex

SEX IS THE VITAL PULSE OF "LIFE'S LONGING FOR ITSELF," IN THE WORDS of poet Khalil Gibran.

Sex is the juice of attraction, the polarity that makes sparks, the mating urge that produces life. It's the primal power of sperm chasing egg, of egg embracing and enveloping sperm. It's what creates life in all its wondrous diversity and multi-cellular complexity.

It's the ancient archetypal God and Goddess—Shiva and Shakti in the Hindu tradition—merging in divine union to birth the orgasmic universe.

Sex is the grand dance of masculine and feminine energy, played out in the joy of genitals, of slippery flesh and juicy connection. Eros is what fuels the relentless and irrepressible tide of passion, lust and desire. Sex is the potent, mysterious, and alluring power that draws you to desire and connect. It moves within each of us like a deep inexorable tide, whether we like it or not.

Bijou Xochi, *At the Fall*

Your sexuality is a common thread that connects you not just to other people, but to all life on earth. You share with mating tigers and spawning salmon the urge to mate and reproduce.

For millions of years, living creatures danced to the tune of elaborately orchestrated mating routines. For the vast majority of animals, the sex act is still that way—an entirely utilitarian event that is compelling only when the heat is on, at which point it's all-consuming. It's entirely instinct-driven: The mating dance is a defined and repeated choreography, enacted without imagination or variety.

Not so for humans. Unusual animals that we are, we've developed the remarkable ability to have sex whenever we want, regardless of fertility status or the possibility of offspring.

*The ability to make love frivolously is the chief characteristic which distinguishes human beings from the beasts.*

HEYWOOD BROUN

Developing this capacity was part of becoming human, the upright big-brained social animals we are. We're foragers and opportunists, clever story-makers, and innovative tool users extraordinaire. Along with other remarkable evolutionary accomplishments like opposable thumbs and the art of the joke, we evolved sex far beyond mere reproduction.

For us, it's not just sex —it's sexuality, the act surrounded, embroidered, and elaborated, enabling our sexuality to encompass all and touch everything. Sex provides us with comedy, with tragedy, with drama. It permeates everything from entertainment to education, from profane to profound, from secular to spiritual. It is ubiquitous and omnipresent despite the calls from priests and politicians to rise above it and look the other way.

*Sex* is something all animals do, the human animal, included. *Sexuality* is different, and it's unique to our species (with a few possible exceptions). Sexuality pervades our conscious awareness and our unconscious even more so. Whether we want it to or not, whether we admit it to ourselves or not, this is the milieu we

*Sex is something you do, sexuality is something you are.*

ANNA FREUD

inhabit. Our sexuality is brought to us courtesy of our ancient DNA coding as it's been molded by our complex surroundings. It's mediated by custom, physiology and not least of all by our amazing—and amazingly lusty—imaginations.

Our relationship with sexuality—our own, our culture's and all nature's—is fundamental to the experience of being human.

---

* Big-brained dolphins don't have sex only to procreate. They're one species that, like humans, express their sexuality through sexual play.

# Succulent Summary

## What Is Sex?

SEX IS ANY EROTIC ACTIVITY: it's something you do. *Sexuality* encompasses the whole of who we are. It incorporates our thoughts, emotions, stories, beliefs, values, relationships, boundaries, choices, behaviors, knowledge and experiences.

Sex makes life. It made you—the one and only complex entity you are.

Sex is the vital life force, the energy that infuses all living creatures. It connects all life (including you).

Sex is the pervasive power of creation, the force that fuels sexual reproduction. It drives evolution's mix of competition and cooperation. It generates diversity, beauty and complexity.

Sex permeates everything. Our political systems, spiritual traditions, institutions, mythologies and cultures are shaped by it in myriad ways, both positive and negative. Eros fuels fertility, creativity, connection and love.

*Sex is the gateway to life.*

FRANK HARRIS

PLAY & PRACTICE

FOOD FOR THOUGHT

## What Is Sex For You?

FOR STARTERS, PONDER THESE questions, remembering that there are no right answers. If you choose, record your responses in your journal.

- How do you define sex?
- What did you think sex was when you were a child?
- What would you like your sex life to be like?
- What do you like about your current sex life? What do you dislike about it?
- What are some positive feelings you have about your sexuality?
- What are some negative feelings?
- What do you believe would make your sex life more fulfilling?
- What would you like to learn?

Extra credit homeplay assignment: Come back to these questions after finishing this book. Compare and contrast your answers.

## The Domestication of Sex

Sex is the glue and lubricant of our intimate relationships. It's probably been this way for as long as we've been human. In our dim prehistory, the bonding that resulted from sex was an exquisite and ingenious way for hunter-gatherers to increase their tribe's odds of survival. For hundreds of thousands of years, this 'babies, bliss and bonding' system supported pleasure, procreation, partnering and parenting while also building tribal cohesiveness.

But that was before. Before we enslaved animals and domesticated the land. Before we owned property—not just things but other peoples, including women and slaves.

That's when we tamed sex, shackling it with prohibitions and taboos. Culture after culture meted out punishment for pleasure practiced outside the rules. We brought sex into our farms from its home in the woods and wilderness. We domesticated our bodies. And most of all, we domesticated sex.

Mihály Zichy

Or at least we tried to. For thousands of years, we tried to sanitize, hide, bury and deny one of nature's most powerful forces. We pathologized and subjugated our erotic energy. We factory-farmed desire.

We decided wildness was bad and decried sex as base and animal, which is totally ironic, given that all the civilization in the world couldn't keep us from being the most sex-obsessed creatures on the planet. And so it remains to this day: No tilled field can contain our appetite, no monoculture can suppress the diversity of our lust. We stray beyond containers of rank, beyond arrangements of marriage, over walls of class. Our desire burrows beyond culture's rules and regulations. It directs our eyes beyond our borders to where the jungle calls. We know what awaits us there and we hunger for it—erotic connection so deep, so consuming, that it sends us literally out of our minds. We yearn for ecstatic tsunamis that will carry us beyond all pretense of good behavior, erasing boundaries and overriding edges. Our desire calls us to return to the ecstatic earth, to go back to the wildness that once upon a time was our home.

The Biblical story has it that we were thrown out of the garden, but that's backwards. We weren't thrown out of the garden—we were thrown *into* it. We left the rough paradise of the wilderness and became enamored of cultivation, which propelled us into civilization with its many pros and cons. We gained culture, consciousness, and choice. We got indoor plumbing and the Internet. We gained mobility and material goods.

But we sustained grievous losses, too. We lost touch with the Sacred Feminine; we became disengaged from the Erotic Divine. Our natural connection to our animal selves, our tribe, all nature and the web of life was severed. As we grew more self-conscious, we became less able to experience the unalloyed pleasure of our animal self and the bliss of unadulterated erotic connection.

Can we go back? No. But we can go forward, creating a new and integral understanding of what sex is and can be. Through conscious choice we can regain access to our erotic innocence, to our ecstatic birthright, to pure pleasure. We can recover our capacity to experience untamed sexual connection—and we can do so in a context of consciousness, integrity and responsibility. We can recreate a sexuality that's in wholistic relationship with, well, everything.

Would you like to find that place inside yourself where wildness couples with civilization to create a liberated, empowered and amazingly ecstatic you?

*The Bible contains six admonishments to homosexuals and 362 admonishments to heterosexuals. That doesn't mean that God doesn't love heterosexuals. It's just that they need more supervision.*

LYNN LAVNER

Eric Gill, *Eve*

## A Sea of Sex-Negative Stories

Before any of this can happen, though, we must free ourselves of the misguided and ugly stories that thousands of years of sex-negative culture have handed down to us. Our mainstream narratives about sex are shallow, flawed, incomplete and, quite frankly, dysfunctional. We're told that sex is about getting laid, putting out, getting some, giving it up, hooking up, scoring, getting off, getting it on, getting down. There's a whole lot of getting going on! But where's the giving? The sharing, the connecting?

Culturally we're all confused about sex. It's full of false dichotomies and contradictions. Good girls, bad girls. Prudes and sluts. Studs and players. Just say no. Just say yes. Sex is flaunted non-stop in our entertainment and advertising in a confusing stream of mixed messages.

*Only the liberation of the natural capacity for love in human beings can master their sadistic destructiveness.*

WILHELM REICH

It's alluring and shameful, taboo and tempting, pleasurable and profane. It's trivialized and vulgarized by being positioned as much more about appearances—how you look, dress and act—than about intimate connection with yourself and others.

The consequences are profound. The compelling force of reproductive energy cannot be denied or annihilated, despite the enormous effort over the centuries to suppress and even eradicate it. When people try to squelch Eros, it emerges anyway but perversely, creating pathological power dynamics and driving much of the evil that humanity has proven itself capable of.

But things are also changing for the better. Homophobia is on the wane as evidenced by the increasing acceptance of gay marriage. Women, while still disadvantaged, have made enormous gains in recent times (at least in the West). A new, more respectful and responsible culture is emerging that decries sexual violence. We remain a long way from being sexually celebratory, though. Women are still supposed to look sexy but not be too

*Sex education is legitimate in that girls cannot be taught soon enough how children don't come into the world.*

KARL KRAUS

sexual. Men are still supposed to be strong silent types who intuitively know how to please their partners. We remain at best a sexually confused culture, at worst a sex-negative one.

It's no surprise, then, that for many sex is an ongoing source of unhappiness, dissatisfaction and frustration. It's fraught with challenges. Many people's sexuality is constrained by ignorance, fear, inhibitions, body image issues, low self-esteem and shame. Far too many people feel wounded and powerless sexually.

Combine the ubiquitous sexy surface with the underlying guilt and shame and it's no surprise that we're surrounded by a welter of counter-productive stories about sex. We're given very little help to really understand what sex is or how our sexuality operates, much less how to do it well and be deeply ecstatic. Virtually none of our sex education, formal or informal, encourages us to say "yes" to responsible, celebratory sex. Abstinence-only sex ed programs insist that you "just say no" to premarital sex, which is kind of like standing on the shore and demanding that the tide stop coming in. (And we know how well that works!) Even so-called 'comprehensive' sex education programs tend to focus primarily on preventing infections and unwanted pregnancies. While that's important information, it's far from the visionary, transformative message it could be.

*Conservatives say teaching sex education in the public schools will promote promiscuity. With our education system? If we promote promiscuity the same way we promote math or science, they've got nothing to worry about.*

BEVERLY MICKINS

Being 'sexually free' has come to be associated with having bad boundaries and being sexually promiscuous. That's not what it means to me. I see it as being about liberating ourselves from the stories of our dominant culture's sex-negativity. It's about making choices that are responsible and respectful to ourselves and others. It's about choosing to honor pleasure and the profound power of Eros while conducting oneself with integrity. I'm all for being sexually free in this unequivocally positive sense of the term, and I wish it for everyone.

When you honor the power of sexuality and channel it appropriately, you transform your sex life for the better—and the benefits of having a sex-positive framework extend far beyond that. Your sex-positive way of being ripples out and helps propel a cultural shift in consciousness that honors the connectedness of all life.

Thomas Rowlandson

## Take a Stroll Down Memory Lane

GET COMFORTABLE. Close or blindfold your eyes. Relax with breathing.

Take a few moments and let your mind wander back to your earliest sexual experiences with yourself. How did you discover your sexuality? Do you recall touching yourself? Exploring your body? When is the first time you remember experiencing erotic pleasure by yourself? What happened? Were your experiences positive, negative or mixed?

Do you remember your early attractions? Reminisce about them.

Can you recall your early fantasies? What were they like?

How old were you when you first explored erotically with someone else? What happened? What did you learn? Were your early experiences positive, negative or mixed?

Think back to a few of your most significant early sexual experiences. What happened? Again: Were your experiences positive, negative or mixed?

You may want to record your memories and recollections in your notebook. I encourage you to focus especially on what you learned from your experiences and whether you still believe those lessons to be true.

*Partner Play Option:* If you have a partner, share some or all your stories.

## You and Your Sexuality

Since this book focuses on understanding what sex is and what it can be for you, the time has come to get personal. As we've seen, your sexuality is an inherent and integral aspect of who you are, as individual as your fingerprints yet utterly universal. However you express your sexuality, even if you don't act on it, it's a central force in your life. This is why, if you want to explore and expand your pleasure potential, the place to start is with yourself.

Two main lines of learning are involved. One, become conscious of any negative stories you have about sex and replace them with beautiful new ones. Two, learn to use your internal sexcraft toolkit to enhance your pleasure so you can realize your full and amazing sexual potential.

Rembrandt, *Nu Masculino Sentado*, 1646

FOOD FOR THOUGHT

## My Sex Life Story

HERE'S AN OPPORTUNITY to reflect on and summarize your sexuality journey. You can do it once or create as many versions as you want. If you like, share with friends and partners.

- OPTION #1. My Sex Life In Brief
  Write the story of your sex life in 50 words or less.

- OPTION #2. My Sex Life In A Tweet
  Write the story of your sex life in 140 characters or less.

PS. WANT EXTRA CREDIT? Then post your tweet, anonymously of course, on our website! We'll be compiling them for you and others to enjoy. We're also planning on running a contest and invite you to enter it. Enjoy!

To post, go to GetSexCrafty.com

If you tweet yours, use #SexLifeIB

Here's Carl's 140-character story: *Busted by Mom in my bedroom who pretended not to notice. Thought I knew it all until I knew I didn't. Ai yi yi! An eager, happy student now.*

And Sheri's: *So curious & precocious. Just try it all. Learned to love it, w/i my own boundaries. I'm really good at this! Pleasure = POWER! Yay for sex!*

### BEYOND BABIES

Why do we have sex? Unlike other animals, we rarely intend to reproduce. (In fact, most of us expend quite a bit of effort ensuring pregnancy doesn't happen!) Let's delve a bit deeper into what motivates our randy sex drive.

While we do sometimes have sex to procreate, most of our erotic encounters are for other reasons. We do it for pleasure. We do it for power. We do it to bond with

> *A promiscuous person is a person who is getting more sex than you are.*
>
> VICTOR LOWNES

others. It can get us ecstatic and put us in touch with the Divine. Some do it for money, some out of boredom, for ego gratification or out of pity. The reasons are myriad—for the thrill, for the touch, out of curiosity or a sense of obligation.

The more important question, though, isn't about why other people have sex. It's why do *you* have sex?

FOOD FOR THOUGHT

## Why Do It?

WHY DO YOU HAVE SEX, both with yourself and others?

Make a list of your motives for having solo sex.

Make a list of your reasons for being sexual with others now and in the past (if this is part of your life experience).

Have you discovered after the fact that you and a partner had different intentions for being sexual? (If you haven't, you're in a small minority.) What were your motivations and those of your partner?

Have you ever had sex when you really didn't want to? Note the reasons why you acquiesced in an activity that wasn't thoroughly pleasurable and positive for you.

Why do you think other people have sex? Note the purposes that aren't on your personal list.

🍒 We're compiling a list of why people have sex. Come check it out and feel free to add to it (anonymously)! *Visit GetSexCrafty.com.*

### THOSE BEDROOM ADVENTURES WHEN WE'RE YOUNG

Whatever your background, there probably came a time when you began exploring your capacity for sexual pleasure. Do you remember those early experiences? For me, it was like wandering around in a vaguely familiar yet new and exciting forest where I followed ancient paths, some overgrown and some obvious, all of which led toward a destination that I didn't know much about beyond being certain that I wanted to get there.

Franz von Bayros

Sooner or later, most of us stumbled around enough to find the land of orgasm. And my, was it good! So we went back again (and again, and again), typically following the same path that got us to our climax the first time. We were like rats in a maze, following the same trusty trail that got us to our cheese—were rats ever happier? Soon enough, we developed a reliable path to take us from point A to point O.

Paths are wonderful. They make it easier to get where you want to go. The problem is that when you use the same path over and over again, it can turn into a rut, and if you stay in

*It is a miracle that curiosity survives formal education.*

ALBERT EINSTEIN

that same rut, over time it can become a trench. After a while, you can't see any other way to go. While it's great to be able to achieve an orgasm more or less dependably, it can be restricting if the price you pay is a cap on your pleasure. Following the one path we know can cause us to miss out on the virtually infinite variety of other ways we can get turned on and orgasmic. It can also put blinders on us that keep us from envisioning our full sexual potential.

## GREAT SEX IS JUST THE BEGINNING

People rarely go to places they don't know exist. If you want to expand your erotic pathways and have more sexual pleasure, it's helpful to have a map of what's possible so you know where you can go.

How good can it get? Wildly so. Just for the fun of it, I've created a spectrum of positive erotic experiences:

- *Good sex.* This is what sex is for many people. While it doesn't live up to the passionate embraces you see in the movies, it's a delightful experience and it helps you feel connected in the moment. Orgasms are probably genital rather than whole-body. Sometimes the feeling of connection ends when the orgasm subsides.

- *Great sex.* These experiences are intensely pleasurable, feel deeply intimate and are extremely rewarding. For many people, this level of pleasure is as good as it gets—and great is, well, pretty great!

- *Fabulous sex.* This is sex with fireworks finales. It's romantic movie sex. It's multi-orgasmic and leaves you 'cumatose.' Fabulous sex typically requires you to be deeply connected with yourself and your partners. It usually emerges out of a high level of reciprocal love or caring and establishes a genuine bond, be it temporary or long-term (although casual spontaneous 'cumbustion' has been known to occur).

- *Transcendent sex.* At this level, sex strips away our sense of separation from everything we usually experience as 'other.' It's a mystical encounter: Our spirit merges with the All. It can heal our deepest, darkest wounds and impart a profound sense of joy. The bliss we experience is truly divine!

## GETTING THERE

For some of you, experiences at the top of the spectrum may seem painfully far away. Sexual challenges show up in a variety of ways.

If you haven't yet had an orgasm, you're probably a woman. Although it's not a happy place to be, you can take consolation in the fact that you're not alone. While it's far from definitive, research suggests that about 10% of women haven't yet found their path to orgasm. If you're in this group, there's nothing wrong with you—there's just stuff you haven't learned yet. You are 'orgasmically naive.'

If you have orgasms sometimes but not whenever you want to, then you belong to a large group of women (and some men) who have not yet developed what I call 'orgasmic proficiency'—the ability to always have an orgasm, sooner or later, one way or another.

Men's bedroom issues are usually different from women's. They're typically not so much about getting to the land of orgasm as they are about the ability to get an erection at all or to get one when you want to and to ejaculate when the moment is right.

And then there are the people who think that they don't have the right kind of orgasms or don't come from the right kinds of stimulation. A very common example is women who don't have orgasms from penis-in-vagina penetration.

Eric Gill
*Art and Love*

SUCCULENT SEX CRAFT

## Fascinating Facts

### Orgasmic Challenges

75% OF MEN AND 29% OF WOMEN report always having orgasms with their partner in a 1994 study of Sexual Practices in the US.

A 2005 study found that one in three women reported never or seldom achieving orgasm during intercourse, and only one in ten always orgasmed.

### SIMULTANEOUS ORGASM

46% of all adults do not regularly achieve orgasm simultaneously. In fact, more than a third of those surveyed said that it hardly ever—or never—happens.
  —*Condom company Durex® 2012 poll of 1,000 adults, married and single.*

Many women (and their partners) think there's something wrong with this even though over half of women don't reach orgasm this way. Men can also have orgasm-with-intercourse challenges.

If you have one or more of these issues or challenges, don't despair! For one thing, there are no right kinds of orgasms or right ways to have them. For another, arousal and orgasm pathways are learned, and all the potential pathways are already there inside you. What you've been lacking is information and support. You haven't been given useful, accurate maps or the encouragement you need to go inside yourself and find the connections that will get you to your promised land, whatever and wherever that may be.

### WORD NERD

#### Levels of Orgasmic Ability

- *Orgasmic Novice*: Not yet having learned the skills and pathways that will take you to your orgasm(s).

- *Orgasmic Proficiency*: The ability to always have an orgasm, sooner or later, one way or another.

- *Orgasmic Mastery*: The ability to always have at least one, often multiple orgasms, utilizing a variety of pathways and/or multiple forms of stimulation. For men: Includes having the ability to exercise ejaculatory choice (when to come) and to have non-ejaculatory orgasms.

FOOD FOR THOUGHT

## Where Are You and How Did You Get Here?

IN YOUR MIND OR JOURNAL, answer the following questions:

- BASED ON WHAT YOU'VE READ, do you view yourself as orgasmically naïve, proficient or masterful?

- IF YOU'RE ORGASMICALLY PROFICIENT or masterful, how old were you when you reached your current level (and any earlier ones)? How did you develop these abilities?

- HAVE YOU EVER HAD GREAT SEX? Fabulous sex? Transcendent sex? How often? What were (or are) the circumstances and what was the 'special sauce,' if any, that made these experiences possible?

No matter where you are today, you can achieve 'orgasmic mastery'—the ability to have a variety of orgasmic experiences including multiple climaxes and expanded full-body orgasms. As a budding erotic virtuoso, you'll discover your network of arousal pathways so you can get turned on faster and by many different kinds of stimulation. You already possess the sexcraft tools you need that make this possible. Your next step is to become more skilled at using them.

Ecstasy in all its forms is learnable. If you believe it is.

William-Adolphe
Bouguereau
*Nymphs and Satyr*

SUCCULENT SEX CRAFT

# CHAPTER THREE

# A VISION OF SEX FUTURE

*May my mind come alive today*
*To the invisible geography*
*That invites me to new frontiers,*
*To break the dead shell of yesterdays,*
*To risk being disturbed and changed.*

JOHN O'DONOHUE

## Whole Sex

HOW DO YOU FREE YOURSELF FROM OUR CULTURE'S SEX-NEGATIVE stories? What do you replace them with? It starts with embracing a new understanding of sex and sexuality—specifically, *your* sex and sexuality—so you can weave a healthier, more beautiful and celebratory narrative about Eros.

We already had a sexual revolution, with significant but bumpy gains, imperfect progress and some serious backlash. Where do we go next? How do we progress to a world where the power of sex is honored as an essential, inherent aspect of being a whole and healthy human being, where sexual freedom is balanced with respect and responsibility and everyone recognizes that erotic and relationship skills are learnable?

A sexual evolution? Well, yes, but that would take too long—we need more rapid progress. So how about this: It's time for a sexual transformation! One that's both personal and cultural.

I'm happy to say this shift is underway. Many different communities—including gay, trans and intersex rights activists, feminists, kinky folks, open expanded relationship people, holistic healers and others—are driving this change. An entire sub-culture, the 'sex-positive movement,' has emerged. While sex-positive activists don't agree about everything, for the most part there's a striking consensus about what a healthy relationship to our sexuality means for the 21st Century and beyond. Here's a short list of attitudes and beliefs that are common in sex-positive communities:

- Sex is normal and natural. It's a good, healthy, vital and powerful aspect of us all.

- We have autonomy and freedom with regard to our sexuality. No one can tell us what we can or can't do so long as our behavior is responsible and ethical.

- Our capacity for erotic pleasure is a gift. Rejoice in it! It's our birthright and nothing to be ashamed of. It's beautiful, amazing and healthy, so go for it!

- The body-mind is inherently wise, crafted by evolutionary processes to work perfectly, including our entire sexual apparatus.

- In your sexual conduct, it's essential to behave responsibly and respectfully and to be in integrity with yourself and others. This includes such things as practicing safer sex, respecting other people's autonomy, having healthy boundaries, and having sex for emotionally healthy and celebratory reasons. It also includes being sure that all sexual encounters honor personal and relational boundaries and are based on enthusiastic, clear consent and honest and transparent communication. No lying. No cheating.

- Sexuality is a shame-free zone. There is no need to be ashamed or embarrassed about our bodies, our desires, our fantasies, our solo sex or our erotic connections with others. We're entitled to do as we please, so long as it's consensual.

- Diversity is appreciated, celebrated and valued. All orientations, preferences, levels of ability, inclinations, bodies and genders (including the ones in between) are honored equally.

In addition, many in the sex-positive world believe that sex is inherently sacred. Since our sexuality is how we manifest the universal life force, it is seen as an aspect of the divine.

I'm a proud member of this movement and look forward to the day, hopefully not too far away, when these values and attitudes are mainstream.

There's no one right way to be sex-positive or to transform your erotic life into one that's more integrated and empowered. My own journey showed me what was possible and inspired me to create the Wholistic Sexuality model I share here. I offer it as one possible path—and the most integral one I know—for guiding you on your erotic learning journey and creating a future where sex is seen as natural, beautiful and *learnable* as well as a source of empowerment

> *You never change things by fighting the existing reality. To change something, build a new model that makes the old model obsolete.*
>
> BUCKMINSTER FULLER

SUCCULENT SEX CRAFT

and joy. Imagine a world where sex is celebrated in a responsible and respectful way and how those attitudes would affect the planet!

In the balance of this chapter, we'll examine the basic ideas that underlie the Wholistic Sexuality model. Later in the book, we'll go into more detail about playing with your sexcraft tools and how to use then fully.

## The Wholistic Sexuality Vision

### THE PRIME DIRECTIVE: WHOLISTIC SEXUALITY IS ABOUT CONNECTION

By now, this point is probably familiar: Sex isn't just about copulating to create unique new beings. It's about connection. While the basic biological template is about males and females mating to produce offspring, for us humans, sex is about connecting beyond the mechanics of reproduction. It's about connecting with ourselves and our partners at multiple levels, including the physical, mental, emotional, spiritual and energetic. It's also about connecting to the life force, Eros, that underlies and unifies everything.

### ONE: YOUR PRIMARY SEXUAL RELATIONSHIP IS WITH YOURSELF

More than anything, your sexuality is about your relationship with yourself. By 'self' I mean all of you: your body, mind, heart and spirit; your past, present and future; your genetics and your environment—everything that makes you uniquely and completely you.

Your sexuality is about *who you are*, not about who you do (or don't) have sex with. Your sexual activities don't define your sexual identity—they emanate from and are expressions of it. Your sexuality is an inherent, inseparable and essential aspect of the complex person that is you.

You can break up with other people. They can die or go away. You can't leave or be left by yourself, though. Wherever you go, there you are. You are your primary partner, the only one who has been and always will be with you.

What this means is that if you want to have better sex, start with yourself. If you want to have better relationships with other people, start with yourself. If you want

Kseniya Vlasova, *Valentina: The Renaissance Woman*

more love, connection and pleasure in your life, the place to start is, you guessed it, with yourself.

There's a straightforward reason for this: Your foundational relationship to yourself is the basis of all your other relationships (not just the sexual ones). All your other connections are shaped by your relationship with yourself.

This self-relationship includes the entirety of your history and life experiences. It's grounded in your relationship with your body at all levels—physical, mental, spiritual, emotional and energetic. Your inner relationship includes the beliefs and values you were exposed to growing up as well as those you hold now. It incorporates your current and past relationships and your connection to all the communities you participate in. It starts with your family and extends to your neighborhood, work, education and recreational activities. It proceeds from there to our local, regional and national spiritual and political institutions, and, ultimately, extends out to include the whole world. It also includes all the media messages you've absorbed throughout your life. All these and more are the threads that weave the tapestry of your relationship with your sexual self.

> *You were wild once.*
> *Don't let them tame you.*
>
> ISADORA DUNCAN

Titian, *Venus in Front of the Mirror*

SUCCULENT SEX CRAFT

In addition to being your own primary partner, there's another reason why sexual self-improvement starts with your relationship with yourself. For better and worse, how you think and feel about yourself profoundly influences your sexual beliefs, choices and behavior. For instance, how do you feel about your body? Do you love it? Like it? Hate it? Take a moment to give some thought to the many messages you've absorbed over the years about how you should look. Our entertainment and advertising cultures do a particularly effective—maybe the better word is nasty—job of making us

Achille Devéria

hate our bodies and feel ashamed of our genitals. If you've been lucky enough to escape these insidious messages, congratulations! But for most women and many men, negative body issues regularly block their ability to open to erotic delight and love. You can't revel in your pleasure when you're wondering if your ass looks too fat. And what about your genitals? Do you view them as powerful and attractive or as dirty and repulsive? Are they sacred and celebrated? Or are they shameful, unnamed and ignored? We've all received innumerable messages about our genitals—which ones have lodged in your programming? How do your stories about yourself affect your sexuality?

Here are a few examples of belief systems we sometimes fail to question:

- WHAT ASSUMPTIONS do you make about men and women? If your father abandoned your family, do you assume all men are untrustworthy? If your mother let herself get pushed around, do you assume all women are doormats?

- HOW ABOUT SELF-PLEASURING? Do you see that as a guilty pleasure or not a pleasure at all? As an expedient way to release sexual tension? Or, as I recommend, as a way to explore your sexuality and love yourself well (and thoroughly)?

- WHAT ABOUT SEXUAL ORIENTATION? Somewhere along the way, did you come to believe the stereotypes that gay men are sexually promiscuous or lesbians hate men?

If you're living with stories that don't serve you or wrong others, there's only one person who can get rid of them—you. It takes time to reprogram negative belief systems, especially if you've had them since early childhood, but it's definitely do-able. You can replace your negative stories with positive ones.

When you recognize the web of connection, influences, bonds and beliefs you have around sexuality, you have more power to choose stories and relationships that are healthy, appropriate and fulfilling for you. The more you consciously examine your narratives, the easier it becomes to choose meanings that enhance your life and help you become the most authentic person you can be. Separating yourself from your stories—owning them, rather than being owned by them—is one of the great life tasks that goes with being in conscious relationship with yourself.

*Everyone is born a genius, but the process of living de-geniuses them.*

BUCKMINSTER FULLER

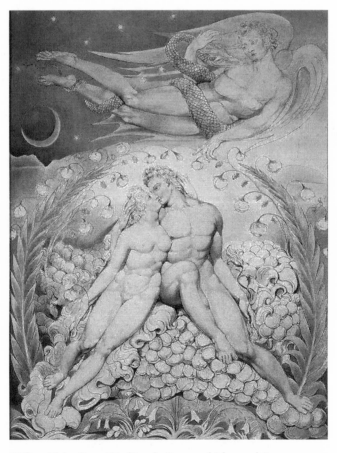

William Blake, *Satan Watching the Caresses of Adam and Eve*

## Your Sexual Stories

LET'S LOOK AT YOUR PERSONAL, complex and utterly unique 'sexual stories.' (Feel free to write your responses in your notebook or simply to ponder your answers.)

- WHEN, WHERE AND HOW did you learn about sex?

- HOW DO YOU WISH you'd learned about sex? What do you wish you'd learned?

- DID YOU GROW UP in a religious tradition that shamed or honored you? Your body? Your sexuality? Your desires? Your orientation?

- HOW DO YOU FEEL ABOUT your genitals and other sexual parts such as your anus? What about those same parts when they belong to others?

- IN YOUR FAMILY OF ORIGIN, how was pleasure viewed? As a sin, a waste of time or something to delight in?

- WHAT ABOUT DESIRE? Do you view it as delightful or dangerous?

- WHAT WORDS COME TO MIND when you think about sex? Is it passionate? Overwhelming? Challenging? Sinful? Blissful?

- WHAT STORIES AND BELIEFS do you have about relationships? Do you expect Prince Charming to arrive someday and sweep you off your feet? Is Sleeping Beauty waiting for you to kiss her awake? Are you planning on finding your soulmate? On living happily ever after?

- HOW DO YOU BELIEVE real men behave? How about real women?

- WHEN YOU HAVE PARTNER SEX, what are your assumptions about who does what to whom? What's permitted? What isn't? Who decides? How it is it supposed to look?

- HOW DO YOU LEARN about partners and what they do and don't like?

- WHEN IS IT OKAY to have sex with someone?

- Is SEX supposed to be fun? Is it fun?

- IN YOUR IMMEDIATE CULTURAL CIRCLES, what types of sexual behavior are accepted? What types aren't?

- WHAT ABOUT YOUR SEXUAL FANTASY LIFE—what's allowed in that private world? What isn't?

 *Want more "Questions to Ponder?" Come visit GetSexCrafty.com.*

## Two: Your Sexuality Is Connected With Everything

Like a hologram, your sexuality is a microcosm that reflects and manifests everything from the personal to the planetary. The erotic surrounds us; it contains us; it penetrates us down to the cellular level. Sexual reproduction creates diversity, novelty and complexity. It makes life, including the unique complex being that's you. Wholistic Sexuality is about recognizing our connectedness to all life. More than an intellectual construct, it's about owning that truth with your entire being.

*We cannot live only for ourselves. A thousand fibres connect with our fellow men; and among those fibres, as sympathetic threads, our actions run as causes, and they come back to us as effects.*

HERMAN MELVILLE

Because your sexuality is an integral aspect of who you are, Eros shows up in all your interactions and relationships, including the many that aren't sexual. All your other relationships are influenced by your core connection with yourself, just as you have been shaped by all that surrounds you. You're at the center of a great web of connection. This includes your relationships with partners, families, communities, culture and ultimately the whole wide world. Whatever you do, however you're connected, your sexuality is part of it.

We were all born with a natural capacity for extraordinary pleasure and deep connection. Correction: we were all conceived with the capacity for these things. With sophisticated ultrasound, we can now see fetuses—both boys and girls—not only sucking their thumbs but also playing with their genitals. Babies born naturally in a peaceful, calm environment come out blissful and beaming. We come into the world pre-wired for pleasure. It's pleasure that draws us to connect. That's one reason your relationships with others is an aspect of your sexuality even if you're not having sex with them. As humans, we evolved to be a tribal species, deeply bonded to our families, communities and partners. Our internal wiring predisposes us to seek connection. Our need for acceptance, pleasure and love drives us to form the kinship ties we need to ensure survival.

Connection is your most basic way of being, from infancy to old age. The more you can experience and celebrate your connection with yourself, your partners, and with everyone and everything in your lives, the more you become able to access your

Charles Edouard de Beaumont

SUCCULENT SEX CRAFT

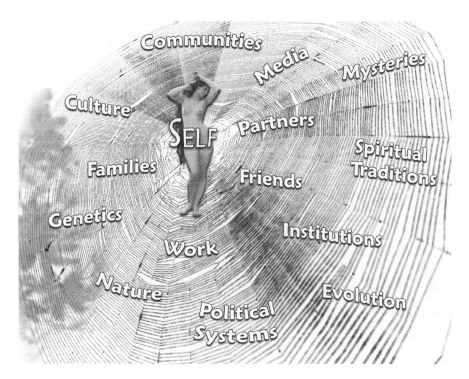

Sheri Winston, *Your Self in Web of Everything*

capacity for pleasure and ecstasy. Embracing the fact that we're hardwired for connection and pleasure is a great starting point.

Certainly, your sexuality is also about having sex with other people or desiring to do so. Our ancient mating template fuels our desire for sexual connection. There are several deep, inexorable drives at play here. One is the magical falling-in-love drive, the starry-eyed obsessive euphoria of passion and romance. Another driver of sexual connection is the powerful falling-in-lust force. They are not necessarily concurrent or directed at the same person. When these two overlap, it's a force that sweeps us off our feet.

There's also a third loop—the drive for attachment; to feel safe, secure and known; to feel cared for and cared about. Attachment often occurs with lovers and it also happens in non-sexual contexts such as with friends and family.

I'm not suggesting that sexual fulfillment and empowerment entails your being sexually active with anyone other than yourself. Nothing requires you to have a partner or partners. Your sexuality is about who you are, not who you do. What matters most is that you be in a positive sexual relationship with yourself, and that you be in conscious relationship with your partners, friends, families, communities and the rest of the living, pulsing world. If you can do that, you will be opening yourself to the omnipresent spirit of Eros and well on your way to fulfilling your sexual potential.

# Succulent Summary

## Connections

YOUR SEXUALITY IS CONNECTED to everyone and everything. Here are aspects of the web of life that surrounds and supports you, and that co-created you:

YOU

- Hardware: Nature, evolution, genetics
- Software: Learning, environment, culture
- Mind, body, heart and spirit
- Energy and matter

EVERYTHING ELSE

**FAMILIES**
- your family of origin (the place where nature and nurture overlap and sometimes collide)
- your families of choice (the people you choose to create family with)
- your families of creation (your kids, if you have them)

**PARTNERS**
- including any people with whom you are or have been intimate, sexual, and/or romantic
- current partners
- past partners
- fantasy partners
- potential partners

**COMMUNITIES**
- friends, acquaintances, and all other communities and connections
- Where you live
- Political institutions, spiritual, religious and other institutions
- Other institutions
- The media
- Your work
- All living beings
- The world
- The ALL . . . The mysteries (leaving room for all of the energies and influences that we don't know or understand)

FOOD FOR THOUGHT

## Your Connection Stories

DELVE INTO THE STORIES you've absorbed from various sources. You can draw from the "Connections" sidebar if you wish. Write down one or more common beliefs or stories about sex, relationships, gender, bodies and pleasure. Here's an example of what I have in mind.

What stories has our entertainment and advertising culture handed me about pleasure, bodies, gender roles, romantic relationships and sex?

- PLEASURE: The Puritan work ethic says that pleasure is indulgent.

- BODIES: TV commercials about women's genitals: My female genitals are 'not so fresh.'

- GENDER ROLES: Books and movies: Women are valued for being beautiful. They need to be rescued and are never the hero. Women will fall down helplessly (and often twist their ankle) when being chased by the villain. Men are valued for being strong, competent, smart and brave. They are heroes and will come to the rescue.

- CHILDHOOD FAIRY TALES: And they lived happily ever after.

- SEX IN THE MOVIES: No talking required. Fireworks every time, including the first time.

This is a fun and edifying game to play with partners and friends. Suggest a number of areas (e.g., TV commercials, family of origin, spiritual traditions) and have each person write down stories they learned from them. Then share.

---

**THREE: SEX IS BOTH NATURAL AND LEARNED:**
**HANDY HARDWARE AND SOPHISTICATED SOFTWARE**

As discussed earlier, the story that 'sex comes naturally' is only partly true. While much of our sexuality is derived from our natural animal templates, an astounding amount of human sexuality is learned. You learn sex, including not just what goes where, but more significantly, your erotic capacities, responses and pathways to pleasure. You are an intricately interwoven combination of hardware and software.

Your hardware is your genetics, the factory-installed equipment that is the unique result of millions of years of evolution. It's your inborn instincts and aptitudes. You can't change your hardware, but you can learn to understand and work with it. And learn how to make it work for you.

A VISION OF SEX FUTURE

Unlike your hardware, your software is the programmable, learned part of who you are. You've been absorbing things like a sponge your whole life, starting with your prenatal environment and continuing through your birth journey up to this very day. You've been shaped by your experience and environment.

Sheri Winston, *Hardware and Software*

The line between what is inborn and what is learned is not clear-cut. There's a gray area between hardware and software, between 'nature' and 'nurture.' In fact, the more we learn about genes, the more we understand that our environment plays a role in turning on or off all sorts of potentials. For now, though, let's just say that humans are made up of both hardware and software, and it's the huge software component that makes us the 'learning animal.'

Much of our sexuality comes from the software side of the divide. You learned to view sex as sinful, sacred or something in between. You learned your concept of foreplay, your beliefs about who is and isn't appropriate to have sex with, and much more. Some of this education has been conscious. Much has been unconscious.

Your ability to learn is innate, while what and how much you learn depends on your social and cultural circumstances. For instance, you were born with the inherent ability to learn language, but your proficiency with your native tongue or how many languages you speak depends on your environment. Another example: Every baby loves

> *It is what we know already that often prevents us from learning.*
>
> CLAUDE BERNARD

music and responds to rhythm—but whether or not you play an instrument depends on what you learned to do with your intrinsic musical aptitude. Essentially, you learn sex the same way you learn to play a musical instrument, dance or become fluent with a foreign language.

We all come equipped with a starter kit of basic capacities such as an inherent sense of rhythm, a body that loves to move, and a brain primed with the ability to learn words and grammar. Our natural aptitudes provide the foundation for learning essential skills. We then build up our skill sets by layering on increasingly complex competencies. While much of our learning is unconscious, it's through conscious learning that we achieve proficiency and ultimately mastery.

## UN-LEARNING

Becoming more erotically adept isn't only about learning. It also requires un-learning. You need to erase limiting and incorrect information from your inner blackboard so there's room for new material. You may need to unlearn negative stories about your body, bad programming about solo sex, limited ideas about gender roles, or inhibitions that block your free experience of arousal.

I encourage you to wipe your slate clean so that new affirming messages and beliefs about yourself and your delicious sexuality can emerge and thrive. Write new stories that celebrate your amazing body, whatever your shape, size, abilities or limitations. Craft a new tale that celebrates Eros: trust pleasure as your guide. Cast yourself in the role of hero or heroine on a grand journey to erotic mastery.

*There is nothing like a dream to create the future.*

VICTOR HUGO

You may think of creating new stories as just 'making stuff up,' but it's much more than that. When you consciously craft new narratives, you're redesigning your inner architecture; you're upgrading your software and importing new programming. In fact, by reading this book, you're in 'install' mode right now— you're learning to be a new you! And that's deep learning.

---

## *Succulent Summary*

### Learning to Play Your Instrument

- Sexual skills can and need to be learned.

- Anyone can learn to achieve basic sexual proficiency, then become more skillful and adept—ultimately developing mastery of their own sexuality. The foundational skill set involves learning to play your own instrument.

- Skills build on each other, with basic skills supplying the foundation for more advanced, complex abilities.

- We all have the capacity to reach our full sexual potential—and even to become a sexual virtuoso—through practice.

- Great sex is an improvisation. Technique is the foundation.

---

## Four: We Need Accurate, Effective Maps and Models

It's not easy to learn complex skills on your own—it helps to have a guide. A teacher can share their knowledge base of accumulated information, wisdom and techniques, offer logical sequences for learning, organize information, provide structure and clarify confusion. A mentor can encourage you on your journey, and also share useful, accurate maps that show you the easy routes and warn you against pitfalls.

*I have an existential map. It has "You are here" written all over it.*

STEVEN WRIGHT

Good guides are especially necessary when the maps you've been using are inaccurate or outdated. Bad maps get you lost! Unfortunately, this is what we get from our mainstream culture, which seems to specialize in offering flawed maps about relationships and sexuality.

To make matters worse, many people don't realize they've been working with faulty maps and instead believe there's something wrong with them. Bad maps about sex, bodies, desire and relationships often leave people feeling broken or like failures. Here are some examples of maps that steer us astray:

- Many of our mainstream maps of sex are based on masculine arousal. This leaves many women (and some men) feeling like there's something wrong with them because their arousal system doesn't zoom them from zero to sixty like a sports car.

- Our cultural maps and stories about the body are incomplete and erroneous. Hard though it may be to believe, there is widespread ignorance and confusion, even among medical professionals, about important reproductive and sexual body parts and how they interact.

- Our mental models of men and women are simplistic and misleading. They tend to overstate similarities ("Any suggestion that men and women are different is sexist") or dissimilarities ("Men and women are from different planets"). Models like these don't help us navigate the gender divide and they don't build bridges across it, either.

Egon Schiele, *Girl Masturbating*

- We tend to divide people into two genders, male and female, while disregarding the many variations on this theme—people who are a blend of both genders, those who feel like they're a different gender than their plumbing or chromosomes indicate, people with both male and female sexual characteristics, and so on.

- Our relationship models are simplistic and sometimes plain silly. Culturally, we're caught up in the myth of true love that lasts forever and doesn't require care and feeding. All those "happily ever after" stories echo in our heads. If only the 'true-love' story were true! A more accurate model would tell us that wonderful falling-in-love feeling involves a biochemical cascade that typically fades out after a couple of years. Real relationships can be romantic, but they're not a starry-eyed fairy tale. They're challenging and require emotional maturity and hard work seasoned with a plentiful measure of play. Yet our media myths portray romantic fluff as real and ideal, leaving many people feeling frustrated, disappointed and deprived when things don't work out that way.

Hopefully, some of the models in this book will provide you with practical maps that will help you effectively navigate the tricky waters of sex, partners and relationships and find your way to your own land of healthy loving connection.

For all their value, though, it's essential to remember that the map is not the territory. It's a representation of reality, not the actual thing. That's why you can have many maps of the same thing, with each one emphasizing a different perspective. A street map, a population map and a topographical one can be simultaneously true yet all look different and be useful in different ways. As I've mentioned, I provide lots of maps and models in these pages, some of which describe the same thing differently. That doesn't make one right and the other wrong—they just offer multiple lenses so you can get a bigger and more multifaceted picture.

The important thing to ask about a map or model is if it's useful and true. Does it confirm or invalidate your experience? Does it get you lost or help you get where you want to go? If you want to find a special swimming hole you've heard about, you're much likelier to get there if you've got an accurate trail map that has a big 'X' marking the sweet spot.

Of course, you'll only know if it's correct if you actually take that walk in the woods and find out for yourself if that idyllic place exists.

Maps are a supremely useful tool for getting where you want to go. Without them, you're just fumbling in the dark.

## Your SexCraft Toolkit

Later we'll go into exquisite detail about what you've got and how to use it, but for now, here's an overview of your sexcraft toolkit.

You were born fully equipped with everything you need to have fabulous sex. Each and every one of you has all the tools you need right there inside you. What you may not yet know is how to squeeze the most out of your equipment. (So to speak.)

The Wholistic Sexuality model can help you do that. You have an inner sexcraft toolkit that's made up of four discrete but interconnected domains—mind, body, heart and spirit. These domains are interwoven, overlapping aspects of the whole you. While dividing them makes them easier to discuss and learn about, they—and you—are ultimately inseparable. There's a paradox here: They're separate, and they're not.

Each domain has its own bucket of tools. (Or boxes of instruments. Or sets of skills. I use all those words interchangeably and invite you to do the same.) When I talk about tools, I'm not referring to external things like sex toys. I have in mind the internal tools you were born with. You don't need to strap on a tool belt (or anything else) to expand your pleasure. You just need to learn how to play skillfully with the various parts of your multi-faceted self.

Sheri Winston,
*Venus in a Toolbelt*

# Your Sexcraft Toolkit

| MIND | BODY | HEART | SPIRIT |
|---|---|---|---|
| Awareness | Breath | Loving Intention | Sacred Intention |
| Attention | Sound | Loving Action | Sacred Sound |
| Intention | Movement | Courage | Meditation |
| Presence | Vision | Forgiveness | Manifestation |
| Authenticity | Touch | Witnessing | Ritual |
| Trance States of Consciousness | Smell & Taste | Giving & Receiving | Ceremony |
| Imagination | | | |

The table above sets out an hors d'oeuvre version of your inner instruments. You'll find the main course in Section 3, where I go into delicious detail about all your sexcraft tools and how to use them.

We all already use these tools in many different ways in our lives, including during sex. Movement, for instance, is pretty basic: We're all programmed to make the familiar (and hardwired) mammalian mating motion. We all see things that turn us on, we all breathe faster as we get aroused, and we all use our imaginations when we fantasize.

The Wholistic Sexuality approach isn't simply about using your inborn tools—it's about going off automatic pilot and activating them *consciously*. It's about learning to use all of them and to use them more skillfully.

Which ones you choose to focus on is entirely up to you. If you're not a ritual kind of person, nothing requires you to do ritual. You're the owner and operator of your own experience.

Ultimately, your sexcraft skills are not about technique per se. They are in service to your cultivation of your erotic energy—the unique, spontaneous musical improv that you create anew each time you play.

# Succulent Summary

### 🍒 Wholistic Sexuality Overview

THE PRIME DIRECTIVE: SEX IS ABOUT CONNECTION.

THE FOUR PREMISES:

1. Your sexuality is first and foremost about your connection to your self. Your whole self.

2. Your sexuality is also about your connection to others. Naturally that includes the people you have sex with—partner sex is fundamentally about connection. And it's also about your connection to everyone and everything, including all life on this planet.

3. Sex is both natural and learned. While an important part of our sexuality is based on our inborn animal templates, an astounding amount of human sexuality is learned.

4. To fulfill your sexual potential, it helps to have structure, support and guidance—and, more specifically, accurate and effective maps and models. Anything short of that is like trying to find a special spot in the woods without a map (or with one that's just plain wrong).

Sir Frank Dicksee, *The Mirror*

## Levels of Learning

Your sexcraft tools can be used at two levels. Level one is using them to go solo. The next level, partner skills, is how you use them to play duets. Playing solo is your most important learning lab—in fact, it's so important that I've dedicated an entire chapter to it (Chapter Four—*It's All About You*).

### GOING SOLO

You can use your solo erotic tools to get centered and present, turn off your chatterbox front brain, and focus your attention where you want it. You can amplify your pleasure, get more turned-on and expand your orgasms. You can use your tools to get unstuck, ramp things up or slow them down.

You can develop your solo skills to a very sophisticated (and super-hot) level. You don't need a partner to discover and explore your erotic potential. Partners are a nice option but not required. You can learn anything you want by yourself. And, it's convenient (and motivating) that the more proficiency you develop on your own, the more expertise you'll have for playing duets with others.

### DELIGHTFUL DUETS

Your partner skills involve the same mind, body, heart and spirit tools you use to play with yourself. With a lover, you use them to connect energetically, synchronize your rhythms, deepen your (and their) arousal and get into shared erotic space.

Duets are inherently more complicated than playing solo. You need to pay attention to the other person's needs and desires. You also have to coordinate and harmonize how you play with them if you wish to co-create great improvisations. That's why musicians practice their skills solo even when they regularly play

Alméry Lobel-Riche

with others—you hone your chops by yourself so your duets can go smoothly and you can make sultry sexy songs together.

## *Succulent Summary*

### SexCraft Skill Levels

**YOUR SEXCRAFT TOOLKITS: MIND, BODY, HEART AND SPIRIT**

- **LEVEL ONE:** Solo Skills. Using your toolkit with yourself to play your own instrument.

- **LEVEL TWO:** Partner Skills. Using your toolkit to play with others.

**ADVANCED SEXCRAFT RELATIONSKILLS**

- **LEVEL THREE:** Advanced Partner Skills. Additional advanced skills beyond your sexcraft toolkit are needed to create and sustain conscious, intimate connection.

*If you have built castles in the air, your work need not be lost, that is where they should be. Now put foundations under them.*

HENRY DAVID
THOREAU

Sheri Winston, *Venus and Domains*

**RELATIONSKILLS—BEYOND YOUR TOOLKIT**

Beyond your toolkit, there are additional skills that you need to create and sustain healthy, functional and conscious relationships. For this, our erotic tools aren't enough. We need what I call relationskills—which include having exquisite boundaries, exercising personal responsibility, treating oneself and others with respect, and communicating and negotiating skillfully. While a more extended discussion of them is beyond the scope of this book, I note them here so you're aware that there's more to being a great partner then being a skilled lover.

**Level Three: SexCraft Relationskills**

These are the advanced partner tools and skills needed to create and maintain healthy intimate relationships.

AWARENESS BALANCE BETWEEN:
- SELF-AWARENESS ("I")
- PARTNER-AWARENESS ("You")
- PARTNERSHIP AWARENESS ("Us")

COMMUNICATION SKILLS: Techniques of compassionate, non-violent, conscious communication

BOUNDARY SKILLS: Combine awareness, communication, respect, responsibility and protection

PARTNER PLEASURE SKILLS: Techniques of pleasuring others

PARTNERED OR GROUP ENERGY—Includes energy sex

SEXUAL TELEPATHY: A magical trance state of ultimate connection

## Whole Wholistic Sexuality

The Wholistic Sexuality approach offers a loving, responsible, respectful and ecstatic vision of what sexuality can be for you and for us all. I invite you to imagine a world where:

- It's understood that to be a connected, conscious, well-adjusted person, you need to be in a healthy relationship with yourself about your sexuality.

- Eros's power is affirmed and celebrated.

- People spend their time in loving relationship with themselves and others.

- They feel viscerally connected to all life on the planet.

It's understandable if this seems utopian. But dramatic change can happen very quickly. Fifty years ago, unmarried women couldn't get contraception. Twenty years ago, gay marriage seemed like a pipe dream. So did the election of a black President. Now look where we are!

How does such huge change happen? One person at a time, starting with you. When you discover your own erotic power, it's transformative and empowering.

Your sexual confidence and ease are an inner shift that influences how you interact with your family, your friends and communities and ultimately, the world. Your transformation ripples out. Then the next person's change ripples out. When the time is right, the tide turns and washes walls away.

If more people were sexually responsible, self-loving and empowered, we'd have less violence in general and, more specifically, less sexual violence, intolerance of diversity, and disempowering sexual experiences. People would appreciate the value of pleasure for its many benefits and for its own sake. A sex-positive world would offer truly comprehensive sex education for everyone and the curriculum would include how to have amazing sex.

> *The future belongs to those who believe in the beauty of their dreams.*
>
> ELEANOR ROOSEVELT

Together, we can collectively co-create a world that values connection over domination and greed. We can craft a world based on the principles that pleasure is our birthright and that we're connected at all levels with all beings. Granted, it's an ambitious dream—but that's how transformation happens.

Where to begin? With our primary relationship—the one we have with ourselves.

And that's a beautiful new story.

Eric Gill, *Lovers*

# CHAPTER FOUR

# IT'S ALL ABOUT YOU

*We have it in us to be splendid.*

MAYA ANGELOU

## You Are a Village

WHEN MOST PEOPLE THINK ABOUT SEX, THEY USUALLY IMAGINE TWO people rolling around in bed together. Sex, in other words, is something you do with someone else. At the heart of the Wholistic Sexuality vision is a fundamentally different view of sex. It proposes that *your sexuality is first and foremost about your relationship with yourself.* While solo sex is an essential component, your self-relationship is about much more than the time you spend playing with your juicy bits.

It's understandable if this feels counter-intuitive. A relationship with myself? How is that even possible? To be in relationship means that there has to be an other. I'm in a relationship with Joe or Jill or my cat. Or my work. Or the planet. How can I be in relationship with me when I *am* me?

Here's the answer to this very reasonable question. While you may think of yourself as a singular person, the truth is we are each many. The old story is that you're a unitary and consistent self. I'd like to offer an alternative narrative— inside you lives a multitude of sub-personalities, a committee of personas, various versions of you that show up depending on mood and circumstance. You are an ensemble with a cast of characters inside who may have different ideas, beliefs and yearnings.

The notion that you're a unitary being is actually kind of delusional. You've got an entire village living inside you.

There are parts of you that have stayed consistent over time and parts that have changed. You have public selves that show up to the world. You have family roles, work roles, social roles. You have private, secret selves that include your shadow parts, the dark sides of your power, the shamed and disowned pieces that you may have a hard time even admitting are a part of you. You have false faces, masks built up out of defenses and invalid counter-productive narratives. There's your inner lover and your inner warrior, your inner critic, your comic and your cynic. You have a passel of inner children, whole and wounded, of all ages. And that's not all, folks . . . there are many more.

And always at your core lies your true essence, your most authentic and pure self.

Your connection to yourself isn't only about your many different you's. It's also about how you relate to the different aspects of yourself, including your relationship with:

- YOUR HARDWARE—including how you feel about, and what you do with, your inherent talents, intelligences, aptitudes and challenges.

- YOUR ENVIRONMENT—including your history and experiences and the meanings you've made about all that, and

- YOUR BODY, mind, heart and spirit.

And so, when I talk about your connection with yourself, I'm really talking about your relationships with all these aspects of the complex person that is you. The real question isn't "How can I possibly be in relationship with myself?" but "How can I not be?"

Alméry Lobel-Riche

*I am large, I contain multitudes.*

WALT WHITMAN

Recognizing that you're an internal community enables you to skillfully manage all your selves in ways that allow your essence to rise and shine. If you choose, you can literally hold committee meetings, allowing each member to have their say, giving each aspect of yourself a voice. Once you start to identify the myriad characters inside yourself, you can begin to hear their stories, opinions and desires. Luckily, you've got a facilitator, mediator, and therapist plus a good mother and father in there since you need them all to manage the fractious family that is you. You can discover whose stories may or may not be useful for you and choose which narratives serve you best.

When you're in healthy inner relationship with yourself, you recognize and honor all the parts of you, while consciously choosing which gets to be the driver behind the wheel. You've achieved true maturity and wisdom when you act from your authentic core essence in every moment.

(Okay, let's be realistic—most of the time.)

One skin, many selves. That's my starting point and why it's not entirely accurate to say that our most important relationship is with our self.

No: Our most important relationship is with our selves.

---

*It is easy to live for others. Everybody does.*
*I call on you to live for yourselves.*

RALPH WALDO EMERSON

## Till Death Do You Part, You'll Be Partnered with ... You

How kind are you to yourself? How much delight do you take in who you are? To what extent are you your own best booster and champion? Do you support yourself to learn and grow? How good a lover are you to yourself?

If you want to have great relationships with others, it starts with your relationship with yourself. If you don't love yourself well, it won't be easy to love others well

Anonymous Indian Painting from 1780

or be loved by them, either. In fact, in order to have ecstatic sex and authentic intimacy with your lovers, you need to have a healthy sexual relationship with your lifelong primary partner—you!

I'm not emphasizing your connection with yourself only because it will improve your partner relationships. Whether or not you have intimate erotic relationships with others is entirely optional. It's not better or worse to be partnered or to be single (or in any particular relationship variation). There's no 'right way.' Nor do you need an intimate partner other than yourself to go on the journey of self-love and erotic discovery I lay out in these pages. While it's delightful to be physically intimate with someone else, you can flourish and be sexually whole and ecstatic without it.

I want to be very clear about this: You can have a full and wonderful sex life while not having sex with others. It's not as if your relationship with yourself needs to be boring!

After all, you contain multitudes.

## You Are Your History

As a midwife, I've been privileged to witness many truly natural woman-centered births where the babies came out beaming like little bodhisattvas. Few of us had such birth experiences, but that's what we were evolutionarily programmed for, to be born in bliss as we inhaled our first breath and our mother fell deeply in primal love with us.

The evolutionary template is to be given the glorious breast with its ideal combination of sustenance and love—the perfect package of warm flesh, delicious milk, safe arms and adoring maternal gaze. Unfortunately, if you're like most people in our culture, a stranger whisked you away from your mother and did uncomfortable things to your body while you cried in fear. Many of you were pacified with a plastic nipple, an object in place of an ecstatic relationship with another human being. And not just any human being, mind you, but the one we've been literally inhabiting for nine months and who is biologically programmed to be madly in love

Auguste Renoir
*Maternite dit aussi l'Enfant au sein*

with us. Instead of being given Mama's bountiful breast, many of us got a bottle filled with nasty-tasting formula that made our little tummies hurt. How could something plastic and unfeeling possibly substitute for a person who bestows on us a perfect combination of food and love?

We can probably all agree that feeling alone and deprived at such an early age is not the ideal foundation for self-love and a healthy inner connection. Or the best blueprint for your adult intimate relationships.

Your relationship with your own sexuality began right there in how you were birthed and cared for afterward, in how you were fed, held and loved. Your inner connection with yourself integrates everything that has happened to you throughout the course of your life, including seemingly minor things such as how your body (and especially your genitals) were handled as your caregivers bathed you, whether someone responded when you cried, and whether you were looked at with smiling eyes full of love . . . or not.

Your self-relationship reflects the patchwork of customs, traditions, values and behaviors of your family of origin. Did you see your parents or siblings comfortably naked? Did you hear adults making love? Were you touched with tenderness, respect and care or with cold efficiency? Were you spanked or otherwise transgressed? Or perhaps not touched at all?

As you grew older and more verbally curious, what were you told about your own and others' bodies? Did your parents have a name for your genitals or were they simply a place 'down there,' as if they were Africa as imagined by white Westerners of the 19th Century—a dark, wild, scary place where no truly civilized person would ever want to go? When you reached down and played with your body, discovering your pleasure, did your caregivers smile or smack you? The list goes on and on. How were you toilet-trained? Fed? Were your feelings respected? Did you feel cherished or violated? Was your truth heard or ignored? What flavor did love come in and was there a limit on how much you got?*

*Sex is hardly ever just about sex.*

SHIRLEY MACLAINE

Unlike other animals, people make meaning constantly, and so you transformed your life experiences into a belief system about how things really are. Whatever happened to you became your truth about your inherent worth, the right way to treat others, the nature and limits of love, and much more.

As you grew into childhood, your sexuality developed along with the rest of you. Did you especially like the smell of one of your playmates? Did you roughhouse or cuddle with them? Did you play "I'll show you mine if you show me yours?" When you asked how babies were made, what were you told—and did you believe it?

And then there are the messages you got as you were rocked by the hormones and confusions of puberty. If you had a penis, what did your parents tell you about the bizarre body behavior called ejaculation? If you were female, how did your caregivers prepare you for your first bleeding? Was it something to celebrate and be proud of, or was it presented as something disgusting and embarrassing?

---

* If you were bottle-fed, the answer is yes. The evolutionary template assumes abundance: breasts don't run dry. Bottles do, though. Along with formula, they deliver a harsh story to babies. There is only so much love. (And it often tastes bad, too.)

What were you told or, more importantly, shown about gender roles? What did the males around you model about how to be a man? What did women teach you about being a woman? Did anyone ever mention people who are in-between? How did you discover your sexual preference? Did you have healthy, loving intimate relationships modeled for you, or did you only see dysfunctional ones?

Your entire life experience, including everything you've learned consciously and unconsciously, shows up in your relationship with yourself. Your history lives inside you.

---

# $\mathcal{S}$ucculent $\mathcal{S}$ummary

## Relationship Status: ~~It's~~ I'm Complicated!

YOUR RELATIONSHIP with your sexuality is as complex, unique and individual as you are. It includes pretty much everything about you, including all your different you's:

- YOUR PHYSICAL, mental, emotional and spiritual relationship with your body, mind, heart and spirit

- YOUR HISTORY and life experiences

- YOUR PAST AND PRESENT values and beliefs

- YOUR PAST AND CURRENT intimate relationships

- YOUR INTERACTIONS with your various local communities, the ubiquitous pervasive media, all aspects of our culture and our world

- YOUR IMAGINED FUTURES

- THE STRUCTURES (including defenses) of your personality

- YOUR DIFFERENT PERSONAS—the full congress of your selves

- YOUR VARIOUS WAYS OF BEING, which often depend on the circumstances of the moment (for example, how you are at work or when you're with your family of origin)

- ALL OF THE AGES you've been

- YOUR IMAGINED SELVES, including your ideal self

- YOUR DIVINE ESSENCE.

## A Hologram of Yourself

Your life experience shows up vividly in your relationship with your sexuality, which is a hologram—a distillation and representation of everything that you are and that has formed you to this day. Your sex life is a microcosm of your whole life.

Unfortunately, most of us grow up with stories about ourselves and our sexuality that shame and diminish us. One of our most important life tasks is to banish these stories and replace them with ones that help us delight in our sexuality and take a healthy pride in who we are. We need to let the flower of our true self bloom. We do this by unearthing the toxic negative messages about ourselves and our sexuality that have kept us stunted; by fertilizing our garden with positive stories about ourselves and our sexuality; and by shining the light of self-

Franz von Bayros, *Pentamerone*

love on ourselves—on this individual who's the most important person in the world to us, on this being who'll be with us until our dying day.

Healing ourselves is never over; it's always a work-in-progress. And though there never comes a time when you can kick back and say, "Mission accomplished!," you can transform yourself dramatically along the way. You can have compassion for who you were, appreciation for who you've become and acceptance for the forces that shaped you. You can love where there was loathing; you can flourish where you floundered. And, you can accelerate this process by focusing on your sexuality.

*Forget your perfect offering,*
*there is a crack in everything.*
*That's how the light gets in.*

LEONARD COHEN

Here's an important but well-kept secret: When you explore your sexual potential, you're not just working with your capacity for pleasure and ecstasy. You're transforming all of who you are.

Your sexuality is a gateway to yourself.

## Map Your Sexual Self

THIS IS BEST DONE as a writing exercise, but it can also be a meditation.

On a blank page, draw a circle in the middle and put your sexual self inside (Write "Sexual Me" or "My Sexual Self.") Write whatever words pop into your mind, then circle each one and draw connecting lines between them, allowing a web of connections to emerge.

Art Option: Make a collage of images.

However you do it, keep playing with it and adding to it.

*Sex is a discovery.*

FANNIE HURST

FOOD FOR THOUGHT

## Know Thyself

Do this as a spontaneous writing exercise. Don't think about it—just write the first things that pop into your head. Write as much as you want for each.

- SEX IS . . .

- WHEN I IMAGINE myself having sex, I feel . . .

- WHEN I DESCRIBE my sexual self, I say I am . . .

- MY BODY IS . . .

- MY DARKEST FANTASIES are or include . . .

- IF MY GENITALS could speak, they'd say . . .

## Play with Yourself (But Don't Masturbate)

In our culture, masturbation still gets a bad rap. While we may no longer believe it causes degeneracy and disease or causes people to go blind (although I do know a lot of folks who wear glasses!), we still don't celebrate solo sex for the wonderful, self-loving, healthy and pleasurable practice it is.

Anonymous, possibly Deveria

We don't even have a good name for it. I rarely use the word masturbation, preferring to call it solo sex, sexual self-love, playing with yourself, or self-pleasuring. I never cared for the M-word and now that I know the derivation of the word, I like it even less. The Latin roots of the word mean 'to pollute with your hand.' That's certainly not what I'm doing with my hand when it's busy down below! Nor am I committing 'self-abuse.' When you're self-pleasuring, you're doing lots of things—giving yourself sexual loving, learning how to expand your responses, practicing skills, exploring your fantasies, enhancing your mental and physical well-being, improving your vitality, having a good time, receiving pleasure and relaxing. That sounds like a recipe for health and happiness to me! So I encourage you to play with yourself, but never to "masturbate."

Our dominant culture still encourages guilt, if not of the mortal sin variety, then of the mildly shameful or "You're being self-indulgent and wasting time" kind. I find this ironic since we get many of the same benefits from sexual pleasure (whether solo or partnered) that we derive from exercise and meditation. We feel virtuous when we work out or meditate, while taking the same amount of time to have some juicy solo sex is considered frivolous and decadent or worse. When will our puritan culture get over it and accept that solo sex isn't a dissolute fall into wanton lust, but an ascent into self-love that celebrates your desire, hones your abilities and ultimately honors yourself? While the sex you have with yourself certainly isn't all there is to your relationship with yourself, it's an essential component.

Are you practicing sexual self-love? If your answer is "I don't do that," I strongly encourage you to start now. If you're thinking, "But that's not real sex, it doesn't count," it's time for a new story. Think of your solo sex as an affirmation of your juiciness and an essential practice on your path to becoming sexually masterful.

For those of you who do have 'do-dates' with yourself, I have a question for you: How's it going? While you can't really have bad sex with yourself, you can certainly have mediocre experiences. If you're disconnected from yourself or just going through the motions, your solo sex will reflect that. Do you only give yourself quickies? Just having frantic fast-food snacks? Are you a poor lover to yourself?

I hope not.

How would your dream lover treat you? In what ways would he or she delight you? When you practice solo sex, that's how I invite you to treat yourself.

---

### WORD NERD

## Levels of Self-Pleasure

Here's a simple hierarchy of levels of self-pleasuring:

- *Good* solo sex means you're taking the time to tune in—it's an orgasmic and pleasurable, simple healthy meal.

- You're having *great* solo sex when you're taking time to explore, experiment and expand your erotic repertoire with a gourmet repast full of depth, variety and deliciousness. It's leisurely and luscious and a break from your normal routine.

- You're in the *ecstatic* zone when you take yourself out, out, out—and then even further out. Ecstatic solo sex may involve ritual or orgasmic meditation practices and is a feast of tranced-out consciousness.

---

FOOD FOR THOUGHT

## Pleasure List

MAKE A LIST OF THINGS that you can do for (and with) yourself that give you pleasure. Include things that you can do in a few minutes, that require a medium chunk of time, and that need a leisurely time span. Include things that are free (although luxuries that cost money are okay, too).

PUT YOUR LIST WHERE YOU'LL SEE IT. Add to it as you discover new ways to nurture, love and pleasure yourself.

TAKE REGULAR PLEASURE BREAKS during your day and do something on your list. Or, start your day by doing something that makes you feel good and happy. Conclude your evening with another pleasurable action or activity.

SUGGESTIONS: Sing a song. Make a piece of art. Read. Stretch. Dance. Have orgasms. Do orgasmic breathing. Take a hot scented bath by candlelight. Listen to the birds. Pat your pet (your four-footed one, not your genital one). Drink water. Get and give massage. Take three deep slow breaths. Listen to music. Take a walk in nature. Chocolate! Mangos!

Don't limit yourself to this list—do what brings you pleasure. Make pleasure a habit. And a practice.

Shunga, *Reading a Shunga Book*

*Don't worry about what the world needs. Ask what makes you come alive—and do that. Because what the world needs are people who have come alive.*

HOWARD
THURMAN

## The Great Solo-Sex Gender Gap

Think of all the slang terms there are for male self-pleasuring—jack off, pull the pud, flog the dolphin, spank the monkey, and many more—and how few there are for the female equivalent. The phrase 'jilling off' is of recent coinage and hasn't caught on. 'Pet the pussy?' 'Rub off?'

We're still waiting for the language around female solo sex to be as evocative and abundant as it is for male self-pleasuring.

This directly reflects the fact that unlike men, a significant number of women don't play with themselves. The real shame is that shame inhibits women from being erotic with themselves—and the result is less sexually satisfied women. Women who self-pleasure have better sex with others, are more orgasmic and are more satisfied with their sexuality. When you practice playing your own instrument, you develop your erotic skills and discover what works for you. So, ladies,

Abigail Ekue, *Untitled*

if you aren't already petting your pussy, there's no time like the present to begin.

Most men don't need to be told to play with themselves. They've got that one under control—you might say they've got a firm grasp on the situation. However, even for those men and women who already engage in solo play, many do so quickly and quietly, without much real attention.

## Love To Love Me, Baby

In large measure, our furtive and minimalist approach to solo sex reflects our dominant culture's shaming of sex in general and self-pleasuring in particular. We just don't devote much thought, time or energy to it. I'm not saying you should never have a quickie with yourself or just do a utilitarian job of getting off so you can sleep or relieve tension. A speedy sex session with yourself is a

*The erotic cannot be felt secondhand.*

AUDRE LORDE

great way to do both. Yet it's also the case that dedicating more time and quality energy to your practice will benefit you in a multitude of ways.

Self-pleasuring is your opportunity to embody self-love—literally. It's where you can practice caring for and being *very* nice to yourself! Solo sex is your learning laboratory for running experiments. It's your rehearsal hall for practicing skills that, if you choose, you can bring to your erotic interactions with others. Solo sex sessions give you the opportunity to pay attention to yourself and your own experience without the distraction of someone else's needs, expectations and desires. It's where you can try new things to see if you like them, discover what works

*Don't knock masturbation— it's sex with someone I love.*

WOODY ALLEN

for you and repeat anything that's good—as often as you want and have time for!

In the Taoist tradition, solo sex is called self-cultivation. I like how that implies that auto-eroticism is beneficial, life-enhancing and something you can develop. If you need a good reason to embrace solo erotic practice, try on the idea that self-pleasuring is part of your ongoing personal growth program.

---

PLAY & PRACTICE

SOLO PLAY

### Make a Date with Yourself

THIS ONE MAY BE HARD for you even to imagine, much less do. Begin by thinking about the wonderful things you'd do on a romantic sexy date.

Vinette Perez, *Vivify*

Imagine a perfect rendezvous with your lover. Envision all the details.

Only—this date is with yourself.

HOW DO YOU PREPARE YOURSELF? Here are some suggestions—feel free to follow your own instincts here. Take a scented, candle-lit bath. Get your body all clean and delicious. Put on your most luscious silky lingerie, a velvet robe or a racy costume. Take the time to groom yourself—a close shave and a manicure, perhaps?

YOU'LL WANT TO PREPARE your love bower. Make it clean and inviting. Be sure it's warm and comfortable and all your supplies are close at hand.

NOW DO ALL THE THINGS you'd do with a lover. Enjoy a delectable meal and a glass of fine wine (not too much!). Move on to a slow, full-body sensuous self-massage. Have a sexy dance to your favorite steamy music. Seduce yourself! Make love to yourself for a good, long, titillating time. Don't forget to have a loving solo cuddle when you're done and to whisper sweet nothings to yourself. "Thanks, it was great for me, too!"

(See *The Well-Stocked Boudoir* sidebar here and *Creating Your Erotic Temple* in chapter 14 for suggestions.)

## Create-A-Space

If you meditate regularly, you may have set up a spot just for that practice. If you're trying to exercise and stretch, having an open area with mats and equipment helps make it happen. The same is true for your erotic practice. Create a beautiful, peaceful and sensuous space that will make it easy and enhance your experience. Set up your boudoir (or den or wherever) with everything you need for your pleasure. If you don't have room for a permanent space just for sex, create a temple-in-a-box and put your sex supplies in a basket so you can quickly transform a mundane space into a special one.

---

PLAY & PRACTICE

HOT AND JUICY TIPS

### The Well-Stocked Boudoir

WHAT TO HAVE:

- Plenty of water
- Bendy straws (so you can hydrate without having to change position)
- Variety of lubricants and massage oils
- Candles or dimmable lights
- Variety of sex cushions
- Incense, aromatherapy spritzers
- Fresh flowers, green plants
- If you have kids—a lock on your door
- Sex toys
- Sensual playthings (feathers, fur and . . .)
- Music
- Breath mints or spray
- If you're planning on having a long playdate, healthy snacks like fruit and nuts

WHAT NOT TO HAVE:

- Mess, disorder
- Any stuff that reminds you of work
- Electronics (TV, computer)—or cover with decorative fabric
- Your phone!
- Clock (cover it up)

---

SUCCULENT SEX CRAFT

Giulio Romano, *The Lovers* (detail)

## Make the Time

To be a good student and learn quickly, you need to practice regularly. This requires you to carve out time in your busy schedule. Yes, the notion of giving your solo-sex practice sessions space on your calendar may seem weird. To overcome this perspective, which really is only a reflection of our broader cultural negativity, I invite you to ask yourself these questions. Is your full sexual empowerment important to you? Do you value your delight enough to make these sessions happen? Do you want more pleasure in your life? Do you desire to become more skilled with your sexual instrument?

If you answered "yes" to any of these questions, do what it takes to give yourself uninterrupted private time. Put it in your calendar. Farm out the kids. Turn off the phone. Put on music you love and pleasure yourself until the music ends. Make dates with yourself and then keep them!

Not occasionally. Regularly. Because your pleasure is worth it!

*how fortunate are you and I, whose home*
*is timelessness: we who have wandered down*
*from fragrant mountains of eternal now*
*to frolic in such mysteries as birth*
*and death a day (or maybe even less)*

E.E.CUMMINGS

# Section Two

# Essential Maps and Models

*The omnipresent process of sex, as it is woven into
the whole texture of our man's or woman's body, is
the pattern of all the process of our life.*

HAVELOCK ELLIS

George Barbier, *Nijinsky*

# CHAPTER FIVE

# THE ALTERED STATES
# OF EROTICA

*I want to do to you what spring
does with the cherry trees.*

PABLO NERUDA

## You Are Getting Sexy, Very Sexy

WHAT IS SEXUAL AROUSAL AND WHAT HAPPENS WHEN WE VISIT THIS
familiar yet mysterious land?

Simply put, it's a particular (and particularly delicious) type of trance state.

A trance is an altered state of consciousness that's different from our everyday
mundane awareness. Also known
as 'non-ordinary reality,' it's any
mind-body state other than our so-
called normal consciousness. While
rational, analytical awareness is the
most valued way to be in Western
culture, we actually move in and out
of different states of consciousness
all the time. Daydreaming, reveries,
doodling and fantasizing are all light
trance states. You can go into trance
by meditating, chanting, dancing or
drumming. Women need to enter
a deeply altered state to labor and
birth successfully.

> **WORD NERD**
> **Body-Mind or Mind-Body:**
> Your physical body and your
> mind are so connected that it's
> often impossible to separate
> them into distinct parts. For
> this reason, I sometimes use the
> phrases body-mind or mind-
> body when the parts are so
> conceptually and functionally
> intertwined as to be essentially
> inseparable.

During sexual arousal, your sense of time shifts, the focus of your attention
alters and you move into a state of flow that feels more attuned to the moment.
While this is true of all altered states of consciousness, your turn-on trance

has some very special qualities. It's characterized by a deepened awareness of bodily sensation, a higher pain threshold and feelings of heightened pleasure. Your heart races, your breath quickens and you dissolve into a state of euphoria as you go 'somewhere else.'

The arousal process begins when we start to leave mundane reality and enter light trance. It builds as we travel more deeply into our altered state. In deep arousal, you become utterly absorbed and entranced. Self-consciousness evaporates and a feeling of relaxed concentration takes over. You don't need to plan or think, you just go with the flow and follow the path of your erotic energy. Your attention becomes intensely attuned to your immediate physical and emotional experience. Your awareness becomes filled with sensational sensation. The clamor of your day-to-day existence melts away as you go deeper into your trance and soar into the realms of the ecstatic.

### WORD NERD

**Ecstasy:** to be outside (*ec*) our usual state (*stasis*).

Whether you think of it as going 'in' or 'out,' you go somewhere—on an erotic voyage that takes you out of yourself for a time. When it's over, you return to the ordinary world. (Hopefully aglow and content.)

While altered states happen naturally, you can also learn how to enhance this innate capability. Cultivate your skills to turn up your turn on and you'll find yourself having the transcendent sex you dream of.

Titian, *Danae and the Shower of Gold*

# Succulent Summary

## What Happens in Altered States of Consciousness?

- You experience reality differently from 'everyday' awareness.

- You lose ego boundaries and self-consciousness—and become, in this limited sense, more like non-human animals.

- You experience changes in attention and awareness including hyper-focus, expanded attention, increased awareness of self, and decreased awareness of anything outside the self.

- Perceptual shifts

- Sense of escape or journey

- Timelessness or shift in time sense

- Access to information that you can't normally discern with your conscious mind.

William-Adolphe Bouguereau, *The Lost Star of the Pleiades*

## An Improvisational Dance of Arousal

The typical Western scenario of partnered sexual encounters tends to follow a standard and woefully limited script. Opening shot—clothes get rapidly shed (or ripped off) at the beginning of your wordless, fast and furious romp. You start off excited and are quickly overwhelmed by desire. You rapidly get more and more turned on, revving up quickly (and quietly) till you reach a single explosive peak of orgasmic explosion—then you're done. You collapse alongside each other in a heap of happy exhaustion. Scene over—cut!

---

### Fascinating Facts

**Fast Food Sex**

The median time for sexual intercourse is 7.3 minutes.
—*From a four-week study of 1,500 couples in 2005*

A full 50 percent of people said they weren't happy with the duration (or lack thereof) of their sex. The average amount of time people reported for their average sexual encounter was 10 minutes, leading 38 percent of respondents to say that their lovemaking is over too fast.
—*Condom company Durex® 2012 poll of 1,000 adults, married and single.*

---

While there's nothing wrong with this scenario, if that's all that's on your menu you're leading a fast-food sex life and probably missing out on enormous amounts of pleasure. I invite you to invoke a different metaphor: Imagine your erotic experiences as a broad assortment of leisurely, luxurious gourmet feasts, as a banquet of slow-cooked passion and possibilities.

Or, to switch metaphors, your arousal trance is like a musical jam session. You enter it not knowing where it's going to go, how long it will continue or what will happen. There's an interplay of sound and silence, motion and stillness, fast and slow. A great improv explores nooks and crannies—it roams and rambles. Sometimes it dallies with delightful deliberateness and at other times it's an intense driving rhythm. Each altered-state occasion is its own inspired and unique improvisational journey whether you're making music or making love.

Kangra style, 1790

# Science Geek Goodies

## Brain Waves and States

Here's a list of different states of consciousness and their characteristics.

─────────────── **'ORDINARY' REALITY** ───────────────

## Beta

- Normal conscious brain activity includes states ranging from calm and relaxed to high excitation, flight-or-fight reactions and panic.
- Thinking, articulate, logical, linear, rational.

─────────────── **ALTERED STATES OF CONSCIOUSNESSS:** ───────────────

## Alpha

- Light trance: Daydream. Reverie. Doodling. Engrossed in TV or movie.
- Greater access to emotions and sensual experience.
- A bridge state from beta/ordinary reality to deeper states. You often shift between beta and alpha as you check to see if it's safe to check out.
- Characteristic of early- to mid-level arousal.

## Theta

- Deep trance.
- Sense of being transported. Often return with deep insights, profound understanding and awareness.
- A potentially powerful healing state
- The realm of the subconscious
- High level, deep arousal. Normal orgasm. Natural birth.

## Delta

- Very deep trance. Deeper than theta.
- The realm of the unconscious.
- Access to the 'collective unconscious,' a storehouse of universal archetypes, memories, instincts, experiences and evolutionary templates.
- Cosmic—ecstatic states including: ecstatic birth; transcendent sex; divine union. Multiple, expanded and mega-orgasms.

## Gamma

- Lacks research; hard to measure.
- Super fast waves.
- Hyper-alertness, integration.
- Acute perception.

Whether you're playing solo or with someone else, arousal doesn't need to be about getting to the promised lands of orgasm or penetrative sex as fast as possible. When done masterfully, it's an extemporaneous work of art, a leisurely and creative journey into pleasure.

### Pleasure and Pain

The experience of sexual arousal alters perceptions of both pain and pleasure in all the right directions. During arousal, you become increasingly sensitive to pleasure as your awareness of it expands and your reactions to it increase. At the same time, your ability to perceive pain diminishes to the extent that it can magically vanish as you get immersed in arousal. Rather than a headache being an excuse to not have sex, it could be a great motivator to get turned on and orgasmic—and be feeling no pain.

This shift in perception explains why people often experience the same stimulation differently at various points in their erotic trance journey. A particular action can be non-arousing, irritating or painful when you're in mundane consciousness or early arousal, yet the same move can give exquisite pleasure when you're in a deep erotic trance. Think how a nipple tweak can be unpleasant or even painful if you're not turned on and how that same pinch can be oh so exciting when you're immersed in your erotic spell.

This is one of the reasons why ongoing communication and feedback are so important during partner play. You're working with a moving target and need to stay apprised of what is and isn't working.

## The Arousal Journey Up the Stairs

Imagine the process of sexual arousal as a flight of ten stairs, with the tenth representing orgasm. (Watch out for that top step—it's a doozy!) When you're not turned on at all, you're on the ground floor. The first stirrings of arousal bring you to step one. Mid-level arousal is the middle of the staircase, step five. Step nine is the highest level of excitement, just before your orgasm. We'll focus later on that very special tenth step, but for now let's concentrate on understanding the experience and dynamics of the arousal journey.

A basic biological reality about arousal is that you can't skip over any steps. No leaping from step two to step eight in a single bound. ("It's a bird! It's a plane! No, it's Super-sexy!") Each step is created by biochemical feedback loops that spiral us up to the next one, which leads to the one after that. While you can't make a super-human leap and omit any steps, you can develop the capacity to 'work the stairs,' so to speak.

That's right, you can become the Stairmaster!

You can learn to climb faster or drop back down. You can get the hang of hanging out and playing on individual steps—which can be a great move to deepen your arousal trance. You can learn how to not get stuck on a step and what to do if you find yourself unable to get where you want to go. You can learn how to stay on your arousal staircase and not fall off despite distractions—you know, like when the phone rings and you suddenly find yourself back in mundane consciousness and turned off.

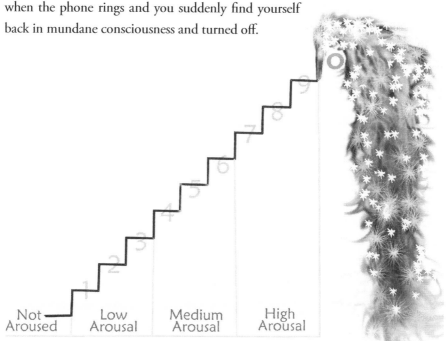

Sheri Winston, *Arousal Stairs (Altered Stairs of Consciousness)*

I find it useful to divide the staircase into three sections. The first three steps are low-level arousal, the middle three are medium, and the top three are high arousal.

Low-level arousal is the warm-up and transition period. Some might say this is the time for foreplay, but I don't like to use that word. I prefer 'warm-up' to 'foreplay.' Foreplay implies it's a mere precursor to the main event, which by implication makes your early arousal activities less important than 'real sex' (for hetero couples, usually penis-in-vagina intercourse).

We typically think of foreplay as something that women need and men don't. A common complaint of hetero women is that men rush through the warm-up phase.

Whatever your gender, preference or orientation, early arousal is your opportunity to get relaxed and present. It's when you loosen up and take the time to awaken your whole body. It's when you let your busy front-brain executive office start to shut down and go off-line.

Warm-up: It's not for women only!

In the early stages of arousal, you're flickering between beta wave 'real world' consciousness and alpha's light trance state. As you feel safe enough to turn off your vigilance centers and leave your alert thinking mentality behind, you start to lose yourself in pleasure. The easier it is to feel safe, the quicker you'll fully enter erotic trance. The more times you have to return to vigilance and thinking, the harder it becomes to relax and move deeper into an altered state.

Your mid-level steps are where you're starting to be taken over by your erotic energy. You're leaving the thoughts and cares of the mundane world behind and getting into the rhythms and delights of your erotic improvisation. You move from beta to theta and become increasingly absorbed in your erotic altered state.

At the highest steps, you're in a state of intense arousal. You're carried higher and higher by the tide of Eros, transported by the powerful sexy flow out of thought and time, beyond self-consciousness—you're zooming into the Erosphere.

## WIDENING THE STAIRS

Our staircase arousal map started out as a flat, two-dimensional model. You could only go up or down. But your actual arousal trance has another, important dimension—depth. I invite you to be aware not only of what step you're on, but also how deeply you're in your trance at each level.

If your trance state is shallow, it's as if your stairs are narrow, which makes it easy to get knocked off and out of your arousal spell. The more deeply entranced you are at each level of the arousal experience, the less likely you are to tumble back to zero and re-enter the world of chattering, thinking, unsexy reality. The wider your stairs—the deeper your trance—the easier it becomes to go in even deeper, get ecstatic and have spectacular orgasms.

How do you deepen your trance? By using your sexcraft toolkit of mind, body, heart and spirit to transport you ever further into your altered state of consciousness, whether alone or accompanied. The more skillfully you play your own instrument, the more entranced you'll become. And, if you're playing with a partner, you can use those same skills to encourage them to go deeper into their trance and to get your states to harmonize and synchronize.

Sheri Winston,
*Widening the Arousal Stairs*

While it can be fun to take a fast run up the stairs culminating in a single orgasmic peak, there are advantages in not just going up, up, up and over. You can deepen your trance by taking your time and dallying on each step. You can intensify it further by playing with bringing the arousal up gradually, dropping it down and raising it up again (and down and up again). Every time you rev up and then downshift, you're widening your arousal stairs, magnifying your erotic energy.

You can breeze up the steps in your rush to get to the big O, but lingering in arousal has big benefits—the longer you hang out, the more charge you build up, and the bigger your orgasmic waves can be.

## AROUSAL SPIRALS

If the linear stairway model doesn't quite work for you, here's an alternative: I call it Arousal Energy Spirals— it's what I see when I'm in my arousal trance. Imagine that erotic energy consists of lots and lots of sparkly particles. Arousal begins when the diffuse particles gather and coalesce. The energy spirals start small and then, as the arousal builds, they expand, growing denser and wider. As the journey progresses, the energy comes together, twisting,

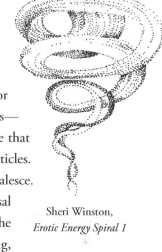

Sheri Winston,
*Erotic Energy Spiral 1*

coiling, and intensifying. As you play with raising and lowering the arousal level, the spirals swirl and dip, tangle and twist, pulsate and pulse, grow and rise. The more you amplify the energy, the more there is to play with and, when the time comes, the more explosive your orgasm (or orgasms) can be.

---

## Succulent Summary

### What Is Sexual Arousal?

SEXUAL AROUSAL IS:

- An altered state of consciousness
- A type of trance
- A journey
- A dynamic interplay of tension and relaxation
- An improvisational dance
- A romp on the 'stairs'

---

### Arousal Awareness

**SOLO:**

AS YOU TAKE YOURSELF THROUGH your next sexual trance journey, pause occasionally and tune into your arousal level. Ask yourself, "What level am I at?"

The first time you do it, you may choose to simply use low, medium or high. The next couple of times, try to get more precise: Use the 'stair' numbers. Start to distinguish what it feels like to be at a four compared to a five. Notice what's happening with your sensations when you're at a two or a six. What's your breathing like at different steps? Do some internal research and notice the differences in how you feel, what you're aware of, your pleasure level, bodily sensations, postures and movements.

Run some experiments and play with bringing your attention to your arousal level during different erotic activities. What brings it up a step? What drops it back down? Can you hang out on the same step for awhile? Can you stay on step five more easily than nine?

Next, notice how deeply you're in trance at each level. Are your stairs wide, medium or narrow? What's the difference between a shallow five and a deep five? How is nine different when you're in a more superficial trance compared to being deeply in?

**PARTNERED:**

At various points in your erotic interaction, share with each other the level of arousal you're at. See if you can guess where your partner is. Notice if it helps refine your partner play when you say things like, "I need to be at an eight or nine for penetration to feel fabulous to me" or "I'm at a nine—let's see how long I can stay there." It can also be useful to share how shallow, moderate or deep your trance state is. Later you can talk about the difference between being on a step in a shallow or deep way.

## Exploring the Wild Woods of Pleasure

The things you imagine and do to get turned on are your paths to arousal and orgasm. These patterns are body-mind habits overlaid on your ancient reproductive templates. If you want to expand your paths to arousal and orgasm, it's usually easiest to begin by working with what you know best. Take your time to explore one technique or facet before moving on to another. If your current approach has become a rut or a trench, don't worry. You learned that pathway

and you can learn other ones, too. *Living erotically is opening oneself up*
You can widen your path, create side *to nature— externally and within.*
trails and, over time, develop a whole
network of conduits and connections. KRISTIE LEVANGIE

Two simple techniques can help you do this. The first, cross-training, involves
doing two things simultaneously. The second, switching, involves alternating a
familiar path with a new one.

### CROSS-TRAINING (OR PAVLOV'S ORGASM)

With cross-training, you teach your body-mind to have the same response
to two different stimuli. It's based on operant conditioning, which was made
famous by Pavlov and his equally celebrated dog. You probably know what
happened: Pavlov fed the dog and rang a bell simultaneously, and kept doing
this until eventually he could make the dog salivate by merely ringing the bell.
By now, Fido associated the bell with eating, so a ting-a-ling was all that was
required to get him thinking, "Meal!"

You can use this same approach to widen your current paths to arousal and
orgasm and to create new ones. The bell can be anything you want. Start by
doing what already works to get you turned on. Bring yourself to deep medium
or high arousal. Now do cross-training, that is, concurrently do two things, the
old stimulation and the new one. Repeat the double stimulation many times.
You're tricking your brain into believing that both forms of stimulation produce
the same response.

After you've done both things lots of times, intermittently discontinue the old
activity while keeping the new type of stimulation going. (An extra trick—one
we'll talk more about later—is to imagine the old stimulation continuing.) Pay
attention to your arousal level and add your tried and true form of stimulation
back into your play whenever your arousal level drops. Eventually your brain
won't know the difference between Stimulation 1 and Stimulation 2. You'll
'salivate,' or maybe even get orgasmic, when the bell is ringing and there's no
food anywhere in sight.

Let's say you want to learn to get turned on, or even have orgasms, from
nipple stimulation. After a hearty warm-up, start your training session by
simultaneously playing with your genitals and nipples. Do both things at
the same time, over and over. After you've practiced doing both many times,
occasionally stop the genital play while continuing with the nipple titillation.
Add direct genital arousal back in if your turn-on turns down. Make sure to
continue nipple stimulation during orgasm—you definitely want your brain to
associate those two activities! Eventually your brain will conclude that nipple

stimulation—the bell, as it were—turns up your turn-on and can sometimes produce orgasms, just like the 'food' of genital stimulation. Voilà! You've cross-trained your brain.

### SWITCHING

With cross-training, you do two things simultaneously. With switching, you go back and forth between two types of stimulation, your known path and a new one. By doing this, you add fun little side trails that with more practice can become their own broad, easy-to-access routes.

Let's take a quick look at how using the switch technique can expand your groove. Let's say you're a woman who can only get turned on and have orgasms by using a vibrator on the head of your clitoris. You'd like to be able to get off by using your hand. (After all, there's not always a handy place to plug in and your hand is, well, handy!)

Start by using the path you already know. Here, this means arousing yourself in the usual way. If your vibrator and some erotic fantasy have been what get you off, start it buzzing and unroll a sexy story in your mind to get yourself to medium or high-level arousal. Take your time and make your arousal trance nice and deep.

Now step a bit off your usual path. Intermittently stop using your vibrator and switch to your hand. Stay attuned to your arousal level. As soon as you notice it dropping down, return your vibrator to your clit—you're stepping back on your established trail. Do this as often as you need to—and do it in a rejoicing, affirming, non-self-critical manner. Instead of being annoyed with yourself ("Damn, I still have to use the effing vibrator," go with "Goody, my trusty vibrator is right here and I can use it to keep my turn-on on!"). Keep going, using your vibrator as much as you need to, but continuing to periodically step off the path by intermittently substituting your hand.

---

## *Succulent Summary*

### How To Create A Network of Arousal Pathways

- DEVELOP AND ESTABLISH your easiest path.

- WIDEN YOUR PATH by using your inner toolkit to enhance your trance.

- USE 'SWITCHING'—create side trails by alternating stimulation

- USE 'CROSS-TRAINING' by doing two (or more) erotic activities at the same time, intermittently stopping one and continuing the other until both elicit the same response.

---

With practice, you'll find that you need to use your vibrator less as your body habituates itself to your new arousal path. Eventually you'll be able to use either your hand or your vibrator to get aroused and reach orgasm.

And then there were two!

Do you want to go for a third path? No problem: Cross-training and switching can do it for you. Simply decide what you want to add to your arousal array and proceed to use cross-training or switching to increase your network of happy trails.

You can learn to get turned on and to come from just about anything. Once you understand the basic premise of how to expand your pathways, the sky's the limit.

HOT & JUICY TIPS

### Take The Easy Road

WE ALL KNOW THAT millions of years of evolution have made some body parts more erogenous than others. What you might not know is that Mother Nature has also created some natural hardwired connections, some of which might surprise you. For example, your nipples and genitals are neurologically linked because it's evolutionarily advantageous for mothers not to die after their baby is born. When Junior fastens onto the nipple, this signals the uterus to contract, which keeps Mom from bleeding to death. This is good news for both Mom and her baby!

Both men and women possess a network of hardwired erogenous pathways that connect the following body parts to each other:

- GENITALS/REPRODUCTIVE ORGANS

- THE BUTTOCKS/ANUS

- NIPPLES, AREOLAS, BREASTS

- MOUTH, LIPS, TONGUE

- FINGERS AND TOES

- NAPE OF THE NECK

- EARS

- THE SEX CENTERS in the brain (and anything that connects to them such as your vision or your imagination)

Why bushwhack through the woods when you can use the deer trails? Start your erotic training regime by using Mother Nature's easy paths!

## Oh-Oh-Oh Orgasm!

When you come, is it a fireworks finale or a small sizzly sparkler? Is it a crashing crescendo or a genital tickle? There's a huge spectrum of orgasmic experience, and it varies from person to person and for the same person from day to day. How are your orgasms—satisfying, satiating or snooze-inducing?

Orgasm comes from the Greek *orgasmos*, meaning organ swelling. And while it's true that organ swelling is usually involved, orgasm

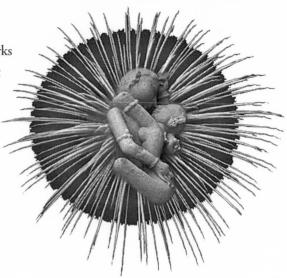

Sheri Winston, *Shakti Shiva Explosion*

is about much more than genital engorgement. The climax produces sensations, emotions, feelings and visual images. On a physical level, you experience rapid heartbeat, throbbing pulse, fast intense breath, sweating, flushing and involuntary muscle movements. Emotionally, you may feel joyful, exultant, intimate, vulnerable or invulnerable. You may have a sense of being at one with yourself, your partner and even the whole universe. Your orgasm can feel sacred, wild or wicked (in a good or bad way). It can be spiritual or carnal, intimate or mechanical.

### Fascinating Facts

**The average duration of orgasm**

MEN: 5—30 seconds

WOMEN: 30—45 seconds

You'd expect such a common and nearly universal experience to be easy to define, but it's not. We don't even have a single accepted definition of orgasm! *The Clinical Psychology Review*, a professional journal, lists twenty-six definitions. Generally they focus on measurable, observable phenomena—muscular contractions and the like. Subjective measures are often disregarded, although happily that's changing.

Still, orgasm does have some aspects that we can pretty much all agree on. It's a pleasurable peak or climax that occurs at the height of sexual excitation. Orgasms are characterized by a series of involuntary contractions of the genitals and pelvic floor muscles along with other body movements. The orgasmic experience is often accompanied by a range of physical sensations and emotions, including euphoria, the release of tension, and a sense of boundlessness.

There's also general agreement that while the process of arousal involves some conscious choice—think of it as climbing to a diving platform—orgasm is different. Like a leap from the high dive, it involves surrendering, releasing control and totally giving oneself over to your involuntary nervous system as you leave the board and plunge into the water.

*Electric flesh-arrows . . . traversing the body. A rainbow of color strikes the eyelids. A foam of music falls over the ears. It is the gong of the orgasm.*

ANAÏS NIN

For our purpose, what's more important than definitions is how you experience orgasm and how you can make them more powerful and pleasurable. Wherever you are on the orgasmic scale, you can make them bigger and better. You can also learn to experience different kinds of orgasms and, as we've seen, to come from a broader range of stimulation.

---

PLAY & PRACTICE

FOOD FOR THOUGHT

### Name That Orgasm!

AS YOU EXPAND your pathways of arousal and explore the land of orgasm, you'll probably discover new types of orgasmic experiences. Here are some that I've named or that have been named by others:

- LAUGH-GASM
- SOB-GASM
- MEGA-GASM
- HEART-GASMS, LOVE-GASMS

 *Do you have any terms to add? Come visit GetSexCrafty.com to do so.*

---

Western culture tends to be goal-oriented when it comes to sex—it's about achieving orgasm. While I don't want you to make orgasm the be-all goal of sex, I do want you to know that everyone can develop orgasmic mastery—in other words, you can learn to have at least one orgasm, pretty much when you want to.

*The orgasm has replaced the Cross as the focus of longing and fulfillment.*

MALCOLM MUGGERIDGE

There's a paradox here, and I invite you to hold it. On the one hand, the erotic journey is full of innumerable pleasures—arousal can be enjoyed for itself. On the other, the ability to have stupendous orgasms is a marvelous—and learnable—skill that everyone can use to further enhance the exquisite pleasures of their erotic life. Yes, enjoy the journey! And the journey is always better when there are fabulous fireworks at the end.

## 8 Hot and Juicy Tips for Starter Orgasms

IF YOU'VE NEVER HAD AN ORGASM, you're probably a woman, so I'm directing this to female-bodied people, although the same general principles apply whatever your plumbing. Don't despair. There's nothing wrong with you and you aren't broken. This is all learnable stuff and you can learn it.

1. CULTIVATE a positive attitude. You'll get there.

2. LEARN TO PLAY your own instrument. Go play with yourself! Have solo sex. Really, loving, good, hot sex with your hot self.

3. MOST WOMEN USUALLY NEED direct clitoral stimulation to have an orgasm. Include playing with your whole clitoris, with emphasis on the head. (See the anatomical details in chapter 7.) Try different strokes—rub, roll, circle, stroke, pat, press, pulse....

Susan Singer, *Celebration of Life*

4. MOST WOMEN BENEFIT from having their whole Erectile Network engorged. (Yes, I'll tell you all about it in chapter 7.) Take the time to play with all of your parts thoroughly.

5. MOST WOMEN BENEFIT from getting their whole body turned on. Touch yourself all over as you'd like a lover to touch you.

6. FOCUS ON YOUR OWN experience to find your inner connections to your erotic energy.

7. BE SELF-LOVING in lots of ways beyond sex.

8. GET HELP, support, information and education.

🍒 *For more tips, please come visit: GetSexCrafty.com*

---

*The Rubicons which women must cross, the sex barriers which they must breach, are ultimately those that exist in their own minds.*

FREDA ADLER

---

## The Big Man-Woman Question

Our cultural story tells us that men and women are different and that you're one or the other. We also have a whole passel of stories about how that defines how you should be and behave. We are so beyond that . . . aren't we? Shouldn't we be living in a gender-free world where we raise our boys and girls to play with dolls and trucks equally? Yes: We shouldn't bring gender biases into how we raise children. And when it comes to workplace issues such as equal opportunity and pay parity, here, too, we definitely need to get beyond gender. But

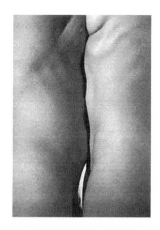

Grace Gelder, *Untitled*

when it comes to the bedroom, and more specifically to sexual behavior and reproductive equipment, maybe we should be saying vive la différence! For there are real differences—at least most of the time, for many people.

I'm not making a case here for simplistic models. The traditional dualistic model of men and women leads to limited gender roles, stereotypes and myriad other problems. Nor does a dualistic model account for the full range of people in their wondrous diversity, including people whose body parts don't match their erotic energy or those that don't clearly fall into one or the other category.

But assuming there are no gender differences is also problematic. As with all mammals, sperm-making males and egg-bearing females have different roles to play in reproduction. For many if not most of us, our biological makeup affects how quickly we get aroused, what turns us on and more.

In the next chapter, we'll examine a model that offers a more nuanced, flexible and multifaceted way of understanding gender. It focuses on energy, not plumbing. For now, though, let's look at how the experience of arousal and orgasm plays out in men and women with their differently wonderful or, is it "wonderfully different?" body parts.

## Gender Differences in Arousal and Orgasm

In many ways, the orgasmic experience is universal. Whether you're male, female or somewhere in between, you breathe intensely, your heart races and when you come your body is flooded with a feel-good chemical soup of orgasmic pleasure.

At the same time, the experience of arousal and orgasm can be quite different depending on your plumbing and wiring. The vast majority of men find their path to orgasm early and easily. Not most women. Some haven't found it yet, while for others the sexual experience is a challenging process with an uncertain finale. Most women need time and experimentation to discover how to get turned on and for orgasm to become a guaranteed destination on their erotic journey.

---

## Fascinating Facts

### The Orgasm Gap

AGGREGATED DATA from various surveys suggests that about 15% of women report difficulties with orgasm. Ten percent have never climaxed, while 40–50% have either complained about sexual dissatisfaction or experienced difficulty becoming sexually aroused at some point in their lives.

About 85% of men report that their partner had an orgasm at their most recent sexual encounter, compared to 64% of women who report having had an orgasm at their most recent tryst.

Men are more likely to orgasm when sex includes vaginal intercourse; women are more likely to orgasm when vaginal intercourse is supplemented by oral and manual activities.

—*Sex in America Survey (2009). This survey reported on the sexual behaviors of 5,865 Americans aged 14 to 94. From researchers at Indiana University's Center for Sexual Health Promotion*

---

In order to expand their sexual capacity, men and women tend to need to learn different things. While penis owners typically don't have trouble having a single, ejaculatory orgasm, learning to have non-ejaculatory and multiple orgasms is often challenging. Some men also have difficulty getting and sustaining an erection and mastering ejaculatory timing. For most female-bodied people, the path to orgasm may be difficult to establish, but once discovered and established, many women can fairly easily learn to have expanded experiences such as multiple orgasms.

*The Female Orgasm. The Big O. That elusive, reclusive Loch Ness of the labia. Does it prove the existence of God, or just His twisted sense of humor?*

KIRSTIE COLLINS BROTE

The tools and skills discussed in this book are gender-neutral. They can help anyone learn to become an erotic virtuoso, whatever their equipment and abilities. Whether you need to get better at slowing down or speeding up, at relaxing more or getting more excited, discovering and learning how to use your internal toolkit will help you get there.

Now let's look more deeply at some maps that will support you on your learning journey.

# CHAPTER SIX

# THE WHOLE
# YIN YANG THANG

*You must know that I do not love and I love you,*
*because everything alive has its two sides; a word*
*is one wing of the silence, fire has its cold half.*

PABLO NERUDA

## Energy, Not Anatomy

IN THIS CHAPTER, I OFFER MODELS OF MALE AND FEMALE SEXUALITY. Doing this is inherently tricky business. For one thing, there are always exceptions to any generalizations about sexuality. For another, it's fraught because some people believe that making any generalizations at all about gender and sexuality is by definition sexist and offensive. So let me launch this chapter with these caveats:

- People are complicated, sexuality is complicated and desire is complicated. Simple models can't do justice to this complexity. Even nuanced high-level models that are genuinely inclusive of diversity can only come close.

- For any general model, there are always exceptions. Not all men demonstrate 'male sexual behavior' nor do all women demonstrate 'female sexual behavior.' For any model, it's important to understand that we're talking about tendencies across a spectrum, not absolutes, and that individuals come in a wonderful variety of non-gender-bound configurations.

- Not everyone fits into a male or female pigeonhole. There are people who are in-between, intersex, transgender and gender-fluid.

The fact is that when it comes to sexuality, men and women tend to be different. We serve no one by pretending these differences aren't there. The challenge lies in accounting for the differences without falling into stereotypes.

This is why the models I offer focus on energy, not anatomy. It's a way to steer clear of all the traps this conversation is prey to.

There's another reason, too. Energy is ultimately more important than anatomy. It's energy, after all, that drives sexual behavior—the anatomy comes along for the ride.

Masculine and feminine energy are cosmic and eternal forces and not at all political. Sexual politics matter—they matter a lot. But they're not germane to this topic.

Sheri Winston,
*Yin Yang Symbol*

So much for framing. Now on to the meat of the matter.

## A World of Polarities

Let's start with an elegant, simple yet profound map that's central to the ancient philosophy of Taoism—that all life is a dynamic interplay of complementary forces.

We live in world rich with opposites. We experience light and dark, sun and moon, summer's heat and winter's cold. None of these is better or worse than the other. They are what they are and they're different. They don't clash, they co-exist. They're not really opposite, they're complementary.

Together these polarities create the dynamic homeostasis that is life. You consume and excrete. You inhale and exhale, wake and sleep. There's day and night, matter and energy, masculine and feminine and all the other dualities. These seemingly opposite forces require each other. To see, we need both light and dark. Without illumination, we'd be stumbling around in the dark. Without shadows to give us contours and edges, we'd have only blinding light.

These polarities are truly universal. At a micro level, atomic particles have positive and negative forces that attract and repel, that bond and release. At a macro level, our planet is polarized by its north and south poles. Somewhere in between, you were created by a sperm and an egg.

These forces pull and push in the dynamic, eternal dance of life.

And sometimes they connect in a fiery explosion, with polarity providing the spark.

Sheri Winston
*Yin Yang Masculine Feminine*

## Yin and Yang

Broadly stated, there are two kinds of energy in the world (and us). There is the hot, steady fire of the sun and the cool, fluid, watery energy of the moon. Taoists call the solar type of energy yang and the lunar type of energy yin.

Yang is the initiatory, active, focused energy associated with the masculine. Yin is commonly associated with qualities that we think of as feminine: it's receptive, creative energy. These polarities aren't in opposition—they're two ends of a spectrum.

YANG
Male
Masculine
Positive Pole
Li (form)
Inhalation
Fire
Container
Sperm

Female
Feminine
Negative Pole
Chi (energy)
Exhalation
Water
Flow
Egg
YIN

Sheri Winston,
*Yin Yang Qualities*

WORD NERD:

## Can't Tell Your Yin from Your Yang?

CAN'T REMEMBER which word is associated with qualities? Try this silly ditty.

*Yin goes in. It's a yinni yoni! Yang has a wang and likes to bang.*

### SEXUAL WIRING TENDS TO BE POLARIZED

The majority of people are most polarized when it comes to their erotic energy.

People are usually wired in the way that male-female stereotypes predict—people with male equipment have core yang energy and those with female equipment have core yin. A small percentage of people are wired in the opposite manner—male plumbing and core yin energy, or female apparatus and core yang. For those people who are trans or intersex, any variation is possible.

It's important to remember that we're talking about how you're wired sexually, not about your social or workplace self, where you may be energetically quite different, although there is usually some connection and overlap.

*Neither sex, without some fertilization of the complimentary characters of the other, is capable of the highest reaches of human endeavor.*

JEAN-PAUL SARTRE

### YOUR CORE AND COMPLEMENT

Although we all have both yin and yang energy within us, for most people one forms their primary, dominant sexual polarity. Your core erotic energy is considerably stronger and more central. Your core polarity is your most potent, central power. Think of it as your default position. It's where you tend to start from and where you go more often. It's your more natural preference.

Our core polarity usually manifests in our sexual expression and attracts us to those with the opposite polarity.

The opposite pole is your secondary, complementary energy. It balances and leavens your dominant aspect; it's where you are less often. Although it is your peripheral, less powerful energy, it's no less important than your primary. To be healthy and internally balanced, your primary core aspect needs to be complemented and counter-balanced by your secondary aspect.

A small percentage of people are evenly balanced in their sexual energy. If that's you, you're just as happy being on top or on the bottom: you're turned on by being the doer as much as the do-ee. You're bi-energetic—an energetic switch, so to speak.

A very tiny number of people are asexual and don't carry a sexual polarity: they're sexually neutral.

All this is normal! However you're wired, it's perfect. There is no right or wrong way to be, no better or worse. Nothing to try to change, be ashamed of, or aspire to. The goal is to understand your own energetics and that of your playmates.

## Pussycats and Puppy Dogs

There's another map that gives a related but different perspective on men and women and everyone in between. I call it the Pussies and Puppies School of Love. It's a simple way to understand yourself and your partners. Core yin folk tend to be like pussycats while core yang folk tend to be like puppy-dogs. I'll give you more information about that map in the next pages where I integrate the pussies and puppies and yin-yang models.

J. J. Grandville

## Feminine Yin Energy

Yin energy is like a lazy river, slow, cool and watery. Feminine yin power is associated with darkness, the night and the moon. Yin energy flows and fluctuates, waxes and wanes, shifting from expansion to contraction, growing and diminishing in a cyclic rhythm.

These qualities have been associated with women since time immemorial because of the very real link between women's fertility cycles and the changing moon. Although it's less so now due to the advent of electric lights and other factors, in primal cultures women's menstrual cycles were closely linked to the moon's phases. The Greek deity Artemis is (among other things) a goddess of the moon.

Feminine energy is changeable because women do, in fact, go through numerous transformations. The fluctuations of menarche, menstruation, pregnancy, birth, postpartum, breast-feeding and menopause all come with the territory, so to speak, of women's sexuality.

Yin has the quality of opening or closing. She can open to receive or she can contract, clam up, deny permission to enter. When open, yin radiates invitation. It's the same energy that all female mammals put out when they're in heat. She dilates wide, taking in the big picture. Yin energy is great for multi-tasking and integrating a wide perspective. Yin beings long to surrender. But this cannot be forced. Their owners can allow yin body parts like the yoni and ass to open, their visitors can encourage it, an environment can be created that facilitates it, but they cannot be made to bloom. Unless yin feels safe, she cannot relax and open.

*Be not ashamed, women—your privilege encloses the rest, and is the exit of the rest; You are the gates of the body, and you are the gates of the soul.*

WALT WHITMAN

Yin energy has a deep and special magic to it—the power of transformation. As the feminine principle, yin makes magic manifest with her miraculous power of creation, gestation and birth. She receives something (sperm, inspiration, ideas), cooks it up in her cauldron of transformation, and then births something new into being. She showers forth abundance in the form of love, amrita (the sacred name for female ejaculate), a child, and every other ecstatic form of creation. All acts of creativity use yin magic. Regardless of your plumbing, if you're creating and then birthing your creation, you're using your yin power.

Yin is the core energy and primary quality of most (but not all) women. It's often (but not always) the secondary, complementary energy of men.

*This is the female form; A divine nimbus exhales from it from head to foot; It attracts with fierce undeniable attraction! I am drawn by its breath as if I were no more than a helpless vapor—all falls aside but myself and it.*

WALT WHITMAN

### THE YIN PUSSY

We refer to female genitalia as a pussy for good reason. Besides being furry and fun to pet—kitties are great exemplars of feminine yin energy. Cats are cool. They flow. They're experts at relaxing and receiving. Cats want to be served (and even revered). When a pussy is properly attended to, she relaxes open and surrenders to pleasure. If you go too fast, if you don't attend to her signals of what pleases her, of her relaxing open or tensing closed, you'll lose her trust. She'll clam up and you will not get to pet the pussy.

Shuncho, c 1800, Woodblock Print

## The Masculine Yang Energy

Steady and stalwart, yang is the energy of flame and light. Yang is fast, fiery and focused. It's the power of the sun and the dependable circadian daily rhythm. This is consistent with many mythologies—Artemis's twin brother, the sun-god Apollo, is the hunky charioteer who travels daily through the sky.

Yang energy is commonly associated with qualities we tend to think of as masculine. Yang is initiatory. It's about direction, about moving in and out, or towards and away. Yang penetrates, inserts, puts forth. It loves to be doing. It seeks to fix, to accomplish, to work, to serve. It desires to penetrate the world with action, to offer its gifts and assert (and insert) its influence.

Yang energy is the container, the form that gives shape to the flow, much like the banks of a stream keep the water from flooding. Yang provides the structure within which spontaneity can erupt. In dancing the tango, it's the lead dancer (traditionally but not necessarily male) who provides the container and the direction within which his partner can spin and swirl.

Yang is the energy that drives the archetypes of the Guardian who protects and the Warrior who defends the vulnerable and defenseless.

Yang energy tends to be genitally focused. This explains why people who have a lot of yang erotic energy often ignite rapidly with fast easy arousal and can just as quickly erupt in a blaze and burn out.

Yang is the core energy and primary quality of most (but not all) men. It's often (but not always) the secondary, complementary energy of women.

Dogs are wonderful exemplars of yang energy. Our canine companions are active, enthusiastic and focused. Dogs love to have a job! They're happiest when they have work to do, guarding the house, herding the sheep, tracking a hot scent. Fido (the word comes from *fidelis*, Latin for faithful) wants to do a good job, and his favorite reward is to be praised for doing so. Dogs lap up appreciation!

The dog is goal-oriented—get that squirrel! And focused—keep your eye on the ball, get the ball, bring the ball back.

Your pooch is almost always up for a game. Hey boy, wanna go for a walk? Woof, yes! Wanna play ball? Woof, yes! Wanna have sex? Woof, yes! At his most well trained and mature, the dog is about service. That's why we don't have seeing-eye cats. Dogs make great service animals and are proud to do their jobs well.

Dogs are courageous and loyal companions. They protect, guard and care-take. Although it may seem strange to link pooch energy with heroism, it's actually a heroic archetype. Heroes are like dogs in that they choose duty first, act with courage and offer their gift, their service, to a world that needs them.

PLAY & PRACTICE

PARTNER PLAY

### Pussy and Puppy Playtime

A FUN GAME TO PLAY is to pretend to be animals! No language or even costumes needed. Just allow your animal selves to rub and pet, romp and roll around. Lick and suck, nuzzle, and nibble. Play with animal sounds—growl and yowl, moan and purr. Cats and dogs too tame for you? Try the game with a tigress and a wolf instead. Now you can really roar!

## Playing with Pussies and Puppies

You don't play with a cat the same way you play with a dog. Cats don't fetch (unless they feel like it). By understanding your core energy and that of your partners, you'll be able to figure out how to play with them in the ways they like best.

In general, dogs are easy. For most dogs it doesn't take long before you can have them on their back, begging you to rub their tummy. ("Please, rub it, please, please!")

Those puppy dog, core yang folk are usually happy to play almost anytime as long as it's not interfering with their job. If your partner is more dog-like, he'll probably be delighted when you offer sex play. They love to get their doggy bits focused on—you'll rarely go wrong by spending a lot of time focusing on his

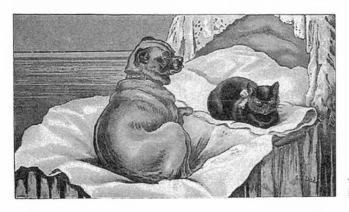

Anonymous vintage illustration

genitals. He will respond very positively to praise and appreciation (and won't mind getting tasty treats, either!)

Core yin pussycat people tend to be moodier. If you have a pussycat partner, you'll do best by tuning in to her moods and making sure she has what she needs to feel safe, comfortable and relaxed. Start with creating a feeling of connection. Listen. Pay attention to what pleases her and give her that. She'll probably want to feel nurtured before she's ready to play. She's prone to distraction so help her focus. Take your time pleasuring her whole body, with emphasis on the non-sexual parts. Tease and tantalize her. Use your attuned attention to tune in to her signals. Arouse her desire by giving her a little less than she wants so she's hungry for more. When your yang dog energy is relentlessly focused on the yin kitty, you are in service to joint pleasure.

*Dogs come when they're called; cats take a message and get back to you later.*

MARY BLY

Remember, everyone has some cat and dog inside them. Your usually slow-to-get-going pussycat might one night go canine and playfully attack and jump all over you (much to your delight if you're a dog). Your always-raring-to-go puppy might have a kittycat sort of a day and want to be petted and served. When it comes to play, the usual way isn't always the right way. You'll probably never go wrong by being attuned, present and creating connection. Once you're there, play with your pet with inspiration, creativity and fun—that's the recipe for very happy animals.

Each of us has both aspects within us. Masculine and feminine, yin and yang, estrogen and testosterone, fire and water, sun and moon, cat and dog, we each contain them all.

The sexual polarity of yin and yang is what creates the exhilarating dance of attraction that fuels our desire to connect and to merge, the yearning to enter or be filled, to play in the fields of erotic delight.

## Succulent Summary

### Polarity Basics

- YIN: Feminine energy, dark, receptive, cool, slow, watery

- YANG: Masculine energy, light, penetrative, hot, fast, fiery

- WE ALL HAVE BOTH yin and yang energy.

- WE ALL NEED BOTH.

- NEITHER is better or worse, superior or inferior.

- THE POLARITIES are complementary, not opposite.

- THERE IS A SPECTRUM of qualities.

- YIN AND YANG are not stagnant—they move in an ever-dynamic dance.

- EACH POLARIZATION has in its heart the seed of the other.

## Your Core Energy

When we talk about how 'female sexuality is' or 'how men are,' what we're really discussing is how people who have that core erotic energy are. Or how they tend to be.

Which core energy are you? Ask yourself, would I rather pursue (yang) or be pursued (yin)? Am I more comfortable being the yang seducer or the yin seducee? Do I prefer to be the yang driver or the yin passenger? Since we've all got both energies, everyone does both at some point. The one you prefer more often is your dominant polarity.

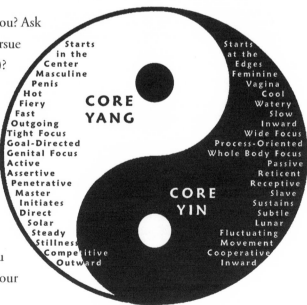

Sheri Winston, *Core Yin and Yang*

## How Are You Wired?

JUST FROM READING the previous section, you may already have a good sense of how you're wired. Remember, it's not about how you are all the time in all the areas of your life. This is about how you are, erotically, most of the time. Look over the core yin and yang qualities below and note which are more strongly true for you sexually. (This is an utterly unscientific study, just a fun little game.)

Rate yourself on a scale of 1–5.

| 1 | 2 | 3 | 4 | 5 |
|---|---|---|---|---|
| STRONGLY DISAGREE | DISAGREE | NEUTRAL | AGREE | STRONGLY AGREE |

1. I PREFER NOT TO initiate erotic encounters.

2. I LOVE TO OPEN and receive.

3. I LOVE IT WHEN my partner enters and penetrates me.

4. IN MY SEXUAL FANTASIES, I like to be submissive and my partner to be dominant.

5. I LIKE TO SURRENDER to my partner.

6. I LOVE IT WHEN my partner makes plans for us and takes care of arrangements.

7. I LIKE IT WHEN the other person makes the first move.

8. IF SOMEONE WANTS ME, they need to pursue me.

9. I LOVE IT when my partner directs our sexual encounters.

10. WHEN IT COMES TO SEX, I long to relax and not be in control.

### SCORING: Add up your points.

VERY YANG ........................................................... 10 - 15

MODERATELY YANG ............................................... 15 - 20

BALANCED ............................................................. 21 - 29

MODERATELY YIN ................................................... 30 - 45

VERY YIN ............................................................... 45 - 50

## Your Complementary Energy

Once you recognize your core sexual energy, you've also identified your secondary or complementary sexual energy.

Ideally your primary aspect is balanced, tempered and seasoned by your secondary one. Yin helps yang be in attunement. Yang gives yin direction. Without effective complementary energy, your core will be out-of-control.

One reason our mainstream model of gender is so dysfunctional is because it misses the importance of this counterbalance. It proposes that to be a real man you need to be all aggressive yang, and to be a real woman you need to be all yielding yin. Not so: You need both energies working harmoniously together to be a fully evolved, mature and

*You know, God, the power that makes life, whatever it is, had just to make two things, masculine and feminine, for all this mischief. And made them so there is this entirely different point of view about love and sex.*

BEATRICE WOOD

conscious loving being. You're not less of a man to be in touch with your feminine aspect—doing so guides your aggressive instincts into service. You're not less of a woman if you have active yang—it gives you ambition and healthy boundaries, and it helps you focus your creative energy.

As in the yin yang symbol, your core and complementary energies aren't static: they move in a dynamic flow. Sometimes you'll be more in your yang energy—doing, directing, initiating action. At other times, you'll be more in your yin aspect, relaxing, receiving and just being. A healthy person is in an internal ever-changing dance, moving from yin to yang and back again, balancing and re-balancing their equilibrium within.

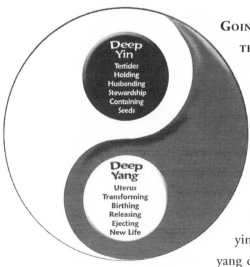

**Deep Yin**
Testicles
Holding
Husbanding
Stewardship
Containing
Seeds

**Deep Yang**
Uterus
Transforming
Birthing
Releasing
Ejecting
New Life

Sheri Winston, *Deep Yin and Yang*

### GOING DEEP—THE YIN OF YANG AND THE YANG OF YIN

The Taoist map offers not two quadrants, but four—it's one reason this model is so elegant and deep. Each polarization, yin and yang, has in its heart the power of the other.

Inside yin there is yang. While the vagina exemplifies the receptive yin, the uterus represents the deep yang qualities of yin with its astounding ability to birth, propelling new life out into the world. The uterus exemplifies the fierce and spontaneous feminine yang. It's the power of an erupting volcano or a birthing woman unstoppably pushing out creation.

Just as yin contains yang, yang contains a deeper yin aspect that is about holding and husbanding. While the penis exemplifies the core yang qualities of being the stalwart directive penetrator, the testicles embody the deep masculine yin.

> *Water is fluid, soft, and yielding. But water will wear away rock, which is rigid and cannot yield. As a rule, whatever is fluid, soft, and yielding will overcome whatever is rigid and hard. This is another paradox: what is soft is strong.*
>
> LAO-TZU

The source of semen, it's the container that holds the spark of beginnings. It husbands the seed of life in stewardship for the future.

Everyone contains both core and deep yin and yang qualities, energy and body parts. We all have parts that can penetrate (fingers, words, gaze) and those that can receive (anus, mouth, ears). We all have parts that hold seed for the future (ovaries, testes) and ones that give birth (your mind pushes out ideas, your hands birth art). All these realms are present and accessible to all—all can be cultivated.

## Yin, Yang and Your Many Selves

Remember how we all have a big cast of characters inside us? These sub-personalities can have different yin-yang configurations. Joe may have a Macho Man inside him who's very yang (and comes out after a couple of drinks) along with a Sweet Sensitive Side who wants nothing more than to feel safe, be held and gently opened. Our sexual polarity varies depending not only on what we're doing, but on which of our sub-personalities has been called forth. Each member of your inner cast of characters has its own polarities and tendencies. Although your most essential core polarity will still tend to dominate, part of the flow of the sexual dance involves moving from one pole to the other, from one persona to another, shifting between giving and receiving, from doing to being done.

We contain multitudes in the yin-yang context, too.

Jessica Prentice, *Yin Yang*

SUCCULENT SEX CRAFT

# Yin and Yang in the Bedroom

Both yin and yang energies have characteristic qualities and patterns of movement that help us understand how they each like to play and be played with.

## YIN GOES IN

The direction of yin energy goes from out to in. It begins outside the body in the context and the connection. Yin then moves to the outer edges, and over time moves into the center.

Yin energy starts cool and is slow to heat up. She takes awhile to come to a boil, but once the water's roiling, she can stay hot for a long time.

If yin energy is ignored and shut down, its cool quality can get cold and even freeze. That's why it's important for core yin folks to fire up their erotic energy regularly. That's right—if you're a core yin person, the way to keep your sexual juice flowing is to use it regularly. And take your time doing so. If you're suffering from low libido or very slow arousal, you can ramp up your desire by getting stimulated and aroused on a fairly regular basis: it'll turn on your desire to desire. The more often you boil your water, the easier it will be to fire it up again. The less often you heat your energy, the likelier it is to get frozen.

If you want to relate to a yin being, start with creating connection. Be patient—her energy takes time to move inward and coalesce in her sex centers. The best way to turn her on is by not heading directly toward your goal. The better approach is akin to piloting a sailboat— you have to take the boat, the sails, the water currents and the wind into account. You rarely go straight to the destination. Instead you tack

Paul-Émile Bécat

back and forth as you work with the water and wind, finessing your way across the bay. While you're still yangly focused on the ultimate destination, you understand that the fastest way to get there is by honoring the yin nature of your partner and following the cues of her desire. The path you take today won't be the same as the one you'll use tomorrow when the currents and the weather are different. Each journey is attuned to the unique conditions of the moment.

What yin longs for most is to release her boundaries, open wide and receive fully. She yearns to give up control. But she needs to feel safe in order to do so. When yin dissolves in surrender and ecstasy, becoming a conduit for bliss, it's beautiful to behold.

## Yang Out

Naturally, yang energy moves in the opposite direction, from in to out. For core yang folks, arousal starts with the genital ignition switch. While other sex centers in the brain are also activated during initial yang arousal (specifically, the "yum, that looks good!" brain region), the predominant energetic focal point is usually the genitals (typically a penis). This explains the common pattern in men (or any primarily yang person) to become quickly and easily aroused. Yang energy is like a fire in dry tinder. It's quick to ignite and if not husbanded carefully, quick to consume its fuel and burn out. Core yang folk need to learn to keep their fire burning long enough to boil their yin-partner's water. They'll also increase their own pleasure when they learn to steward and spread their yang energy.

For core yang people, their arousal typically begins at the genital center and travels outward, either with a short quick eruptive ejaculation or, if they've learned how to moderate and channel the energy, in a slower, more whole-body movement.

> *Scientists now believe that the primary biological function of breasts is to make males stupid.*
>
> DAVE BARRY

Yang loves to head straight for the goal. It's much like steering a motorboat directly toward your destination, swift as an arrow aiming for the target. If you partner with core yang people, they'll usually appreciate it when your sex play dives right in to their sexy bits.

Yang energy is interested in surfaces and attracted to external qualities while yin is drawn to depth and internal qualities. Thus core yang people tend to be attracted by visual stimuli while yin is likelier to be turned on by touch and scent.

Yang is the power that provides the focus, discipline and direction that enable yin creativity to take shape and manifest. It's the channel for the current. Core yang folks (or anyone in a yang mood) longs to serve yin, to provide the cauldron for her ecstatic magic. Yang loves to be the one that's responsible for—and gets to watch—their yin partners dissolve in rapture.

## Healthy Yin-Yang Balance

When you have a healthy inner equilibrium, your primary core power is balanced by your secondary complementary force. What this looks like depends on if your core is yin or yang.

### Yang Mellowed by Yin

Yang energy is about containing, initiating, and penetrating, about actively inserting, about pushing something out into the world. When yang's penetrating force is complemented by healthy and well-developed secondary yin energy, it gives rise to *appropriate, attuned and attentive giving*. It's about giving your partner exactly what they want, exactly how and when they want it, about penetrating your partner with love, about using your direction and focus to put out your gift to those that want and need it. Ultimately, it's about being in service, about contributing what is most desired and required—to yourself, your partner and the world. You offer your service, provide aim and attention, and do what needs to be done to penetrate the planet (or your partner) with love.

### APPROPRIATE, ATTUNED AND ATTENTIVE PUSSY-PETTING

Imagine for a moment that you want to befriend a beautiful kitty. You are the yang pursuer. Do you run up and grab her and roll her on her back and rub her tummy? I think not. Did you miss the warning signs of her ears back and her swishing annoyed tail? If you tried to grab her anyway, you'd probably be bleeding and she'd be out of there. And you'd have a hard time getting a second shot at that pussy!

You know better, of course. You use your yang mellowed by yin, your appropriate attuned attention. You start by creating connection. You get her attention and make eye contact. Since yin pussycats can only relax and open when they feel secure, she checks you out to see if you're safe. You approach her slowly, attending to her responses. You notice if she's opening in interest or closing and withdrawing. If you go at the right pace—her pace—at some point you'll get to pet her. Don't overwhelm her or move too fast to her tender parts. You wisely start with the less vulnerable parts of her body. You watch her signals. You give her pleasure, but not too much. If you're very clever, you'll arouse her desire. Pet and rub her just a little bit less then she wants—then she'll want more. Take your time, prove you're safe and can be trusted to give pleasure. If you pet her the way she loves to be petted, sooner or later you'll have a purring puddle of pussy.

### YIN DIRECTED BY YANG

Yin has the essential quality of opening or closing, of being amenable to receiving or alternatively being tightly furled in protection. When core yin is balanced, contained and fortified by healthy well-developed secondary yang, then you have *active conscious reception*. You choose who and what you open for. When you consciously choose to open, you do so actively, sucking in delightedly, like a snake ingesting delicious prey.

Yin balanced by yang isn't passive. You can be a yin flower without being a wall flower. You can receive enthusiastically, delightedly and voraciously. Hungry receptivity is a really hot combination.

When you practice conscious active reception and attuned appropriate giving, you create a circuit of giving and receiving. At some point, it no longer matters who is doing what to whom—both people are being filled and nurtured. A special kind of magic occurs and giving and receiving become the same thing. You actually start to experience the pleasure that you give someone else inside your own brain and body, as if what you're doing to them is also happening to you.

---

## Succulent Summary

### Healthy Core and Complement

HEALTHY CORE YANG complemented by healthy yin—appropriate, attuned and attentive giving

HEALTHY CORE YIN complemented by healthy yang—active conscious reception

---

## Inner Imbalance

You may or may not have already developed both of your polarities. If you've done this successfully, good for you! For most of us, for whatever reason, it's a work-in-progress—we're better at one or the other set of skills. Some people are better at operating from their core, but haven't developed their secondary energy. Others have over-developed their complementary force and their core could use some work.

*Sometimes I wonder if men and women really suit each other. Perhaps they should live next door and just visit now and then.*

KATHARINE HEPBURN

Unbalanced energy is the source of much confusion, violence and unhappiness. For millennia, we've tended to undervalue feminine energy while according unmitigated yang energy far too much power and control. This is still the rule, although the tide does appear to be turning. The consequences have been and remain catastrophic. We have a cultural epidemic of badly trained dogs—yang energy unmitigated by leavening yin. When people (usually men) are driven by unleavened yang energy, the result is often anger, violence (including sexual violence) and the pathological pursuit of power over others. Unbalanced yin energy leads to the passive victim full of simmering resentment, depressed, helpless and hopeless. At the level of individual interactions, it often leads to unsatisfying, unconnected sex and failed relationships.

FOOD FOR THOUGHT

## Yin Yang Journal Notes

TAKE A FEW MOMENTS to reflect on the yin yang model as it applies to yourself. If you have one or more partners, you may want to also think about how this model applies to them.

Here are a few questions to get you started:

- WHAT IS your core erotic energy?

- WHICH IS your erotic complement?

- DO YOU HAVE A SENSE of how strongly you are each? 90/10? 60/40?

- ARE YOU energetically balanced?

- THINK ABOUT THE PEOPLE you are attracted to. Are they core yin or yang? Evenly balanced? Has it been similar over time or has it varied?

- THINK ABOUT THE PEOPLE you have been in intimate relationships with. What would you guess their make-up to be? How well did their energy fit with yours? Was the energetic fit an issue?

- THINK ABOUT YOUR FANTASY LIFE. What kind of fantasies, porn or erotica turn you on? What sort of dynamic is at play in terms of yin yang polarity? Does this tell you something about yourself?

- ANY OTHER THOUGHTS or responses to this model?

### THE DANCE OF MATURITY AND BALANCE

In order to be emotionally healthy, functional and whole we need to develop both our core and complementary energies along with our deep yin and yang qualities. We need to be able to initiate and focus as well as receive and flow. We need to be able to do and be done, to both ravish and surrender into ecstasy. We need to both husband and birth.

When all of your energetic aspects are functional and developed, you can flow between the polarities and call on the appropriate energy when needed.

Ideally, we are always in process, always learning to do a better job of calling forth these aspects of ourselves as circumstances require. Mature skill at balancing these polarities is a gift we give to the world—and it's also one we bring into the bedroom. Only when we learn to tap deeply into our core energy while also honoring and dancing with our complementary one does it become possible to unleash our full sexual potential. There needs to be a healthy marriage of yin and yang—and it's a marriage that takes place inside yourself.

This is yet another reason why "it all begins with you."

Kathleen Mandeville, *Belt Buckle*

## Solo Sex Celebrates Both

When you play with yourself, you get to be both yin and yang. After all, if you don't use your yang to initiate, solo sex won't happen. If you don't access your yin to open and receive sensation, you won't get off. Self-pleasuring provides a great opportunity to explore and expand all aspects of your energy. You get to do and be done—how good is that!

### SOLO YANG

You use your yang to create a generous amount of time for your solo sex sessions. It's the container energy that helps you define a space for pleasure practice and remove all distractions. You also call on your yang to heat up the experience, push for the peaks and drive through blockages.

> *If God had intended us not to masturbate, he would have made our arms shorter.*
>
> GEORGE CARLIN

For women who are experimenting with having multiple orgasms, use your yang energy to pick up the stimulation after your first climax and see if you can keep going. Be in your attuned attentive yang place, though, and find the right level of stimulation that will keep you going (or coming). For many women, the first orgasm makes your clit super-sensitive, so you may find that the way to continue involves less direct stimulation. However you play with yourself, use your yang to push through (gently) any resistance to giving yourself more pleasure.

## SOLO YIN

Your yin abilities will open you up and help you tune in to your pleasure. They enable you to flow with the energy, take your time and attend to the sensations. You augment your attention and magnify awareness when use your yin to slow down. You're utilizing your ultimate yin when you pause, going from movement to stillness and just relaxing into the rapture.

For guys, assuming you're having an ejaculatory orgasm, use your yin skills to prolong your arousal journey and delay your arrival at the peak. Practice bringing yourself close to the point of no return and seeing if you can stay just under that threshold. When you do start to come, instead of tensing into your climax, see if you can go all yin and relax into your orgasm.

PLAY & PRACTICE

SOLO PLAY

### Dancing With Yin & Yang—A Self Pleasure Celebration

HAVE A SOLO SEX SESSION where you focus on both your yin and yang skills.

Alternate yin and yang. Move from slow to fast, cool to hot, exquisitely indolent to intensely active. Go from deliberate and leisurely to aggressively egging yourself on. Ramp your energy way up, accelerating your arousal, then drop it back down. See how far you can take yourself out.

When you're done, don't forget to cuddle with yourself. Give yourself big snuggly hugs. Enjoy your relaxed post-orgasmic state.

### THE MAGNETIC DANCE OF POLARITY

Attraction is about the pull of one kind of energy towards its complement. It's the magnetic force that acts between oppositely charged bodies, drawing them together.

An important component of attraction is partner polarity, the affinity of your opposite forces, the lure of your complementary energies. Sexual desire is very much like the pull of two magnets towards each other. If there isn't a positive and a negative pole, then you just have two lumps of metal lying there. That's what we have with our friends (well, the ones we don't want to get naked and play with). For sexual attraction to exist, you need to the opposite forces that create desire.

Most people tend to be attracted to other people who possess the opposite polarity—yin is drawn to yang and vice-versa. This is also true at a more granular level: strongly yin people tend to be attracted to strongly yang people while more energetically balanced people tend to be drawn to each other.

If you're weak in either your primary or secondary energy, you'll tend to be attracted to someone who compensates for that inadequacy. When your weaknesses are prominent, you're more likely to get together with someone who seems to make up for your lacks. People may believe, usually unconsciously, that their partner will compensate for their weakness.

If you have developed both your core and complement, you'll tend to be attracted to people who are equally healthy and balanced. You'll be drawn to the each other's energetic strengths and be good counterparts. The more whole you are, the healthier your attractions and relationships will be.

In long-term relationships, over time, we tend to de-polarize, hence the common decrease in attraction and sexual activity. To create sustainable long-term juiciness in your relationship, it's important to become adroit at increasing your own erotic energy, and playing with your own and your partner's polarity.

Erotic virtuosos know how to play with polarity and keep the current flowing. When you can fully and actively open your yin and also access and harness your yang, you will be experiencing divine dialog within yourself and with others.

Vinette Perez, *Vigorous*

It's the stuff of mythical origin stories: The spark of polarity caused energy to combine with matter and brought the universe into being. The mating dance of yin and yang, the combustion of masculine and feminine energies, the play of puppies and pussies, creates the cosmic dance that makes life—and it's also what makes it worth living.

# CHAPTER SEVEN

# YOUR GENITALS IN A NUTSHELL

*Does my sexiness offend you?*
*Does it come as a surprise*
*That I dance as if I have diamonds*
*At the meeting of my thighs?*

MAYA ANGELOU

## Maps of the Body

WE BASE OUR STORIES ABOUT OUR BODIES ON THE MAPS OUR CULTURE provides—in anatomy illustrations and textbooks, in sex books and pornography. Unfortunately, our cultural maps and stories about the body are replete

with problems and misrepresentations. In particular, men and women's erotic equipment is portrayed inaccurately. Books have been censored, parts have been ignored, structures lost and information that's wrong passed on as true. Here are some new stories and more accurate maps so you can have a more useful and blissful connection to your own and your partners' sexual parts.

Bijou Xochi, *The Bite*

In this chapter, we'll take a brief tour of our two basic types of genitals. We'll start with the body parts both women and men have, then move to female and male equipment, respectively. But first, a few words about the wonders of genital evolution.

## Genital Co-Evolution

Human genitals are the product of millions of years of co-evolution. They are constructed to increase the chances of successful reproduction, and since mutual pleasure is part of what inspires people to insert Tab A into Slot B, they are also designed to deliver delight. The female and male body/brain circuitry and their complementary genital systems are brilliantly evolved for mutual stimulation and satisfaction. While we big-brained humans use our equipment in ingenious ways that have absolutely nothing to do with actual procreation, the underlying template is reproductive.

We're not alone in this process. Every species has evolved to have their male and female parts mesh perfectly together. There are some amazing variations here. He-possums have a forked penis that exactly fits the duplex vagina of the she-possum. There's a male duck with a corkscrew penis, so of course his mate has a spiral vagina. Fascinating, right? Evolution is nothing if not inventive. All species have genitals that co-evolved to produce the reproductive triumph that is pregnancy.

Not only do humans need to successfully make babies, we also need to raise them, which is a long and often tedious job. It behooves us to try to have our mates hang around so we can work together to rear our offspring. This makes it particularly important for us to share the intense pleasure, intimacy and bonding that sex can evoke. Our genitals are perfectly designed to work together to produce the exquisite pleasure that inspires attachment.

---

PLAY & PRACTICE

FOOD FOR THOUGHT

### Genitals (A Rose By Any Other Name . . .)

THE LANGUAGE PROBLEM really rears its ugly head when we talk about genitals. Here's some food for thought on the topic.

Make a list of terms for male and female genitals and other sexual body parts. Include euphemisms, baby talk, scientific jargon and the lewdest of the lewd.

Look over the list. Note the positive and negative connotations of the words and phrases.

- HOW MANY OF THE TERMS are insulting, derogatory? How many of the words are also used as insults?

- HOW MANY WERE loving, caring, reverent, respectful or appreciative?

- WERE ANY SACRED?

- DO YOU LIKE ANY OF THEM? What are your favorites?

- DO YOU USE ANY OF THEM?

- WHICH DO YOU DISLIKE? Are there any that you actively hate?

---

NAMES HAVE POWER and reflect cultural assumptions, usually unconscious ones. For a good contrast to our cultural story (and, quite possibly, to your own beliefs), check out these names for sexual parts from cultures that revered sex.

**THE FEMALE GENITALS (VULVA AND VAGINA):**
- Yoni (Sanskrit for "divine passage," "place of origin" or "entrance to the universe")
- The Jade Gate, Jade Pavilion
- The Cinnabar Grotto or Gate

  **THE CLITORIS:**
- The Pearl on the Jade Stem
- The Jewel Terrace

**THE MALE GENITALS:**
- Lingam (Sanskrit for "Wand of Light")
- The Jeweled Scepter
- Vajra (Tibetan for "diamond" or "thunderbolt")

**THE ANUS:**
- Rosebud

Hokusai, *Mr. Prick and Mrs. Cunt,* c. 19th century

 *Visit GetSexCrafty.com for more sacred names of parts and erotic activities—and to add to the lists.*

## Unisex Body Parts

### THE FLEXIBLE FLOOR

Whatever version of plumbing you have, inside the bottom of your torso lies a hammock of muscles that surrounds your genitalia and associated organs. These muscles encase your genitals, hold up your pelvic and abdominal organs, and help you manage both your waste flow (keeping it in and letting it out) and your pleasure play (including what goes in and out).

> *The man's body is sacred, and the woman's body is sacred; No matter who it is, it is sacred.*
>
> WALT WHITMAN

These internal pelvic muscles are commonly called the *pubococcygeus muscle* (or PC muscle). This is inaccurate because the pubococcygeus muscle is only one of the multilayered sling of muscles that make up the pelvic floor. They are many, not one. So let's call them the *pelvic floor muscles* (PFM) instead.

The PFMs in men are the same as in women with a few variations. They're smaller because the male pelvis is narrower than the female's. In embryological development, some muscles that split open in women join together in men, resulting in three holes for women and two for men.

In both men and women, the muscles are arranged in multiple layers. The erogenous structures of the genitals are enveloped in the muscle layers and some pass through them. Different muscle shapes and locations

Anonymous, *Soldier Rewarded with Giant Vulva*

translate into different actions—you have muscles that can cinch together, draw in, pull up, open, close, push down and thrust out. For example, the sphincter muscles form circular bands that act as drawstring-type closures.

Your pelvic floor muscles are essential to intensifying your sexual pleasure. Pumping them ramps up blood flow, activates nerves, moves erotic energy and heightens arousal. Since your especially sexy parts are sandwiched in between the muscle layers, every time you grasp and release these muscles, you're squeezing, rubbing and fondling your sexy parts. Essentially, you're playing with yourself without using your hands—which is convenient since, during sex, your hands are often busy elsewhere!

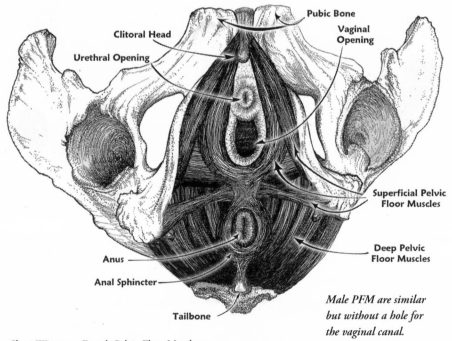

*Male PFM are similar but without a hole for the vaginal canal.*

Sheri Winston, *Female Pelvic Floor Muscles*

SUCCULENT SEX CRAFT

Whatever your plumbing, learning to be in touch with these muscles will help you to develop erotic mastery. Men, if you develop skill with these muscles you can improve the firmness of your hard-on and your ability to sustain it. Pelvic floor muscle control helps you learn to separate orgasm from ejaculation. Women, using your PFMs can help you have orgasms from a greater variety of stimuli, including penetration and intercourse, and to have ejaculatory orgasms. For everyone, developing PFM dexterity can help you make wonderfully subtle intercourse motions. It also makes it easier to experience and share energy orgasms.

## NERVES

Nerves are like trees, with your spinal cord being the main trunk out of which come your spinal nerves, the paired major branches. These then fork, splitting into smaller and then smaller boughs eventually ending in twigs—the nerve endings. (By the way, all the nerves discussed here

Anonymous, *Penis Walking Out Of Vagina*

come in pairs, although I'll refer to them in the singular for simplicity's sake.)

Describing nerve pathways is a tricky business. Like country roads, the names change as you go along. Nerve patterns also have more uniqueness and diversity than many other body systems. The following is a simplified, general description—your mileage may vary.

### YOU'VE GOT A SEX NERVE (ACTUALLY, YOU'VE GOT THREE!)

While most textbooks posit one significant sexual nerve, there are actually three major nerve pathways that innervate both men's and women's sexual equipment.

The nerve that is classically considered the 'sex nerve' is the *pudendal nerve*. I prefer to call this the *primary genital nerve*. It innervates the more external and surface structures, including the genital skin; the more superficial layers of the pelvic floor muscles; the sphincters for the bladder and rectum; in men, the penis, scrotum and testes, and in women, the vulva, the three parts of the clitoris, the vestibular bulbs and the more external aspect of the urethral sponge. (If you're not familiar with all these parts, don't worry—we'll cover them later in this chapter.)

The second major sexual pathway is the *pelvic nerve plexus*. (In anatomy-speak, a plexus is a place where a bunch of nerves join, interweave and split.) The *pelvic nerve* divides into many branches that innervate the more internal structures and organs. This includes the deeper layers of pelvic floor muscles, the bladder, the anus and rectum. In men it connects to the prostate. In women, branches innervate the uterus, the vagina, the perineal sponge and the more internal aspects of the urethral sponge.

> **WORD NERD**
>
> *Pudendum* is Latin for "shame," which makes the pudendal nerve the shame nerve. Perhaps someday we'll shed ourselves of this anti-sex bias and rename it. Pudendum has also been used to refer to female genitalia. Talk about 'the nerve!'

Lastly, there is the *vagus nerve*, the wandering cranial nerve that starts in your brain and meanders through most of the body, connecting to almost every major organ group. It has branches that innervate the heart, the respiratory and gastrointestinal systems as well as the sexual and reproductive organs.

For any of these pathways, when you pleasurably stimulate their respective nerve endings, they send happy messages to your brain to light up and turn on. The more you use them, the more neural connections are made and the easier it is for the impulse to travel the path.

If you predominantly stimulate one nerve pathway, you're most likely to experience arousal and orgasm that are focused on its end-organ system. Thus, when you mostly play with the parts connected to the primary genital (pudendal) pathway, you're likely to have a clitoral or penile orgasm. Utilize the pelvic nerve path and you'll get orgasms that feel more internal, more uterine, vaginal, prostate and anally focused. Use both pathways and you'll get more intense experiences centered on more of your yummy parts. Add in the things that stimulate the vagus nerve, such as using your breathing, making sound, focusing your awareness and using your imagination, and you're on your way to full-body orgasmic explosions. The more paths you use, the more turn-on you'll get and the more outrageous your orgasmic paroxysms will be. When you want the full-on symphony of orgasmic delight, use all your pathways! (More on how to do this when we discuss your toolkit.)

## Partner Particulars

Discover the preferences of your particular partner(s). Everyone is unique, so find out what they love and do exactly that. When something really flips your playmate's switch, make a mental note so you can whip out that move again.

At the same time, bear in mind that the same person may like different things at different times. At least partly, this will depend on where they are in their arousal journey. Timing matters! You'll want to add 'when' to 'what' in learning what turns your partner on.

Your partner's particular preferences may not always be predictable, but many of the moves that really ring their bell are learnable.

### EVERYBODY'S GOT AN ANUS

The much maligned and unisex asshole is a wondrous component of our pleasure system. The *anus* is richly supplied with nerves, surrounded by powerful muscles and has a delicate mucosal lining, making it a sublimely responsive piece of equipment. In its sensitivity, it is second only to our slightly more anterior genitals. Despite its bad rap as shameful and dirty, your ass is a gold mine of potential pleasure.

Eusebi Planas Franquesa

The anus is composed of two overlapping sphincter muscles, the round drawstring-like muscles that can dilate open and contract closed. The outer ring is innervated by your voluntary nervous system. You can consciously relax it. The inner ring is innervated by your autonomic nervous system. You can't make it release, but you can allow it to open. To do this, you need to surrender, to let go—your anus is a wonderfully yin orifice. Men and women and everyone in between can benefit from exploring their back door and expanding their receptive yin abilities.

Inside the anus is the anal canal. Deeper in is the rectum. Beyond that is the sigmoid colon. Anything beyond the rectum isn't usually reachable with fingers, penises or toys and isn't discussed here. For sexual hygiene purposes, though, it's helpful to know that your stool remains in the sigmoid colon, only moving into your accessible ass parts when you get the "I have to poop" sensation. That's why, generally speaking, a healthy ass is not full of shit. But you still need to be aware of bacteria-filled traces of poop and keep contaminated toys and body parts segregated and out of vaginas and mouths until washed.

## Guided Tour of Your Back Door / Part 1

EQUIPMENT: LUBE, GLOVES, TRASH CAN, TISSUES, NATURAL BABY WIPES.

If you've never explored your own back door, now is a great time to begin. As with any new practice, this is best done with yourself, by yourself. If you have a partner urging you to open your butt to their plundering, I encourage you to decline until you've determined that it gives you pleasure. Pain is not a part of this agenda. If it hurts, stop! While your anus has enormous pleasure potential, you have to open to it, both literally and figuratively.

YOU MAY WANT TO START YOUR EXPLORATION either in or after a shower or bath. You're likelier to be relaxed and have fewer hygiene issues.

HAVE YOU EVER LOOKED AT YOUR ASSHOLE? Use a mirror and take a peek. See if you can open and close it, giving yourself a cute little anal wink! That ability to relax and dilate your anal sphincter will help when you want to open and receive something like a flanged toy, finger or penis.

PLAY WITH YOURSELF IN YOUR USUAL WAYS, including lots of yummy genital stimulation, and get pleasantly aroused. If you're using a glove, put it on. Put some lube on your finger and begin to stroke the outer areas of your ass crack. Gradually bring your digital attention to the outer pucker of your anus. For starters, just focus on the sensations from your external ass play. For a while, that may be all you do. (If you like it and it feels arousing, this is a great starter way to add anal play to your partner sessions.)

ONCE YOU'RE ENJOYING PLAYING WITH YOUR OUTER ANUS, it's time to try some self-penetration. Don't forget to simultaneously continue genital play or alternate the two types of stimulation. Start with your finger, wriggling just the tip into your anal sphincter. Allow your anus to relax around your finger. You may want to vibrate it slightly or hold it still. Apply some pressure to the tight circular band of muscle until you feel it melt open. Breathe. Allow your mouth and throat to dilate and make open-mouthed sounds.

WHEN YOU FEEL YOUR INNER SPHINCTER MUSCLES RELEASING, penetrate further. At this point, you may want to experiment with a small, flanged ass toy. (The flange part is really important—you do not want to lose a toy in anal space!) Continue to play with your genitals to keep your arousal turned on. Later I'll offer more tools to use for amplifying the pleasurable sensations, but, for now, use deep slow breathing and relaxing sounds. Tune in to the sensations. Enjoy!

## Guided Tour of Your Back Door / Part 2

ONCE YOU KNOW YOU LIKE THESE ACTIVITIES, if you have a partner, add your favorite types of ass play to your shared agenda.

For full-on anal intercourse or penetration with a strap-on dildo, wait until you're really ready, meaning you feel relaxed, in deep trusting communication with your partner, and it feels fabulous to have smaller things penetrating your back door. A good way to warm up your butt sphincters is to insert a small or medium-sized flanged toy during the early part of your play session. Take the time to get to full-on arousal and then go slow—really, really slow. As long as you're enjoying it, keep going. If anything feels uncomfortable, slow down or pause until it starts to feel great again. If you're pausing in the ass probing, don't forget you can play with other body parts to increase the arousal level, which heightens pleasure and decreases pain. As I said, there should never be any pain. If it doesn't feel fabulous, don't do it!

## Female Genitalia

You may think you know your way around 'down there,' but there are parts most people haven't yet discovered—it's one of those areas where our cultural maps fall short in important ways. What follows is a brief discussion of what's actually there, how and why it connects, and how to make it very happy. I've left out parts like the ovaries and fallopian tubes that don't play a major role in generating pleasure.*

Shunga, *Vulvae*

### A GARDEN OF VULVAS

Vulvas are like faces—they all have the same basic design yet can look remarkably different. Genitals have an enormous range of normal. If you happen to be one of the many women out there who believes that what you've got is weird or ugly, let me reassure you: You are normal! Female genitalia come in a vast variety of sizes, shapes and colors, and they're all just fine. Don't worry if you don't look the way you're 'supposed' to. There is no right way for your genitals to look. Every vulva is beautiful.

---

* For a much more in-depth discussion, along with extensive and unique anatomy illustrations, see my *Women's Anatomy of Arousal: Secret Maps to Buried Pleasure.*

PARTNER PLAY

### Admire From A Distance

BEFORE YOU LAY HANDS or mouth upon the glistening genital jewel before you, pause and really look at it. Take time to admire it. Appreciate its beauty and mystery, its ripe redolence and tempting textures. Reverently contemplate your partner's most sensitive parts. Let them know how much pleasure you receive from their genitals. Shower their owner with words of admiration and praise. (This practice is applicable to all forms of erotic equipment)

## The External Equipment

Starting on the outside, we have the parts that are common knowledge. *Vulva* is the inclusive term that describes the whole enchilada (not vagina, which only refers to the inner canal). The vulva includes the *mons pubis* or pubic mound, the triangular area over the pubic bone. Although many women these days remove the hair, it's natural for most of the vulva to be fur-covered in post-adolescent women. The skin of the mons has abundant scent glands that produce a faint, pheromone-laden odor (for good reason—smell is one of the oldest sex signals).

Continuing down, we find the *outer lips* (also known as the *labia majora* or large lips). I prefer to name them by their location rather than size since these fleshy parentheses can be petite or pudgy. The outer lips form a pair of longitudinal folds. Fatty tissue underlies the skin. The pubic hair from the mons continues down, covering the labia majora's outer surfaces. I call this whole area the yard.

The *inner lips* (also known as the *labia minora* or small lips) come in a delightful variety of sizes, colors and shapes. These fleshy folds can be tiny frills or opulent drapes. They can be slim and svelte or corrugated and ruffled. They may be hidden by the outer lips or extend far beyond them like a pair of exuberant, lavish flower petals. The variety of inner lips is astonishing. Whatever kind you have, enjoy them!

Opening the lips reveals the area called the *vestibule*, which I think of as the porch of the vulva. From the porch you can see the *vaginal orifice* (the opening or *introitus*), which continues internally as the moist, elastic and extremely popular *vagina*. The vaginal canal is a collapsed tube, its inner walls

Sarah Nicholson
*Mystery and Beauty*

like a folded-up accordion that is closed at rest but can open widely.

Above the vaginal opening, you'll find the urethral orifice or pee hole. It's a small aperture usually tucked into a puckery fold of vulval flesh. In some women it's found low down, practically inside the top of the vaginal opening. In others it's further up, closer to the clitoral head.

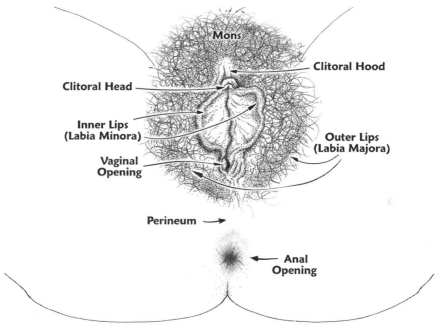

Sheri Winston, *External Female Genitalia*

## Science Geek Goodies

### Vaginal Ecology

I HAVE TWO IMPORTANT NOTES for you about female genital hygiene. First, female genitalia are not supposed to smell like fake flowers (from the use of unnecessary artificial products) or fish (a sign of infection). The smell and taste of a healthy vagina is mild, earthy and slightly pungent with a pleasant, musky aroma.

Second, women, you have a self-cleaning vagina, or at least you do when you have an intact and healthy vaginal environment. The ideal way to clean the outer parts of a pussy is with a hand-held shower head and lots of clean running water. Mild, unscented, natural soap on the outer parts is okay, but no soap or feminine hygiene crap on the mucus membranes or inside the vagina, ever, please! It causes infections and dries and irritates your mucus membranes.

Avoid so-called 'feminine hygiene products'—they destroy the ecology of the vaginal environment and cause infections.

*Come to GetSexCrafty.com for more Vaginal Ecology information.*

## The Female Erectile Network

You may not know exactly what erectile tissue is, but you can probably guess what it does. It's what gives the penis its hallmark ability to go from small and soft to big and hard. Here's an anatomical fact that isn't revealed in our mainstream model of female genitalia—and that most people find astonishing: *Women have as much erectile tissue as men do.* Pound for pound, inch for inch, female genitals contain just as much of this wonderful, sensitive, expandable, engorgeable equipment as male genitals.

Erectile tissue—it's not just for penises anymore.

Allow me to introduce you to the *female erectile network*. It's made up of linked structures, all comprised of enlargeable, sweetly swelling, inflatable erectile tissue.

Women have an erector set of their own.

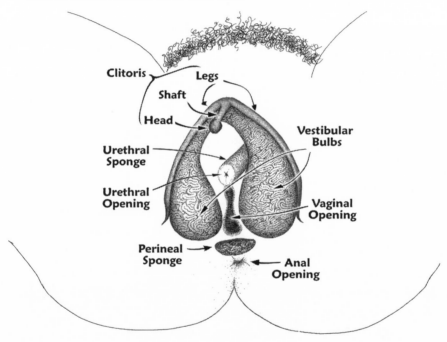

Sheri Winston, *The Female Erectile Network and Associated Orifices*

Let's start our tour with that object of much affection, attention and speculation—the clitoris. Despite the common misconception that the clitoris is only the acorn-shaped nub, it actually has three parts. What is generally thought of as the clitoris is actually the *clitoral head*, or *glans*. With 6,000-8,000 nerve endings, it's the jewel in the crown of the female pleasure system—the tip of the volcano, as it were. This is the largest concentration of nerve endings in the male or female body. It's supersensitive, so be careful—it loves appropriate attention and can also be easily over-stimulated.

The glans can be as small as a baby pea or as big as a giant olive. It may or may not be covered with the fleshy folds of the *clitoral hood*. Just like the rest of the female equipment, the hood comes in a wide range of variations and can be barely there or a substantial and generous cover. Both 'innies' (covered) and 'outties' (protuberant) are normal variations that have no effect whatsoever on the clitoral head's pleasure potential.

The next part of the clitoris, the *clitoral shaft* (also known as the *body* or *corpus*), can be found under the hood, just above the head of the clitoris. This small pole is about the width of a chopstick or a pencil, and about one-half to one inch long. It rests in a slightly mobile tube.

The third part of the clitoris, the paired *clitoral legs*, are more difficult to feel. They branch from the base of the shaft like a wishbone and head south, running along the sides of the bony pubic arch. They're each about 3-4 inches long.

All three parts of the clitoris, the head, shaft and paired legs, are made up of erectile tissue. And, just like a penis, the whole clitoris has the ability to become engorged, filling with blood and getting bigger, firmer and more sensitive. And that is a very good thing! "And, there's more!"

*Why do people say "grow some balls"? Balls are weak and sensitive! If you really wanna get tough, grow a vagina. Those things take a pounding.*

Inaccurately attributed to B E T T Y   W H I T E , possibly originated by S H E N G   W A N G

The clitoral structures aren't the only part of the female genitals that are comprised of erectile tissue.

Under the outer labia are two big wads of engorgeable erogenous tissue—the paired *vestibular bulbs*. Each is shaped like an upside-down comma, fat at the bottom, thin at the top. They bracket the vaginal opening. When swollen, they help form the sides of the snug cuff that encircles the vaginal opening. Not only do they provide a pleasurable platform for play on the porch, but the top of each bulb connects to the shaft of the clitoris. When they're tumescent, they transmit delightful sensations to the sensitive clitoral system.

Inside the female body are two more erectile structures. The *urethral sponge* (also known as the G-spot) is a cylinder of erectile tissue that surrounds the tube of the urethra.* It lies just above and parallel to the roof of the vagina. Imagine the urethral sponge as a roll of paper towels. The *urethra* (the pee tube) is the cardboard cylinder and the sponge is like the paper towels. Since this is erectile tissue, it varies in size depending on the level of arousal. When the sponge hasn't been stimulated, it's like you're at the end of the roll. When the sponge has gotten the attention and stimulation it so richly deserves, it engorges and becomes like a brand-new jumbo roll.

---

\* I prefer not to call this area the G-spot. For one thing, it's a tube, not a spot. For another, its namesake, Dr. Gräfenberg, was male and didn't have one. Every woman does, though. It's standard equipment.

When un-engorged, the urethral sponge is difficult to see or feel. Stimulating it will often feel irritating and can make the owner feel like she needs to pee. However, playing with the sponge after the woman is at high-level arousal will often be appreciated. (Very appreciated!) If playing with it doesn't feel fabulous, retreat. Get to high-level arousal first, then go back to exploring the pleasure potential of this part of the erectile matrix.

Whether you're a visitor or the owner, you'll find that it's much easier to appreciate the urethral sponge's size, shape, contour and erotic potential when it's engorged.

*The Majority of women (happily for them) are not very much troubled by sexual feelings of any kind.*

WILLIAM ACTON, *English urologist, 1857*

In addition to being part of the erectile network, the urethral sponge serves another function. It houses the *paraurethral glands*—the source of female ejaculate. Although there isn't scientific consensus on this point, I'm convinced this fluid is part of the immune system and that it helps protect women from urinary tract infections. All women have the equipment and the capacity to produce 'shejaculate.' Some women are natural ejaculators—they always gush abundantly at some point in arousal or with orgasm. For other women, obvious and abundant ejaculation is a learned experience—they've discovered how to squirt or to amplify their gushability.

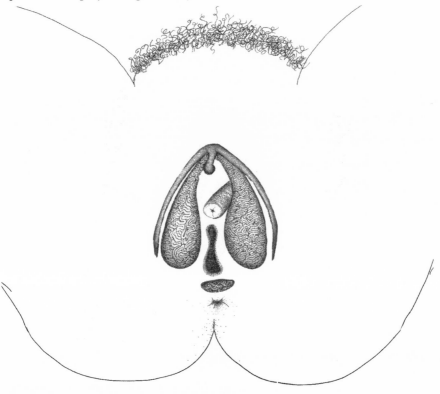

Sheri Winston, *Erectile Network Flaccid (Unengorged)*

SUCCULENT SEX CRAFT

While not all women squirt copiously, I believe all women produce at least a small amount of fluid during arousal. Every woman, can, if she wishes, learn to enhance this natural process and to gush more profusely. It's an amazing sensation: Generous gushing, especially in concert with orgasm, feels intensely sacred and ecstatic.

There's one more wad of genital erectile tissue, the *perineal sponge* or *perineal body*. It lies under the floor of the vagina, in the wall between the vaginal and anal canals. You'll find it an inch, more or less, inside the vagina and just past the anal sphincter.

Unlike penises, which are more of an all-or-nothing apparatus, some parts of the female erectile network can be engorged while others remain flaccid. In women, if you don't play with each of the structures, they may not swell.

For a woman to achieve her prodigious pleasure potential, get this snug, expandable erectile cuff totally stimulated. When all these parts are aroused, they form a circuit of delightfully swollen erectile tissue—a 'she-rection.' Only when you attend to every bit of the engorgeable equipment do you get the connected circuit of structures along with the full and spectacular effects of the connections—a deep, thorough arousal trance and easier access to a woman's full orgasmic capability.

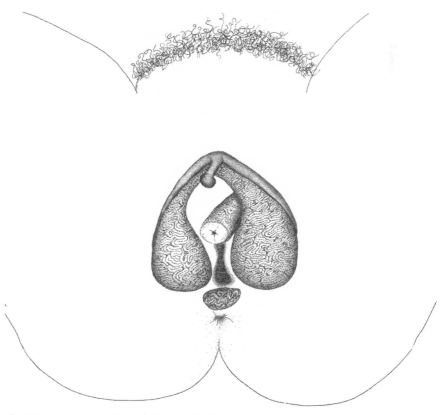

Sheri Winston, *Erectile Network Engorged (Fully Aroused)*

As I said, both male and female bodies have the same amount of erectile tissue—it's just arranged differently. All bodies also have erectile tissue in other locations including the areole, nipples, nostrils, lips and earlobes. But everyone regardless of their plumbing has plenty of delicious, nerve-packed sensation-rich erectile material.

SOLO AND PARTNER PRACTICE

### Female Guided Tour—Take a Look Under the Hood

TRY THIS AS A SOLO TOUR FIRST! Start in a state of non-arousal. Using a light and a magnifying mirror, take a good look at all your visible equipment. Using the eyes in your head as well as the eyes at the end of your fingers, see and feel all the parts. Note the size, shape, position, color and sensitivity.

Now play with yourself and get to medium-level arousal. Make sure to pleasure each of the components of your network. Take your time and be thorough. Pause in your play and check out all your juicy bits again. Notice the changes.

Return to your self-pleasuring. Use whatever works to get yourself to a high-level, deep arousal trance, which often takes 30-60 minutes. Be a really fabulous lover to yourself and get yourself utterly turned on.

Now for the hard part of the homeplay assignment—stop! Check everything out again, attending to the changes.

Finish your solo sex session however you like, ideally with one or more orgasms. Do one more check-in, noting what your sweet satisfied snatch looks and feels like.

Appreciate the dramatic changes that your external vulva and erectile network undergoes. Delight in your new knowledge about all the parts you have and how they're connected.

#### PARTNER PLAY

TAKE YOUR PARTNER on a guided tour, pointing out the landmarks and the changes.

#### FOLLOW THE BOUNCING UTERUS

In addition to all this delightfully erectable equipment, there's another female body part that's included in her pleasure equipment. As with the erectile network, it's not mentioned in most textbooks, sex books, medical diagrams and other cultural maps—at least, not as having anything to do with sexual pleasure.

Despite being considered a purely reproductive organ, the other part that's pleasurable is the *uterus*.

The uterus or womb is made up of three layers of muscle with a cavity inside. The bottom part, the *cervix*, dips down into the back of the vagina. It contains the opening (or *os*).

You may think of the uterus as a fixed organ, but it's actually mobile within a limited range. During a woman's fertile years, the uterus moves higher or lower in the pelvis at different points of her cycle. Just before and during bleeding, it rests lowest in the pelvis. At ovulation, it perches higher. The uterus also moves in response to arousal, sitting down lower in a non-aroused state and gradually moving up as the turn-on heats up. At high-level arousal, it's pulled way up and forward, like a taut bowstring. During orgasm, the muscular womb contracts and releases while bouncing up and down, pulsing and bopping to the orgasmic beat.

If you think that the uterus isn't a player in the symphony of orgasm, think again. Its pleasurable motion is an intensely exquisite aspect of the orgasmic crescendo.

---

PLAY & PRACTICE

SOLO PLAY

### The Two Rhythms of Orgasm

UTERUS OWNERS: The next time you get very aroused and have a big ol' orgasm, tune in to what's happening and see if you can identify the two distinct rhythms of orgasm—the rapid contractions of the pelvic floor muscles and the slower 'base note' of the uterus as it bounces up and down.

You can also feel your uterus doing its thing by putting your fingers inside your vagina—you'll feel your cervix rhythmically moving up and down and kissing your fingertips as you come.

If you do this with a partner, the best way they can feel the cervix bobbing up and down is with their fingers.

---

Utagawa Kuniyoshi

## Male Genitalia

While male genitalia aren't quite as mysterious as their female counterpart, here, too, there are misunderstood and unappreciated aspects. I'll gloss over the parts you probably know about and focus on the places that are often ignored or don't get the attention they merit.

## Understand the Energy—The Yang Wang

As we saw in Chapter 5, most men's core sexual energy is yang. Yang energy begins in the sex center and can stay contained in the genitals and the pelvis, exploding forth in a genitally focused ejaculatory orgasm. As men mature and develop their inner erotic skills, they can learn to move that energy out of their crotch, spread it throughout their body and have full-body orgasms. It's possible for men to learn to separate orgasm from ejaculation, and to have multiple and expanded non-ejaculatory orgasms. Coming and coming isn't just for women. Men, too, can have their bodies racked by energy orgasm after energy orgasm, for many minutes at a time.

Alméry Lobel-Riche

How do you say "Yum!" in Guy?

Before any of that can happen, though, you need to re-learn your orgasm pathways along with how to expand your arousal so it includes your whole body.

## Keep It Quick and Quiet

Most men began their sexual explorations by playing with their very own beloved cocks. Since most of you were afraid of getting caught, you learned to do it quickly and quietly. Untutored, you went with your yang energy and took it straight out to your destination. You didn't try to channel it, but instead let it be what it was—a hot, fast fiery explosion.

At some point, you got with a real-life partner. If you only had male lovers with predominantly yang energy, things remained pretty simple. You shared the quick, fiery blaze. But if your tastes ran to women, then you found yourself in very confusing waters, especially if they were core yin. Her sexual energy was different, she had mysterious and confounding equipment, and there were usually quite a few surprises in store. And now, instead of getting off as quickly

*See, the problem is that God gives men a brain and a penis, and only enough blood to run one at a time.*

ROBIN WILLIAMS

as possible, you were expected to last long enough to please this mystifying, complicated creature. What to do? How to keep from bursting at the utter delight and exquisite sensations?

Most men learned to deal with this challenge by containing their yang energy. They then maintain this pattern, often for the rest of their lives. Many men hold their breath and make as little sound as possible (except perhaps at the irresistible end, when it becomes too damn much to bear). They also taught themselves to not be fully present. How many of you guys were advised at some point to think about baseball? In other words, constrain and control the sexual energy by ignoring it until you just can't stand it and it overwhelms you and comes busting out.

There are much better options, as we'll see in Section 3.

## The Luscious Lingam

Now, on to the magic wand—the *penis*. Potent creature of myth, the penis has been lauded, demonized, appreciated, laughed at and desired. It's been hidden and enhanced, paraded and powdered, used for pleasure and plunder. Idolized, admired, scorned and derided, it endures, the stalwart center of masculine sexiness.

---

PLAY & PRACTICE

HOT AND JUICY TIPS

### De-lick-table Devotion

THIS PRACTICE is applicable to all erotic equipment.

While it's lovely to share stimulation and have everyone getting some action at the same time, sometime it's great to take time to devote yourself to doing your partner. Let them be totally yin and solely receive, relaxing into their pleasure and focusing on sensation.

Tell them to get comfortable, really, really comfortable, since they're going to be there for a nice long time. (Who doesn't love to hear that?) Of course, you should get really comfortable, too, since you'll want to focus on this lovely flesh in front of you for a good long while.

Now, hang out and enjoy spending a lavish amount of time in undisturbed genital worship of their sacred sex. You can start by just looking and admiring. Then move on to touch. Physically and energetically connect with their genitals in any and every way you can conjure. Forget about orgasm (yours and theirs) for the time being and just focus on playing, exploring, pleasing and appreciating. Sooner or later, coming may get on the menu. Take your sweet time getting there.

---

## Dick Diversity

Doug Metzger
*Dark Mark*

Penises span a wide range in size, shape and color. As with pussies—and faces, and flowers—there is enormous and wonderful variety and the realm of normal is vast.

As we know, there's a cultural myth that size matters and bigger is better. Not true! Size has nothing to do with the pleasure potential of the penis, either for its owner or its playmates. Most people who like to play with penises enjoy a variety of sizes. Some people do have clear preferences, often for penises that fit their particular orifices best. Some love petite ones, some like medium-sized, while others prefer really big ones. Most people are fine with a wide range of sizes.

One thing men need to be clear about: Having a bigger dick doesn't make you a better lover or more of a man. Being a good (or better yet great) lover is not about the size of your equipment, but about your ability to pay attention, be present, and be a generous, considerate and connected partner.

*The real lover is the man who can thrill you by kissing your forehead.*

MARILYN MONROE

Remember, guys: Skill is what matter most. And if the fit's less than ideal, you can still have an amazing time, especially if you show up with your entire toolkit of mind, body, heart and spirit skills and use everything you've got to maximum effect.

## The Penis is Mightier Than . . .

The multipurpose penis's plebeian function is to provide a passageway for urine and semen. As a semen-depositing device, it's beautifully devised to introduce those fragile little sperm way up near the entrance to the uterus where they'll do the most good. (The little fellas tend to get deposited lots of other places too, but that's a commentary on their owners' lustiness, not the design specs.) And of course the penis performs other functions, too, like delivering enormous pleasure to their owners and the folks on the playing, petting and receiving end of it.

The penis has three sections: the top end called the *head* or *glans*, the mid-section called the *shaft* (also *body* or *corpus*) and the *base* (the *root* or *bulb*). The glans is the helmet or head of the lingam. The rim at the base of the glans is the sensitive *corona*. If you have a *foreskin*, when you draw it back you'll see the Y-shaped elastic tissue bridge of the *frenulum* (just like the one under our tongues). The frenulum is highly sensitive and is mostly removed by circumcision. For circumcised men, what's left of it is often a preferred spot for stimulation.

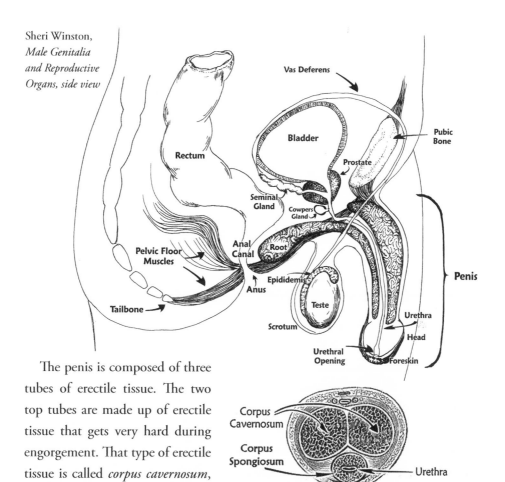

Sheri Winston,
*Male Genitalia
and Reproductive
Organs, side view*

Vas Deferens

Bladder

Pubic
Bone

Prostate

Rectum

Seminal
Gland

Cowpers
Gland

Pelvic Floor
Muscles

Anal
Canal

Root

Penis

Epididemis

Anus

Tailbone

Teste

Urethra

Scrotum

Head

Urethral
Opening

Foreskin

The penis is composed of three tubes of erectile tissue. The two top tubes are made up of erectile tissue that gets very hard during engorgement. That type of erectile tissue is called *corpus cavernosum*, while the lower tube is made of the slightly softer *corpus spongiosum*.

Corpus
Cavernosum

Corpus
Spongiosum

Urethra

Penis, Cross-section, based on *Gray's Anatomy*

The top two tubes run alongside each other until deep inside the body, where they diverge into two branches or legs, called *crura*, which attach to the pelvis. In women, the same embryological structure becomes the clitoral legs.

The base (or root) is the part of the penis that's attached to the body while the shaft is the part that hangs loose. Here's a little-known fact: One-third to one-half the penis is the base, which is contained inside the body. That's right, guys, your magic wand is up to 100% bigger than you thought it was! (Not that size matters.) The penile root is just as full of engorgeable erectile tissue and delights in stimulation. Don't forget to play with the root when pleasuring the male anatomy!

The *testicles*, also known as *gonads* or *balls*, are the sperm factories. They hang in a skin sac called the *scrotum*. As with all the other parts, there is enormous variation among men in how large the balls are and how big, loose or tight the sac is. The scrotum contains involuntary muscles that can let the balls freely hang down or draw them up protectively towards the body when their owner is cold, frightened or at high arousal. The balls and their sac are extremely sensitive and often underutilized in sex play.

## THE URETHRA

The *urethra* is the tube that connects the *bladder* to the outside world, forming the conduit for urine. It runs through the center of the lower erectile tissue cylinder of the penis. This same pipeline is also the delivery chute for semen. There's a valve at the base that closes during arousal, which is why a man can't pee when he's ejaculating. (Obviously, women also have a urethra, although much shorter and lacking that valve.)

## THE PROSTATE

The walnut-sized *prostate gland* rests at the base of the urethra, which passes through it, much like the female urethra passes through the urethral sponge.* The prostate has two lobes with a cleft running between them. Like its female counterpart the urethral sponge, it's composed of both erectile and glandular tissue. It produces prostate fluid, which is a component of semen. This is what mostly makes up pre-cum. It probably has an anti-microbial action as it precedes the rest of the ejaculate out of the urethra.

Sad but true: The prostate doesn't get the respect or attention it deserves. The prostate is very sensitive and can deliver enormous pleasure. By far the best way

Achille Devéria

to play with it involves anal access, so an unfortunately large number of men consider it off limits, being afflicted with the bizarre notion that any kind of anal play may mean they're gay. If you're one of these naysayers, I encourage you to change your story. Enjoying anal play says nothing whatsoever about your sexual preference. (Except for this— you like anal play!) Prostate stimulation can deliver amazing expanded orgasms and also help you learn to have non-ejaculatory orgasms. In addition, it's really healthy for you.

If you aren't a prostate player yet, I invite you to go for it! You can play with it yourself with the aid of specially-designed toys—and you may also have friends out there who are willing to lend a finger.

---

\* Embryologically, the prostate and urethral sponge arise from the same tissue. Thus the urethral sponge can accurately be referred to as the female prostate, and conversely, the prostate could be called the male urethral sponge.

## Male Guided Tour—A New Look at Your Old Friend

### Solo Play

While most men are on intimate terms with their sexual equipment, I'd like to invite you to take another look (and feel) as if it's the first time. As with the female tour, you may want to explore your equipment by yourself and in various states of arousal.

Start in a state of non-arousal. Take a good look at your entire visible apparatus, including using a mirror to see underneath. See and feel all the parts. Note the size, shape, position, color and sensitivity.

Now play with yourself and get to medium-level arousal. Make sure to pleasure your whole penis, including both base and balls. Take your time and be thorough. Pause in your play and check out all of your parts again, noticing how they've changed.

Return to your self-pleasuring. Use whatever works to get yourself to a high-level, deep arousal trance, hovering at step eight or nine but not going over the point of no return. Be a fabulous lover to yourself and get yourself utterly turned on.

Now, for the hard part of the homeplay assignment—don't go over the ejaculatory inevitability line! Not yet, at least. Pause and check everything out again, attending again to all the changes. Check in with the rest of your body and notice what's happening with your breathing, posture, muscle tension, awareness and sensation.

Finish your solo sex session however you like. Assuming that an ejaculatory orgasm is part of your play, try to tune in during the experience and really notice all the sensations. Can you start to distinguish orgasm from ejaculation?

### Partner Play

Take your partner on a guided tour, pointing out the landmarks and the changes.

---

*We have reason to believe that man first walked*
*upright to free his hands for masturbation.*

LILY TOMLIN

---

## Guided Tour: Anus & Prostate

As ALWAYS, I SUGGEST that you explore your inner realms privately before doing so with a partner. If you choose to explore with a partner first, you'll need good communication about your comfort as you go.

HAVE SOME NICE LUBE HANDY. Wear gloves if it makes you more comfortable. Showering and washing well is a great starting point. In fact, you may choose to use your soapy finger for initial anal explorations.

Now, LUBE UP YOUR FINGER and slowly slide it in, bearing down as you do. Take your time, especially if you're an anal virgin. Insert your finger slowly and gently. Go slow and breathe yourself open, releasing your anal sphincter by making soft open-mouth sounds and breathing deeply. Massage the muscle ring and vibrate your finger gently. Notice how the tight drawstring of your sphincter muscles relaxes and opens as you do. You can feel the tight anal band relax around your finger as you let it release

To FEEL YOUR PROSTATE, you'll need to insert all or most of a slippery finger deep into your anus. When your finger is all the way in, curl it, crooking it forward toward the cock. You can also let your finger move in, following the base of the penis, then continue a bit further in and up and you'll feel the firm curve of the back surface of your walnut-sized prostate.

SQUEEZE AND RELEASE your pelvic floor muscles. Notice how it feels to touch your prostate and have it played with. I recommend that you conduct your explorations in both an aroused and non-aroused state. You may wish to use your other hand to play with your cock. Notice how it feels to play with your prostate when you're aroused and how playing with your prostate enhances your penis play.

### PROSTATE PLAY—TIME FOR A TOY

I highly recommend special prostate stimulation toys. You can also use butt plugs or any toy with a flange that prevents it from being inadvertently sucked inside. Use your toy alone and with partner play. When alone, use it to learn which of your pelvic floor muscles squeezes your prostate. This is what you need to do to learn to hold back your ejaculate while releasing your orgasmic energy for male multiple orgasms. For men (usually older men) who need more stimulation to come, a prostate-stimulating toy or your partner rhythmically rubbing it with their finger can provide the necessary stimulus.

## ELEGANT EJACULATION

Male ejaculation generally occurs after erotic stimulation and arousal reach a sufficient peak. In an elegant process, semen, usually containing sperm along with a number of glandular fluids, is forcibly ejected during a series of pleasurable muscular contractions.

While ejaculation usually comes, so to speak, with orgasm, they're actually two separate processes. Ejaculation is the propelling of semen out of the penis. Orgasms are all the other delightful sensations. Men can learn to separate the two processes so they have orgasms without squirting.

Prior to ejaculation, men reach a point of ejaculatory inevitability—the fabled point of no return. After a man ejaculates, he has a refractory period during which he can't get hard again for a while.* As men get older, the calm before the next storm of hard-on energy gets longer. A 16-year-old's refractory period may be a few minutes. For a 60-year-old, it can be hours or even days. Women don't have a refractory period.

## TO CUM OR NOT TO CUM

How often to ejaculate is a hotly debated point in Western science and sacred sexuality traditions. The Taoist view is that ejaculation reduces vital life energy and should therefore be minimized and done less frequently as men age. Modern science seems to be pointing in the opposite direction, with some studies indicating that more frequent emissions reduce rates of prostate cancer. Not owning the equipment myself, I have no advice for men other than to tune into your own experience and discover what works for you.

Martin van Maele

Whether you decide to squirt or not, I encourage you to develop your erotic energy skills so that you can more easily get and sustain your erections, exercise ejaculatory choice and discover the pleasures of non-ejaculatory energy orgasms.

And know that you're blessed with your wonderful wand of light.

---

* The dictionary definition of refractory is "stubborn or unmanageable," which tells us how most people feel about this penile pattern.

## The Pulsing Perineum

The *perineum* is the stretch of skin between the more southerly genitals and the opening of the ass. Some call it the 'taint' because "it ain't the cock and it ain't the ass." Although both men and women have a perineum, I'm discussing it here rather than in the unisex section because it's where a number of male pleasure points are located:

- You can access the base of the lingam from the perineum.

- With very firm pressure, you can stimulate the prostate, albeit somewhat indirectly.

- The perineum is home to the root chakra, one of seven vortices in the Hindu energy system (we'll be discussing it more later) and a powerful place to play with energy. (For women, too!)

- The spot just behind the base of the penis is renowned in Taoist sexuality teachings as the million dollar point. When you press on it, it taps into a powerful masculine sexual energy current. You can play with the deep pulsation that arises there to great effect. You can also press there just before ejaculation to hold back the fluid, producing a 'hand-on' non-ejaculatory orgasm.

---

PLAY & PRACTICE

HOT AND JUICY TIPS

### Play Teacher

REQUEST A PRIVATE show-and-tell lesson in genital stimulation. You can't go wrong with "Hey, honey, I was wondering if you could show me how you pleasure yourself" or "Show me some of the things you'd love to have me do to you." Be attentive—notice what they do and how they do it. Then give it a try, making sure to check in to see if you've got it. Set aside time for teaching and learning and you can become the teacher's pet (and get to pet your teacher).

---

Cynthia Wilson, *Zooming In and Zooming Out*

## The Fabulous Foreskin

Is the foreskin merely an ugly old-fashioned dirt-catching frill that's best removed from all penises as soon as possible? No. In fact, nothing could be further from the truth. The foreskin is an ingenious piece of perfectly co-evolved, multipurpose erogenous equipment.

Natural intact male genitals include a *foreskin* (or *prepuce*), a double-sided sliding sheath of skin. Despite a lot of cultural confusion about this structure, it's not actually separate from the skin of the head and shaft of the penis. The outer foreskin layer is an extension of the skin that covers the shaft of the penis—it folds over to form the highly sensitive inner foreskin layer. The foreskin forms a retractable hood that covers the head of the organ when it's flaccid and everts during erection—the inside layer moves to the outside.

The continuous skin system shifts position as the penis expands and contracts, allowing the penis to enlarge considerably and still be contained within the generous sleeve.

At the tip of the inner foreskin is a ring of tissue, the *frenar* or *ridged band*. This ring of tissue contains the highly sensitive nerve cells

Carl August Ehrensvärd, *Ordensprydd man*

called Meissner's corpuscles. These are the most exquisite nerve cells in the male genitals, responding to fine touch and stretching sensations. Many intact men find this band very erogenous as it evolved to trigger orgasm and ejaculation.

The ridged band forms a softly elastic ring that helps contract the tip of the foreskin, keeping the glans (head of the penis) covered when flaccid. When the cock is erect, the foreskin is drawn down over the expanded shaft, bringing this sensitive tissue to the outer surface.

The super-sensitive nerve cells inside the foreskin's inner band respond to stretch, receiving delicious stimulation when the movable sleeve of skin slides back and forth. The ridged band is stimulated with every stroke, thus providing the mechanism by which the intact man's equipment is naturally most easily aroused.

## Saving the Worst Till Last

I'll put it bluntly, knowing that what I say flies in the face of deeply embedded cultural traditions: Circumcision is an ignorant, hurtful and harmful thing to do. The word is actually a euphemism—the medical term is foreskin amputation, but it's really male genital mutilation.

Here's why this barbaric sado-medical practice should be ended.*

First, circumcision is traumatic. Just because we can't remember an event or tell someone how much it hurt doesn't mean it wasn't horrific. When part of a man's penis is cut off, it's shocking and painful. The emotional and physical trauma it causes is real and has lifelong effects.

Second, removing healthy tissue from a non-consenting person is a human rights violation. We don't condone female genital mutilation in this country and abhor the practice elsewhere. Circumcision is comparable to second-degree female circumcision in terms of the amount of tissue removed. Our baby boys should have the same right as our girls to genital integrity.

Third, circumcision has negative health impacts. One example: The foreskin covers the part of the penile shaft that contains the *preputial glands* or *Tyson's glands* which secrete sebaceous material, as well as pheromones, emollients, lubricants and protective antibodies. Collectively these substances comprise *smeg-*

*Custom will reconcile people to any atrocity.*

GEORGE BERNARD SHAW

*ma*, a much-maligned substance that is a normal aspect of the penile environment. There is an ecology of the foreskin, just as there is an ecology of the vagina. When the prepuce is removed, that natural, healthy ecology is destroyed.

Fourth, circumcised penis owners have less pleasure. The foreskin is exquisitely sensitive. The hood contains approximately 25–50% of the nerve endings and about that much of the male genital skin system. It's the primary and most important sensory tissue of the penis. If you've been circumcised, you lose the nerve endings that deliver all this pleasure.

In addition, the head of the penis is composed of delicate mucosa and isn't supposed to be exposed except during play time. Like the eyelid of the eye, the prepuce covers and protects the delicate tissue underneath. Without that protection, the glans becomes toughened and less responsive to stimuli—and its owner has less pleasure.

Finally—and for those of you who've been circumcised, this may be the hardest part of all to hear—your penis-receiving partners have less pleasure, too.

---

* Term coined by the late great Jeanine Parvati Baker, midwife, herbalist, writer and consciousness-raising pioneer.

Why? To put it bluntly, because you fuck differently.

I'll take an extra moment to explain how this is so.

Why is it that over half of women in our culture don't have orgasms from intercourse? Many women prefer to be pleasured by hands or mouth because they're likelier to have orgasms that way—and it's not just women who don't put coitus at the top of their wish list. For many men, a blowjob beats boinking hands down. (And by even more when the hands are on, not down!)

From an evolutionary point of view, this doesn't make sense. The act that makes babies ought to be what we desire most, but that's not how it is. Why not? Why isn't intercourse the ultimate satisfaction for everyone?

There are basically three explanations. First, women and their partners don't know the truth about female genital anatomy or how to make it purr.

Second, most people don't know how to use all their equipment or that of their playmates to get deeply turned on. When you use your full toolkit of mind, body, heart and spirit skills to fire up your and your partner's erotic energy, it makes for sexual encounters that are likelier to include lots more pleasure and treats like orgasms for women from intercourse.

Finally, there's circumcision. When you remove a functional part of the sexual equipment, guess what the result is? That's right, dysfunction—or at least reduced function. When the skin system of the penis is amputated, our co-created genitals can no longer collaborate as intended.

So how are the intact penis and vagina supposed to work? During vaginal intercourse, the foreskin acts as a loose sleeve that remains relatively motionless inside the vagina, allowing the penis to glide in and out in a mostly friction-free

## Circumcised Sex (Love to Lube Ya, Baby)

FOR COUPLES WHO FACE a friction challenge because they're playing without a foreskin, the liberal and frequent application of extra lubricant can greatly help reduce this problem. It also helps when only hand play is involved—whether the hand is the owner's or someone else's. So bring on the lube, baby, and keep things gliding smoothly.

My personal favorite is coconut oil. It's all-natural, tastes delicious and lubricates wonderfully, although it's not compatible with latex. For latex-friendly options, I recommend water-based natural lubricants, particularly ones that are aloe-based. For a more long-lasting slip and slide, try silicone lubes.

manner. Circumcised men often need a lot of thrusting to get the extra friction they need to get off since they lack all the foreskin's wonderful nerve endings. Foreskin owners tend to use a connected hip-rocking motion more than the old in-out. Chicks dig this: Less friction means less irritation, and less thrusting means more contact with the entire erectile network. Together this translates into more pleasure. While friction may be the circumcised man's friend, it's often not the woman's.

Foreskins are there for a reason. The prepuce isn't just a little flap of extra tissue that Mother Nature tossed on top of the penis like a useless dust-catching doily. It's part of the integral and elegant skin system of the penis and it performs important functions. It should remain attached, and it is damaging in multiple ways when it's severed.

If you happen to be circumcised—and many men are; in the United States, the number is over 50%—it can be painful to learn about what's been taken from you involuntarily. You may feel that you come into the game at an erotic disadvantage. Please don't stress about it. What's done is done, and more importantly you can still have fabulous, transcendent sex that is totally amazing for both you and your partner. As with any challenge, you can learn to compensate and overcome your disability by maximizing and refining your other abilities.

Utamaro, *Man and Woman*

## Healing Circumcision Trauma

FOR MANY OF YOU, THIS BOOK MAY BE the first time you've realize what you've lost and that you were sexually traumatized as an infant. People will react differently to this news. Possible responses include denial, anger, grief and the surfacing of deep-seated pain.

Our bodies respond to trauma by armoring—your muscles and tissues tighten in a protective contraction. This pattern becomes part of our body-mind's architecture. I'm convinced this is why many men have locked hips and are unable to move their pelvis freely. I also believe it explains many men's deeply held, usually unconscious fears about safety, pleasure and pain.

There are many paths to healing sexual trauma. Here is one option. I understand that this may be a bit much for some of you, especially if you're in the 'real men don't do woo-woo' school. If this isn't for you, that's okay. I do believe that rituals, when entered into respectfully and with real commitment, can change our stories and our lives.

CREATE AN ALTAR TO HONOR YOUR GENITALS. Place items there to represent you, your equipment and whatever symbolizes wholeness and healing for you. Possibilities include a picture or drawing of you, a lingam stone or a picture of an intact and smiling baby boy.

HAVE SOME MASSAGE OIL READY. Begin by taking deep slow breaths. Breathe and pulse your pelvic floor muscles. Hold your hands near your penis, feeling your genital energy field. Visualize your penis surrounded by colored light. Imagine healing energy pouring from your palms into your shaft. Softly cup your hands around your cock. Repeat a healing phrase such as, "I send healing light into my body." You may alternate with a releasing phrase such as, "I release all pain." Breathe deeply and fill your genitals with loving and healing thoughts and images. Put some oil on your hands and begin to stroke your lingam, not like you do when you're trying to get aroused, but like a healer would soothe sore muscles. Continue to focus on healing phrases, breathing deeply as you rub, hold and tenderly love your penis.

END THE MEDITATION QUIETLY, bringing yourself to a calm and centered loving place. Or, if you prefer, move it into sexual energy. If you choose to shift the energy towards the sexual, dedicate it to healing by repeating a mending mantra as you play. Especially think healing thoughts as you come. Let your orgasmic energy pour through your lingam in a burst of rejuvenating love.

The reality is that we all have disabilities; we all have challenges. They may come from negative stories we believe or be due to something physical. But we also have wonderful capacities. Our potential for erotic bliss is amazing and that's true even if you don't have a foreskin or a uterus or some other body part.

We have another wonderful faculty, too—the ability to learn new skills and to re-wire our bodies and brains with new pathways. I know a man who's a quadriplegic. The only thing he can move below his neck is his right arm and the thumb on his right hand. He's learned to run energy through his thumb and experience it as if it were his penis. He can even have energy orgasms from using it! (I hear his partners love his magical thumb, too).

His story is remarkable—and it's also true that if he can learn to do that, the rest of us can learn more modest skills. Like learning to use our entire instrument to have amazing sex whatever parts we have or don't have, including whether we're the owner of, or merely dating, a circumcised penis.

Franz von Bayros, *Sweet Snail*

SUCCULENT SEX CRAFT

# CHAPTER EIGHT

# YOUR INTERTWINED BODY-MIND

*The human mind evolved always in the company of the human body,*
*and of the animal body before it was human. The intricate connections*
*of mind and body must exceed our imagination, as from our point of*
*view we are peculiarly prevented from observing them.*

JOHN DESMOND BERNAL

## It's *Not* All In Your Head

IN THIS CHAPTER, I COVER INFORMATION ABOUT THE INTRICATELY interconnected body-mind that will help you better understand your sexcraft tools and how to use them to your erotic advantage.

Let's start by asking, "What exactly is the mind?" Philosophers, scientists, religious folks and great thinkers have pondered this question for millennia and come up with different responses. One answer is that it's what allows us to ponder such questions! My view: It includes the brain and the body, consciousness and perception, cognition and feeling, agency and judgment. It's what lets us consider the past, imagine the future and strive to be present in the now.

In Western culture, there's been a tendency to separate mind and body, to envision the smarty-pants mind as what's in your head and the 'dumb' body as everything that's below the neck. In this limited picture, all activities of the mind are in the purview of the brain. It assumes that your brain is in charge and tells the rest of you what to do. In truth, while an amazing

> *I think we actually punish children out*
> *of their relationship with their bodies . . .*
> *we categorically separate mind and body*
> *and emotion and intellect.*
>
> SUSAN GRIFFIN

amount of processing and integration does occur inside your skull, the major direction of information flow is from the body to the brain, not the other way around. The brain can't be separated from the body—and, in many ways, the body has a mind of its own.

The idea of the mind-body split is rapidly becoming outdated as mounting scientific evidence demonstrates that this division is simplistic and misguided. Your body-mind is a complex integral system that's woven together by incredibly nuanced and sophisticated neurological and biochemical systems. For example, research on the enteric nervous system, the 'brain in the belly,' shows it has more nerve cells than the central nervous system. Your belly has its own set of smarts and often gives instructions to the brain. Your 'gut brain' includes not just your body's intelligence about what and when to eat, but offers other wisdom such as a 'gut feeling' that can guide your thinking brain's conscious choices. (Your brain may or may not listen, but that's another story.)

The mind-body relationship is, as they say, complicated. While there are still huge mysteries to solve such as what consciousness actually is and how a bunch of tissue and chemicals could create it, at a minimum we know this: The head and the brain are a part of the body and our consciousness includes every last bit of us, top to bottom.

Alméry Lobel-Riche

## Your Nervous System

Here's some anatomy and physiology information that, while geeky, is worth knowing because it can help you better understand and manage your arousal and orgasm.

Your *nervous system* is your internal wiring and signaling system. It controls and coordinates your physical actions, communicates among different parts of your body and integrates your entire body-mind. It includes your brain, spinal cord and the vast network of nerves that branch throughout you. Your *nerve cells*, called *neurons*, are capable of sending rapid and precise electrochemical signals to other neurons and cells. They're what enable the multi-cellular, multi-organ organism that you are to function with grace and sophistication.

On a physical level, you can divide the system into two basic parts, the central nervous system and peripheral nervous system.

The *central nervous system* is your brain and spinal cord. Your brain is your operations center and plays the lead role in coordinating and integrating the systems of the body. The spinal cord mostly relays information.

The *peripheral nervous system* includes the rest of the nerve tissue and is the control, coordination and communication mechanism that connects the central

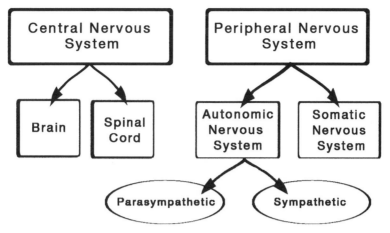

*Divisions of the Nervous System*

nervous system to the rest of the body. It includes the enteric nervous system, the 'gut brain' I discussed above.

The peripheral nervous system is further divided into two parts. The *somatic nervous system* controls the voluntary muscles and their movement. (For this reason, it's also known as the *voluntary nervous system.*) It's operated intentionally and its function is to enable the organism (that would be you) to interact successfully with its environment. It includes motor neurons, which mediate movement, and sensory neurons, which receive stimuli and transmit impulses to your central nervous system, primarily your brain.

The somatic or voluntary nervous system is the part we're most likely to be conscious of, although most of our 'voluntary' actions actually take place at a relatively unconscious level. If you want to reach for your favorite sex toy, you don't put a lot of thought into the action, you just do it—it feels pretty automatic. It's only when we're learning new habits, like learning to ride a bicycle or recovering from a stroke, that we have to consciously think about what we're doing in order to make it happen.

The *autonomic nervous system* is your autopilot, the part of the peripheral nervous system that regulates involuntary body functions like your heartbeat. Generally, what goes on here is beyond conscious control although, as we will see, it's not entirely beyond our conscious influence—we can get into and adjust this machinery. In fact we'll learn how to do this in the next section when we start to play with our sexcraft tools.

The autonomic nervous system has two further divisions, *sympathetic* and *parasympathetic*. In many cases, the two have complementary actions where one activates a physiological response and the other inhibits it. For instance the sympathetic system dilates your pupils while your parasympathetic system contracts them.

Some compare the sympathetic system to an accelerator and the parasympathetic system to a brake, but that's a bit simplistic. The sympathetic system is the excitation system that prepares you to deal with the challenges of sudden stress—to fight or flee. While it acts as an accelerator for some systems, like rapidly increasing your heart rate and pumping more blood to your 'race or rumble' muscles, it also acts as a brake for systems like digestion (if you may become food, you don't need to waste your 'run away' resources on digesting food.)

*Our bodies are at once the receiving and transmitting stations for life itself. It is the highest wisdom to recognize this fact and train our bodies to render the sensitive and responsive to nature, art and religion.*

RUTH ST. DENIS

The sympathetic system operates in quick-response mode because that's what's required if you're in danger. When you see that tiger coming, you don't want to linger, it's time to boogie. It's also what inspires us to 'tend and befriend.' It connects us to other members of our tribe, enabling us to survive and thrive—they may help us fend off that tiger.

The parasympathetic system is the other side of the energetic coin. It's your relaxation mode. It's running the show when you're calm and ready to eat, digest, relax, play and be at ease. The parasympathetic system is thus your internal chill pill while the sympathetic nervous system is your 'kill or be killed' pill. Both systems are active all the time, maintaining a state of homeostasis, although one or the other usually predominates at any given moment.

## Your Sexy Nervous System

Sex is, of course, mediated by your nervous system.

When you're getting hot and bothered, your sympathetic system is predominating. Arousal up-regulates your system, accelerating your heartbeat and respiration and producing generalized feelings of energy and excitation. Increased speed, hot action and ramping it up all activate your sympathetic system, sending you up the arousal ladder and ultimately tipping you into orgasm. It's the yang aspect of your regulatory system.

When you're relaxed, your nervous system is down-regulating with the parasympathetic system predominating. This allows you to feel safe and at ease, focus on sensation and relax into pleasure. Your system is unwinding. You're in your yin energy. Slowness and stillness open you to this relaxed state.

While your sympathetic system will get you to the higher levels of your arousal steps, when you deepen your trance by relaxing into your arousal, it's your parasympathetic nervous system kicking in.

Arousal is thus a dance between the parasympathetic and sympathetic nervous systems, between relaxation and excitement, between yin and yang. Both systems need to be activated to get to the deepest levels of erotic trance. Too much yin parasympathetic relaxing and you're off into snooze-land. Too much yang excitation and your tightness and tension block your ability to fully receive a broad spectrum of pleasure. Sex gets spectacular when you have a delightful dance of interweaving energies.

## *Succulent Summary*

### Actions of the Sympathetic and Parasympathetic Nervous Systems

SYMPATHETIC NERVOUS SYSTEM: Excitation System (or Challenge System)
Prepares your body for action, including 'fight or flee.'

- Diverts blood flow from the gastrointestinal tract, shutting down digestion

- Sends blood to large muscles

- Dilates bronchi (air passages in your lungs)

- Increases respiratory rate

- Increases heart rate

- Dilates pupils

- Constricts internal sphincters of gastrointestinal tract and urinary system

- Stimulates higher arousal, orgasm and ejaculation

PARASYMPATHETIC NERVOUS SYSTEM: Relaxation System
Promotes a 'rest and digest' (a/k/a 'feed and breed') response.

- Sends blood flow to the gastrointestinal tract, enhancing digestion

- Slows heart rate

- Slows respiratory rate

- Constricts pupils

- Stimulates sexual arousal through relaxation and increased sensation

- Increases engorgement of genital erectile tissue

## A Chemical Attraction

Your other important internal control and messaging system is the endocrine system, the tissues that secrete hormones into the bloodstream to control your physiological and behavioral responses. Hormones are chemicals that in very tiny amounts generate a reaction in target tissues. The dynamics are complex, interconnected and still poorly understood by modern medicine.

Anonymous, *Satyr and Nymph*

While the endocrine system, like the nervous system, is designed for information signaling, its effects and mechanisms are quite distinct. The endocrine system's effects are slow and long-lasting while the nervous system signals are rapid and short-lived.

Your endocrine system is responsible for the hormones that generate secondary sexual characteristics (like estrogen, which promotes breast growth in women during puberty) as well as the cyclic hormones of the female fertility cycle, the daily hormonal rhythms of waking and sleeping, and the many chemicals that influence and adjust the nervous system's responses. The endocrine system also generates the biochemicals of falling-in-love, pleasure, attachment and excitement, to name just a few components of your personal chemical cocktail.

While some of these hormones are beyond our conscious control, the production of others can be induced. For example, while the bonding hormone oxytocin is naturally present in high levels when you have an orgasm, any kind of positive touch increases your levels whenever you do it. That's one reason why petting your cat (your actual feline, not your pussy) is so pleasurable!

## Some of Your Sexy Biochemicals

- OXYTOCIN: A bonding and attachment hormone. Stimulated by pleasurable touching. Peaks: orgasm, birth.

- PEA (PHENETHYLAMINE): The falling-in-love hormone. For most people, it has a limited life-span of four years maximum.

- DOPAMINE: Among other things, delivers the rush associated with sexual gratification. Part of your internal reward system.

- ADRENALINE (EPINEPHRINE) and NOREPINEPHRINE: Excitation hormones.

- NITRIC OXIDE: An important biological regulator for a multitude of body systems including the nervous and immune systems. Also an important component of arousal. Among other things, it stimulates increased genital blood flow and engorgement.

- ENDORPHINS: Your internal 'opium,' inner feel-good chemicals that produce a natural high and block pain.

## It Is All In Your Head

In order to perceive something, you need a stimulus, like someone running their mischievous fingers along your thigh. While we tend to assume that the sensation is happening in the leg, it's not that simple. The information "fingers stroking thigh" must be transmitted through the wiring of the nervous system to the part of the brain where you hold a sensory map of your body. Only when the part of the brain map that correlates to the thigh gets the signal and lights up do you perceive that there's something lovely going on down south.

Shunga, *Fingers and Tongue*

Although it appears to occur elsewhere, perception actually occurs in the brain. This is one reason why, when you imagine someone licking your luscious bits, your brain responds as if it's really happening. The mere thought of that naughty (and nice!) tongue lights up the genital zone in the brain-map of your body.

## Sometimes Size Does Matter

The brain-map of your body doesn't have the same proportions as your physical body. The more innervation an area has, the more brain territory it gets. Your fingers, mouth and genitals are allocated a disproportionately large amount of brain-map because they have lots of nerve endings relative to their size. Your super-sensitive genitals are rich with sensation-transmitting nerve-endings and thus get a lot of brain map devoted to them. Body parts like the calf or the middle of your back are less densely packed with nerves and get relatively short shrift upstairs.

## Remodeling Brain Architecture

Is our brain-map fixed and unchangeable? The old thinking about the brain was that after the tumultuous transformations of infancy and early childhood,

*I wish we could treat our bodies as the place we live from, rather than regard it as a place to be worked on, as though it were a disagreeable old kitchen in need of renovation and update.*

SUSIE ORBACH

it was a static organ incapable of further alteration. Now we know better. Current brain research has replaced that idea with a new one. The concept of neuroplasticity proposes that your brain changes its architecture throughout your life based on a range of inputs, including your experience, environment, learning and physical trauma. It turns out that the more you use parts of your body, the bigger its lit-up brain region gets. A trained pianist has larger 'brain hands' than someone who hasn't spent years developing hand and finger skills. Similarly for genitals—if you use them a lot, your corresponding brain-map area will, well, not exactly engorge, but it will become larger.

In addition, neurons form webs of connections to other neurons. In other words, stimulating a nerve pathway sends electro-chemical signals through the network, which causes more connections to be made and speeds the flow of impulses. Contemporary brain researchers like to say that neurons that fire together, wire together (or excite together and light together). When an impulse travels along those well-linked paths, all the connected neurons fire as well.

*In the human mind, the number of possible connections that can be made between neurons greatly exceeds the number of atoms in the universe.*

ALAN MOORE

## Getting In The Groove

When you learn to do something you haven't done before, you have to think about the new behavior and consciously make yourself do it. You're sending nerve impulses along novel pathways. As you practice these actions, new junctions, networks and pathways are formed. After they're used many times, nerve impulses flow quicker and more connections are activated. Over time, they become established neural grooves, automatic and unconscious. That's what learning consists of—reprogramming your body-mind with new connections and patterns, increasing the signal stream and expanding your neural maps.

I hope you see how useful this is in supporting your erotic expansion! These factors will help you become sexually more masterful because, thanks to the new and enlarged genital zone in your brain-map along with lots of linked and well-connected pathways, you will have a more nuanced sensory relationship with your physical genitals and the rest of your body. A well-trained musician or erotic master has cultivated an extensive and well-established network of pathways for musical or erotic pleasure.

*As a single footstep will not make a path on the earth, so a single thought will not make a pathway in the mind. To make a deep physical path, we walk again and again. To make a deep mental path, we must think over and over the kind of thoughts we wish to dominate our lives.*

HENRY DAVID THOREAU

## Mirror, Mirror In the Brain

Our amazing brain has mirrors along with maps. Let's say you see someone smash their thumb with a hammer. You probably wince and go "Ow!" You're not actually getting hit by the hammer, so why this response? Because we have brain cells that fire in response to our perception of other people's experience.

They're called mirror neurons, but they might as well be called empathy neurons, because that's what they do—they connect us emotionally to other people. When you get all weepy at that tear-jerker movie, it's because of mirror neurons.

Mirror neurons are central to our emotional and social development. They are probably the physiological basis for imitative learning (person see, person do) and why we pick up many social cues.

Mirror neurons are also why so many people are aroused by porn: They turn the actors' pleasure (or pseudo-pleasure) into their own. This also explains why fantasy and imagination do such a good job of feeding our turn-on. Mirror neurons don't distinguish between 'real' and 'pretend,' or between my experience and yours—they light up for it all.

When you see your partner get ecstatic and this gets you really turned on—that's right, those are mirror neurons in action. And of course the action doesn't stop there. Picking up on your partner's arousal is exciting and empowering, which triggers a cascade of arousal biochemicals that send blood to your own genitals. This, in turn sends pleasure messages back to your brain, creating a delectable feedback loop of its own.

The more you pay attention to your partner's pleasure and to your own, the more everyone gets turned on, and before you know it the two of you are feedback-looping down the express lane to ecstasy.

Gustav Klimt, *Nuda Veritas*

## Your Triune Brain

There's a simple map that can help you understand your incredibly complex brain. Think of the human brain as having three sections, each of which recapitulates a different chapter in our evolutionary journey and plays a role in helping (or hindering) our erotic experience.

The base of your brain, which is located immediately above the spinal cord, is the *hind-brain*, which evolutionarily speaking is the oldest part. Often called the 'lizard' or 'reptile' brain,' it includes your brain stem, which manages basic life functions, and the cerebellum, which coordinates movement. These brain structures are associated with territoriality, preprogrammed behaviors, aggression, survival, basic life functions and some sexual and reproductive behaviors. It's where your most basic mating motions arise from.

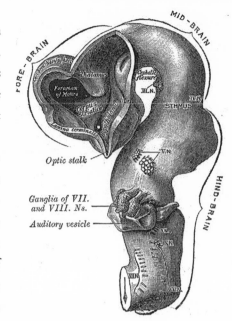

Gray's Anatomy, *Embryonic Brain Formation*

The *mid-brain* is often called the mammalian brain because it's the part that's associated with nurturing, caretaking, attachment and social bonding. It includes much of the emotional brain, also known as the *limbic system*. The biochemicals of love and attachment stimulate multiple areas in your mid-brain. Lovers, babies and companion animals activate our mammalian connection circuits.

The topmost section is the *forebrain*. It includes the *cerebral cortex*, the folded, convoluted layers associated with uniquely human attributes like self-control, self-consciousness, intellect, reasoning and abstract thought. Its outermost layers make up your *neocortex*, our newest evolutionary innovation. Your 'new brain' is the part that anticipates and worries, that imagines and remembers. It's where you make lists and recite poetry, where you simulate possible futures and plan for eventualities (often for things that never happen). Your neocortex attempts to understand and, through understanding, to control (as best it can!)

## This Is Your Brain on Sex

Your neocortex is the executive headquarters of your brain, perched in the penthouse at the front of your skull. This is not where sex takes place. Sexuality is primarily a function of the older, more primitive parts of our brain. Sexual energy is animal energy and our animal selves live in the limbic system and old brain. Sex taps into ancient evolutionary machinery that resides, so to speak, in the cranial basement. You need to go down the brain elevator if you want to really get down sexually.

> *Brainy's the new sexy.*
>
> STEVEN MOFFAT

Your busy babbling executive forebrain can be more of a hindrance than a help. We've probably all had times when our chattering neocortex blocked our sexual energy. People get stuck in their heads—or, rather, neocortex—all the time thinking about things like what you should (or shouldn't) be doing, if you're doing it right, if the ceiling needs painting . . . the list goes on and on.

## Sex Makes You Stupid

How CAN YOU PREVENT morning-after, "I can't believe I was so stupid" syndrome? Understand that once your thinking brain goes offline, you will become essentially brainless (neocortically-speaking). Guaranteed. Nothing personal here, it's just that high arousal makes you unable to plan and judge. This is why conversations about safer sex practices, appropriate boundaries, preferences and practices need to happen before you get turned on or, at the latest, when your arousal level is low.

This is also why I encourage people not to change boundaries when they're deep into a hot session. Your judgment will be impaired and that's no time to be making boundary decisions, especially ones that may affect your life, health or emotional well-being.

Achille Devéria, *Dancing Penis with On-Looking Demons*

🍒 *Come visit GetSexCrafty.com for more info on Safer Sex Conversations and Guidelines.*

The simple fact is that to go into erotic trance at all, and especially to go deep, your forebrain needs to turn off so your animal body can wake up and turn on. Your command center needs to stop thinking, deciding, planning, worrying and judging—it needs to go off-line.

Until that happens, the primal templates that reside in the old parts of your brain can't be accessed.

Turning off the jabbering conver-

*I believe in an open mind, but not so open that your brains fall out.*

ARTHUR HAYS SULZBERGER

sations in your executive office is easier said than done. We can do it, though, with the help of our sexcraft toolkit. Focusing on sound and breath, for instance, takes our attention away from all that administrative prattle and brings us to greater body awareness—it makes us, in this sense, more 'animal.' Similarly, visualizing heart energy stills the mind and activates the limbic system, which, as we've seen, is the mammalian part of the brain that deals with love and attachment.

Great sex brings out the animal in you. Not literally, but not merely figuratively either. You go down into the more animal parts of your brain, on vacation from your control-aholic, hyper-active head office.

The deeper we get into our arousal trance, the more difficult it becomes to communicate coherently. Talking is a fore-brain activity and when we're turned on, we're down in the basement and that upper story is far away. This explains why we tend to communicate in shorthand when we're having sex ("Now!" "Please!" "Yes!") or stay with our animal selves and simply purr and howl.

The three aspects of the brain—the old 'reptile brain,' the 'mammal mid-brain' and the ultra-modern 'human new brain'—can act in coordination or competition. Sex is a great example of how this plays out. It's a journey where you shift from mundane reality to the altered state of intense arousal. At the beginning of the experience, your prattling neocortex predominates. As you go deeper into arousal, it slowly shuts down, allowing you to descend to where the primeval apparatus of sex resides. In between are the connections, emotions and experiences that form the web of who you are, what turns you on, your dreams and fantasies, your hopes and expectations, your anxieties and fears, your thoughts, sensations, meaning and stories. These can facilitate or inhibit your shift into deep erotic trance. For instance, your command center can assist you on your journey by reminding you to use your tools, advising you to take some deep breaths, make pleasure sounds and rock your hips. You can use your sexual imagination to replace negative thoughts with hot scenarios. Brain management is, believe it or not, a bedroom skill. You don't want your forebrain working against you. Learn to harness it in service to your arousal—use your conscious brain to get animal and wild.

You can consciously use your brain to change your mind and you can use your mind to change your brain.

Anonymous, *Dick Rider*

SUCCULENT SEX CRAFT

CHAPTER NINE

# The Geography
# of Energy

*You, yourself, are the eternal energy which appears*
*as this Universe. You didn't come into this world;*
*you came out of it. Like a wave from the ocean.*

ALAN WATTS

## Embodied Energy

ENERGY: IT'S A BROAD CONCEPT AND A WORD WITH MANY CONNOTATIONS.
In one context, its meaning is perfectly clear. No one blinks if you say we need
energy to fuel our cars and heat our homes. We also know that plants get energy
from the sun and animals get energy from food. But there's more to energy than
that. There's also the mysterious 'something' that enters us when we're born and
leaves us when we die. Some sort of life force animates us. Some sort of force
underlies and infuses the physical world. This amazing power connects your
physical body with your mind and emotions and whatever it is that we call spirit.
For lack of a better word, I call this force *energy*.

Ancient cultures have always assumed that we're beings of both energy and
matter. In Traditional Chinese Medicine, the life force is called *chi*, while in India
it's known as *prana* (both of which literally translate as 'breath').

---

### WORD NERD: LIFE'S SUBTLE ENERGY

"Numerous cultures describe a matrix of subtle energies that support,
shape, and animate the physical body, called *qi* or *chi* in China, *prana*
in the yoga tradition of India and Tibet, *yesod* in the Jewish cabalistic
tradition, *ki* in Japan, *baraka* by the Sufis, *wakan* by the Lakotas, *orenda*
by the Iroquois, *megbe* by the Ituri Pygmies, and the Holy Spirit in
Christian tradition. It is hardly a new idea to suggest that subtle energies
operate in tandem with the denser, 'congealed' energies of the material
body." —Donna Eden with David Feinstein in *Energy Medicine*

---

Energy not only suffuses us, it emanates beyond the body, creating a field that is somehow transmitted to others. Take emotional states, for example. If an angry person walks into a room, we pick up their hostile energy. Similarly if a person radiates love—we pick up that vibration. When we're madly in love, a powerful erotic current pulls us to our beloved—we're magnetized by their energy. But what exactly are we registering? What subtle energy is and how it operates are questions science hasn't fully answered yet. But we can probably all agree that energy not only animates us, it connects us—to ourselves, to others and to all life around us.

*Scientists will eventually stop flailing around with solar power and focus their efforts on harnessing the only truly unlimited source of energy on the planet: stupidity. I predict that in the future, scientists will learn how to convert stupidity into clean fuel.*

SCOTT ADAMS

Cutting-edge science is starting to confirm all these ancient intuitions about energy. For instance, while we've known for some time that our brains are abuzz with electrical energy, it has now been demonstrated that our brain waves affect people in our immediate vicinity. In fact, close physical proximity causes brain waves (and the resultant state of consciousness) to align. It turns out that the famous 'contact high' is real!

It also turns out that energetically, our hearts are even more powerful generators than our heads. Like our brains, hearts send out waves—they create emotional fields—that cause a mirrored physical response in those nearby. These heart-wave signals cause our body rhythms to synchronize, especially when we're with people we feel connected to. When your heart is open and loving, you're bathing yourself in a healthy feel-good chemical soup and anyone nearby shares in your positive alchemical broth. When your heart is full of anger or fear, those

around you feel that, too. Strong emotions like anxiety are contagious. So is love.

We are all producers, transmitters and recipients of energetic currents. We bio-regulate each other, harmonizing and entraining our life rhythms with other people. We're a tribal species and evolutionarily designed to connect emotionally and energetically.

Gustav Klimt, *Fischblut*

## Sexual Energy

Erotic energy is the generative aspect of our life energy that arouses the lust to mate and the desire to connect in that special sexual way. It drives our attractions and our passions. Sexual energy channels our personal life force into the compelling desire to merge and create new life (or at least go through the motions!). Whenever you want, you can funnel your vital force, your *chi*, through your erotic channel.

You can celebrate or condemn your sexual energy. You can express it or suppress it, but one thing you can't do is make it go away. It's a built-in part of your operating system. Once you acknowledge that it's a vital aspect of you and all life, you can learn to consciously channel that energy and use it to support love, health, pleasure and connection. It becomes something you can work with (or, better yet, play with).

While there are many ways to conceptualize sexual energy, an easy way to understand it is as the force behind arousal. When your bodymind is turned on, when your genitals swell and throb, you're infused with sexual energy.

I also find it useful to think of sexual energy as the erotic music you orchestrate using your mind, body, heart and spirit instruments.

While the experience of sexual energy varies, there are commonalities. One pretty unanimous perception is that it moves. Energy flows, it pulses, it vibrates. It is never static.

Other ways erotic energy is experienced include:

- As HEAT, especially anything hot that's also moving, like a flow of molten lava or a torrent of rushing hot water.

- As SENSATIONS such as pulsations, vibrations or tingling.

- As VISUALS with lights and colors (fireworks!).

- As SOUNDS, including internal thrumming, toning and beating rhythms.

> *If you want to find the secrets of the universe, think in terms of energy, frequency and vibration.*
>
> NIKOLA TESLA

- As an AWARENESS or awakening of parts of the body or the whole body.

For many people, sexual energy manifests as a mix of sensations and experiences. Often these perceptions shift at different stages of the erotic journey. The same person may perceive erotic energy differently at different times or with different partners.

## Damn That Dam: Sexual Energy Blocks

It's not unusual to run into obstacles when trying to tune in and play with your erotic energy. Everyone experiences times when their erotic energy isn't flowing and they aren't getting turned on. Energy blocks can arise due to particular circumstances, occur occasionally, or be part of a long-term pattern. Rather than bemoan erotic energy constrictions as a problem, I invite you to view them as a learning opportunity, a chance to hear what your unconscious mind is trying to say through your body.

When your sexual energy block is sporadic, it's often because your body-mind is responding appropriately to your current situation. Not getting wet or hard may be your body's way of saying, "There's something here you need to pay attention to!" There are many possible issues. Sometimes the reason is simple—

maybe you just need more time or are feeling performance pressure. You may be having a communication challenge with your partner. Maybe an undisclosed 'something' needs to be aired. Perhaps you're angry with your partner—if so, your emotions need to be dealt with before your amorous energy can flow. If you're being sexual with someone you're not sure you can trust, your lack of arousal may be telling you to stop or slow down, or that playing with this person isn't a good idea at this time. If you're not getting turned on by something that usually gets you going, your body is sending you a message.

Peter Paul Rubens, *Study for a St. Mary Magdalen*

It's your responsibility to listen. Attend to what your lack of sexual energy is saying—and take good care of yourself by responding appropriately. Do what you need to do to respond to your body's communiqué. Talk with your partner. Set different boundaries. End your encounter, if that's what you need to do.

### Persistent Problems

As you become more adept at tuning in to your body and your energy, you may discover chronic blocks. Perhaps you have particular body parts that feel numb or areas where your erotic flow feels inhibited. You might have a general blockage manifesting as reduced libido or a difficult time getting turned on at all.

If your challenge is more persistent and long-term, it probably won't submit to a quick fix. In this case, your erotic energy obstruction may be a big neon arrow pointing to where you need healing or help. Blocks can illuminate stories that need re-writing or parts of your body that need healing. Or serious relationship issues that need addressing.

If your sexual energy isn't flowing, don't just lie there, do something! Check in with yourself, look inside and trust yourself— you do know what you need! If you have regular intimate partners, share with them what's going on. If you need more support, get help. Seek out the people and resources that can give you the healing and care you need.

*The sensation of energy expands with increasing relaxation.*

ILCHI LEE

### STUCK ON THE STAIRS

Not everyone has challenges on the arousal journey, but some people do. Several of the steps on the arousal staircase are especially tricky and common places to get stuck.

Step one, getting from the ground floor into early arousal, can be sticky. A lot of people have difficulty shifting gears from work to play, from thinking to feeling, from doing to being.

We can get stuck in the middle, where we're somewhat aroused but unable to ascend to high-level turn-on. Often it's because we can't turn off our vigilant brain and relinquish control to drop deeper into trance.

Step nine can be another tricky one. Performance anxiety sometimes arises and we worry our way right off the stairs. Or we may try to 'achieve' orgasm, attempting to force it by pushing and tensing instead of allowing and encouraging it to happen. We may resist giving up control and surrendering to the orgasmic wave.

Whatever it is and whenever it happens, don't freak out. Remind yourself that erotic energy blocks happen frequently. Lots of people have to deal with them and you can get through them, too, especially when we understand how we operate and have a full bucket of sexcraft tools at our fingertips.

### EMOTIONAL EROTIC ROADBLOCKS

The stories, beliefs and feelings our history has implanted in us are another obstacle to the free flow of erotic energy. Here are some of the ways we get blocked.

There may be trust issues directed at our self or, during partner sex, at our playmate. It's hard to get entranced and surrender if you don't feel safe.

Inhibition and shame can block arousal. These challenges are often fed by religious or cultural perceptions of the body (especially the sexy bits) as bad, ugly, dirty or evil.

Negative body image is a big issue for many people. To have sublime sex, you need to accept yourself. This can be a big challenge, but it's important to overcome it. You may not like everything about your body, but you can still love it, especially if you appreciate it and focus on the pleasure it can give you. As a woman of abundance myself, I can assure you that it's possible to overcome body issues and have spectacular sex. The key is to focus on your pleasure. Appreciate that you have a body, hardwired for ecstasy and connection. Practice gratitude for the pleasure it can give you. If you don't feel comfortable in your body, you can learn to change that and feel secure and unashamed. If I did it, so can you.

If you want to have great sex, be erotically empowered and be a sex-positive person, it really helps to be body-positive, too. Practice gratitude for your body!

## Embracing Pleasure Means Embracing Your Body

PLEASE BE PATIENT AND SELF-LOVING as you learn to enjoy your body and reclaim your erotic energy.

Appreciate the body you have, whatever its size, shape or limitations. Remember: It gives you the gift of sensation! Your animal body can feel, move, touch and be touched. It can delight, astound and feel bliss.

Learn to celebrate your silky skin, your firm bones, your beautiful eyes and your magnificent genitalia. You've got a body, so please—enjoy all the pleasure it can give you, whatever your size, shape or physical abilities or disabilities. Don't focus on performance, what you look like, or limitations. Put the spotlight on pleasure! When critical or negative thoughts or stories arise, replace them with sensations of pleasure. Your awesome body is animated by erotic energy. It's a conduit for ecstasy!

Henry John Stock, *Rapture*

*I suppose that a lifetime spent hiding one's erotic truth could have a cumulative renunciatory effect. Sexual shame is in itself a kind of death.*

ALISON BECHDEL

Another common block is fear. The list of anxieties around sexuality, sexual performance and the body is long. It includes fears about:

- Surrendering control
- Humiliation
- Performance
- Unleashing an insatiable monster
- Losing boundaries
- Revealing one's real self, including needs, wounds and desires
- Being too powerful (and making your partner feel less powerful)
- Behaving in ways that are inappropriate, illegal or taboo.

A negative history around sex, including abuse, assault and shaming, can be psychologically devastating and painful. Your body is very wise and protective. If you've survived an abusive or traumatic past or you're carrying a burden of negative sexual experiences, your body may be safeguarding you by turning off parts of you or numbing you out. To get past this, you first need to tune into your numb areas. Listen to your body's messages. Gently and self-lovingly open to your erotic energy so you can reclaim your pleasure.

Many people with difficult pasts also find that getting therapeutic and other kinds of support can be helpful. It's often an essential component of their journey from surviving to thriving.

Painful though they may be, I encourage you to do your best to cultivate a positive attitude toward your wounds, fears and issues. I know it's not easy. Yet it's also true they're your teachers and a growth opportunity. Learning to heal your history and recast your stories is key to changing your roadblocks to freeways.

Your obstacles can become your gateways to sexual wholeness.


## The Power of Pleasure

Your sexual energy is, in itself, an important ingredient in your recipe for erotic empowerment and mastery. Pleasure is one of the great healing forces. Sexual arousal and orgasm can open up your blocked passages and pathways. Erotic energy creates its own weather system of positive feedback that can blast you past your obstacles.

In addition, being in an altered state makes you more amenable to positive changes in your mind-body architecture. Any healing work you do while in your sexual trance state is amplified and becomes more potent and effective.

Whether alone or with a partner, the more you can tune in to your sexual energy, the easier it becomes to move past your blocks, trust your body and open up to pleasure.

# Energy Maps

In order to become skilled at using your embodied energy, it's helpful to turn to the many models that have come down to us from primal cultures and sacred sexuality traditions. Here are some energy maps I've found to be especially useful in the study of sexcraft. These models are thousands of years old and share three common understandings. First, energy flows through channels in the body. Second, there are places where these forces form energy centers. Third, we are enveloped in layers of energy.

While these maps tend to be useful for most people, they're only suggestions. As with everything offered here, feel free to find what works for you to enhance your awareness of energy and kindle your erotic fire. Starting in the next chapter, I'll give you tools for working and playing with these maps so you can try them out and see if they're useful.

## THE CENTRAL ENERGY CHANNEL

In Tantra they call it the *inner flute*. The Taoists call it the *hollow bamboo*. In the yoga tradition, it's an *inner channel* that runs up the spine and can open to the energy called *kundalini*. This is usually visualized as a coiled energy serpent that lives in the sacrum, at the base of the spine, and can be released to spiral upward.

All three traditions share the same basic notion, that there's a central conduit inside us, running top to bottom. Your throat, mouth and the crown of your head are at the top of your inner channel, while your genitals, anus and the outlet of your pelvis are at the bottom. When you open your inner tube, you allow more energy to flow.

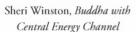

There's a legitimate anatomical foundation for this cross-cultural intuition. At a very early stage in our prenatal development, we were all a bunch of cells that formed just such a tube. Your inner tube is still present and your top and bottom remain anatomically and energetically connected.

Here's an example. Remember sphincter muscles, those round circular muscles that open and close? Well, all your voluntary sphincters at the top (in your mouth, throat and face) and the bottom (in your urinary, genital and anal equipment) are literally connected—they're neurologically hard-wired together. If you want to open your bottom, allow your mouth to dilate and your whole face to relax. Your nether regions will follow suit.

Sheri Winston, *Buddha with Central Energy Channel*

## TAOIST CHANNEL: MICROCOSMIC ORBIT

The Taoists have identified many energy pathways in the body. One of the main ones is the Microcosmic Orbit, so named because it's the 'microcosm of the macrocosm,' a body-sized version of the cosmic path from earth to sky and back again. The Microcosmic Orbit begins in the navel, runs down the front of the body, across the perineum, up the spine, along the back of the head, across the top of your skull and down the front, through the tongue, down the throat and from there back to the navel. It's a fun and powerful circuit of energy to play with.

Sheri Winston
*Microcosmic Orbit on
Gerda Wegener Woman*

---

*You may not feel outstandingly robust, but if you are an average-sized adult you
will contain within your modest frame no less than $7 \times 10^{18}$ joules of potential
energy—enough to explode with the force of thirty very large hydrogen bombs,
assuming you knew how to liberate it and really wished to make a point.*

BILL BRYSON

---

## EMBODIED ENERGY CENTERS

The most familiar and oft-referenced system of energy centers comes to us from India—the chakras (pronounced *sha'-kras* or *cha'-kras*). Chakra is Sanskrit for wheel or vortex. In the most common version there are seven chakras. They are the places in our bodymind where our consciousness, energy systems and embodied matter interconnect.

The chakras function as pumps or valves, regulating how energy flows through us. Although they have physical aspects, they are more fundamentally about how aspects of our psyche manifest.

The chakras interact with the physical body through two major vehicles, the endocrine and nervous systems. Each of the seven chakras is linked with one of the seven major endocrine glands, and also with a group of nerves (called a plexus, as noted earlier). Each chakra is thus associated with specific parts of the body and with particular functions controlled by the associated nerve plexus or endocrine gland. Each chakra is also connected with a color, a sound, a sense, particular emotions and other specific qualities.

That's right, the chakra system is elegant, integral and complex—and will come into play in many suggested practices.

# $\mathcal{S}$ucculent $\mathcal{S}$ummary

## The Seven Chakras

### 1. Root or Perineum Chakra

- Located in the perineum.
- Associated with birth. Life and personal survival. Wild aliveness. Security. The ability to feel grounded. Relationship with the earth. The ability to be present.
- Body: Lymph system, skeletal system (teeth and bones), paraurethral gland (women), prostate gland (men), sacral plexus, bladder, elimination system, lower extremities, nose.
- Sense: Smell
- Color: Red
- Sound: LUM

### 2. Sex Chakra

- Located in the lower belly below the navel. Includes the genitals and reproductive organs.
- Associated with survival of the species. Balance, movement, center of gravity. Fluidity. Food and sex. Relationships with reproduction and creativity.
- Body: Reproductive system, ovaries and testes, sexual organs, lumbar plexus.
- Sense: Taste
- Color: Orange
- Sound: VUM

### 3. Solar Plexus Chakra

- Located in the solar plexus.
- Associated with personal power. Vitality. Control. Freedom. Ease with being yourself.
- Body: Muscles, skin, solar plexus, large intestine, stomach, liver and other organs and glands in the region of the solar plexus, pancreas, eyes and face.
- Sense: Sight
- Color: Yellow
- Sound: RUM

**Crown**
**Third Eye**
**Throat**
**Heart**
**Solar Plexus**
**Sex**
**Root**

Sheri Winston,
*Chakras on
Da Vinci Man*

### 4. HEART CHAKRA

- Located in the center of the chest.
- Associated with the desire to merge and melt. Love. Passion. Perceptions of love, relationships with people close to your heart.
- Body: Heart and the blood circulatory system, the cardiac plexus, the lungs and the entire chest area, thymus gland, breasts.
- Sense: Touch
- Color: Green
- Sound: YUM

### 5. THROAT CHAKRA

- Located at the base of the throat.
- Associated with communication. Authentic expression. Openness to receiving. Trust. Creativity. Abundance. Grace.
- Body: Throat, neck, arms, hands, thyroid gland.
- Sense: Hearing
- Color: Blue
- Sound: HUM

### 6. THIRD EYE OR BROW CHAKRA

- Located in the center of the forehead.
- Associated with intuition. Imagination. Mind. Intellect. Freedom. Spirit. The unconscious or subconscious mind.
- Body: Forehead, temples, faces, pineal gland.
- Sense: Insight (intuition)
- Color: Violet
- Sound: OM

### 7. CROWN CHAKRA

- Located at the top of the head.
- Associated with cosmic or divine energy. Unity or oneness with the universe. Connection with everything and everyone. Divine bliss. Soul. Higher creativity.
- Body: The top of the head, brain, nervous system, pituitary gland.
- Sense: Compassion and empathy
- Color: White
- Sound: Silence

*Energy is the inherent capacity of the universe to make matter exist.*

KEDAR JOSHI

## LAYERS OF ENERGY

Cultures throughout history have recognized that our energy extends beyond our body. While there are many maps of subtle energy, the simplest one consists of concentric fields, like nesting dolls. The closest one, which extends three to six inches from your body, is the easiest one for most people to feel. It's usually called the etheric body and is often experienced as an area of density or heat. The more you charge it up, the most defined and distinct it becomes. During sensual and sexual encounters, it can be great fun to play with this energy field before actually touching the body and intermittently after hands-on play has begun.

Sheri Winston
*Energy Field*

As we explore our sexcraft toolkits in the next section, we'll experiment with different ways to play with the inner channel, the microcosmic orbit, the chakras and the etheric energy field.

## The Matrix and the Connector

As we have seen, in the sexcraft model, here are four domains—mind, body, heart and spirit. Energy plays a crucial role here—it's what connects, surrounds and permeates the four domains.

Energy is also what translates the physical experience of the body into the biochemicals of emotion. When your mood shifts from happy to angry or you toggle from distress to pleasure, it's energy that drives the transformative pathway. Energy is the matrix, the ground, the source.

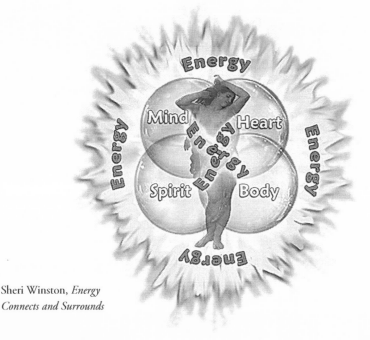

Sheri Winston, *Energy Connects and Surrounds*

## Running Energy

Energy moves inside your body and between bodies. Because of this, you can run circuits of sexual and emotional energy both internally and with partners. Called 'running energy,' it's like plugging into an energetic circuit board that connects you to streams of sensation and awareness.

### Direction

Energy flow often has a sense of directionality. It can be experienced as moving up or down, flowing in or out, or streaming around in a circuit. Energy can ground us by moving up from the earth, entering from below and rising. It can enter us from above and pour down. It can move in waves, pulsing like a tide. You can send it out in a mighty flood.

Alfredo Baruffi, *Woman on a Wave*

### Polarity

Sexual energy also has polarity. The interaction of yin and yang create the charge that causes energy to move.

Your body has 'natural' polarity points. Any part of you that can penetrate (like fingers, penises, tongues) has a positive yang charge while your receptive yin parts (such as mouths, anuses and vaginas) hold the negative charge.

You can play with the polarities during solo sex or with partners. Relatively easy 'transmitting and receiving' spots for plugging into energy include the eyes, ears, mouth, breath, palms of the hands, fingertips, soles of the feet, and all the chakras. Touching anywhere along the spine, on the sacrum or along the centerline of the body can create a contact point for an energy circuit. You can use these connection points in a multitude of ways, including eye-gazing, placing your hands palm-to-palm, putting one hand on the genitals and one on the heart, and synchronizing your breath. These easy connection points are like Lego™—there are limitless ways to put them together. I highly recommend running energy. It's really sexy (in an improbable, almost mystical sort of way) and a great way to enhance your erotic experience.

## Conduct Your Orchestra

YOUR HANDS ARE NATURAL conductors of rhythm and conduits for energy. Utilize their power by orchestrating the movement of your energetic juice. Here are some suggested ways to help your hands make magic:

- Use your hand to focus your attention. Put a hand on the place you want your arousal to go.

- Use your etheric energy field by holding your hand a few inches away from your body over the place where you want your erotic energy to go.

- Add some breaths and imagine you're breathing through your palm.

- Run your hands from one area of your body to another to move your attention and energy. Try three or four firm rhythmic strokes. Want more genital excitement and awareness? Rub from your chest to your crotch. If you already have a lot of genital arousal, you can spread the energy to other parts of your body by stroking from your crotch to your heart or down your legs.

- Use your hands to bridge two areas by putting a hand on each to connect them. Try this with your heart and genitalia, or your belly and crotch.

- You can orchestrate energy by moving your hands about 3-10 inches above the surface of your body, as if you were stirring and swirling the air around you. Try circling your hands above your pelvis during your next climax and see if that keeps your orgasm rolling longer.

PARTNER PLAY: Do the same things with your playmate!

### PLAYING WITH EROTIC ENERGY

How do you tune into and play with sexual energy? In a sense, the entire next section of this book is about learning to orchestrate our erotic energy.

Let's start with this hors d'oeuvre. Before anything else, if you want to play with erotic energy, you have to believe that it actually exists. This can be difficult when so much of our culture scoffs at the concept, but tune in to your own experience and trust it. At a minimum, suspend disbelief.

It helps to know what to look for. We've already identified erotic energy's core characteristics. Be on the lookout for your own special shading of it.

Develop your energy awareness. Start with your internal energy awareness by paying close attention to your intuitions, perceptions and experiences.

*The universe can only be explained in terms of celebration. It is all an exuberant expression of existence itself.*

THOMAS BERRY

Notice what you're feeling and which parts of you feel especially alive. Experiment to discover what awakens your arousal energy. An embodied energy practice like a tai chi, chi gong or reiki can help.

Erotic Bas Relief at Mahadeva Temple, India

Work on developing your external energy awareness by tuning in to the energy of others. Check in with them to find out if your perception of their experience is accurate. If you have the experience of running energy, check in with your playmate. Tell them what you feel, see or sense and find out if they're having a similar experience. See if describing what you're sensing amplifies the energy circuit. (Or just go with the ecstatic flow and save the discussion for later.)

## Succulent Summary

### Energy

ENERGY IS THE MATRIX that surrounds the four sexcraft domains of mind, heart, body and spirit. It also forms the pathways that connect them.

#### THE ENERGY SKILLS

- INTERNAL ENERGY AWARENESS: Consciousness of your own energy.

- EXTERNAL ENERGY AWARENESS: Consciousness of others' energy (and the energy of all life).

- ACCESS: Connecting to inner or outer energy.

- AMPLIFICATION: Magnifying and increasing energy

- MOVING AND CHANNELING: Directing the flow of energy with intention and skill.

- ECSTATIC ENERGY (SEX): Solo, partnered or group energy (includes energy sex).

## It's Better To Give *and* Receive

Remember the giving and receiving circuit we talked about before? One of the easiest ways to create that loop is to become adept at both yin and yang energy skills, whatever your plumbing.

You're using your yang skills when you actively and purposefully send energy

Anonymous Illustration from the *Kama Sutra*

into your lover, and when you push (just the right amount) to take them further out than they'd usually go. You're using your yin skills when you become a magnificent receiver, opening wide to take in all of the abundant pleasure that your lover gives you, until you submit to ecstatic surrender.

When we erase the line between giving and receiving, we enter a magical realm of sex that feels telepathic. The more adept you become at both transmitting and receiving, the easier it is to create loops where it's not clear who's giving, who's receiving and who's getting more pleasure.

### Your Energy Orchestra

Once you start playing with your sexual energy, you'll find that not only can you recognize it, you can amplify it and direct it. You can conduct it the way a musical conductor leads an orchestra.

With practice, you'll get more skilled at consciously playing with energy. As this happens, you can intentionally invoke your erotic energy. Use it to have energy

sex: Clothes-on, (or off), hands-off (or on) energetic erotic experiences. Or use conscious energy play to embellish your more usual physical sexual repertoire. Running energy amplifies your touch and everything else that happens in an erotic encounter. It's the ultimate ecstatic art and raises your sex play to the level of magic.

Franz von Bayros

*Magic is just energy that wants to be something different.*

DANIELLE PAIGE

# Your Sexcraft Toolkit

*In oneself lies the whole world and if you know
how to look and learn, the door is there and the key is
in your hand. Nobody on earth can give you either
the key or the door to open, except yourself.*

KRISHNAMURTI

Franz von Bayros, *Ex Libris*

# CHAPTER TEN

# How To Be a Sex Brainiac

*Live as if you were to die tomorrow.*
*Learn as if you were to live forever.*

MAHATMA GANDHI

## Getting SexCrafty

IN THIS SECTION, WE GET DOWN AND DIRTY (IN A GOOD WAY) WITH our sexcraft skills. It's a practical guide to using your inner tools to become more erotically adept.

To recap, your toolkit has four buckets, each containing a variety of tools (a/k/a skills or instruments). Any of your instruments can be used to play and practice solo or in duets (or trios or moresomes, if that's your inclination).

Sheri Winston, *Venus and the SexCraft Toolkit*

Your domains and their tools are connected by that mysterious but manageable force, energy. It's the magic that weaves musician and instrument together. Remember, these practices aren't just about becoming technically adept, they're about learning to jam with your erotic equipment.

## (Your) Mind Matters

You were born fully equipped with a wealth of mental abilities and cognitive capacities that you can now use to rev your sexual engine and upgrade your erotic experience.

Let's explore what's in your sexy psyche and learn to play some fun head games.

Sheri Winston, *Energy Connects and Surrounds the Four Domains*

Your mind tools are your awareness, attention, intention, presence, authenticity, state of consciousness and imagination.

> *The energy of the mind is the essence of life. Knowing yourself is the beginning of all wisdom.*
>
> ARISTOTLE

### Awareness

Awareness is your foundational mind tool. A function of consciousness, it includes being cognizant of your existence, experiences, thoughts, emotions and surroundings.

At its most basic level, awareness is like your body-mind's operating system, always there, always underlying what you're doing, always working in the background. You're practicing high-level mindfulness when you're deeply tuning into your inner or outer experience.

Beyond that, there's meta-awareness, being aware of your awareness. Meta-awareness is defined by separation—it requires a detached you to be cognizant of your existence.

You have both inner and outer awareness. When you're internally aware, you're being mindful of your perceptions, thoughts, feelings, sensations and reactions. External awareness involves being conscious of what's going on around you. Our

SUCCULENT SEX CRAFT

awareness tends to flicker back and forth, toggling from inner to outer. Self-awareness is not only about being conscious of what's happening with you directly but also about how you're responding to external events. When you're skilled, you can shift between inner and outer awareness as circumstances require.

*I need one of those baby monitors from my subconscious to my consciousness so I can know what the hell I'm really thinking about.*

STEVEN WRIGHT

Your inner self-awareness is the baseline for all your other sexcraft skills.

### ENHANCING EROTIC AWARENESS

Sexual awareness involves being acutely aware of your body-mind during erotic activities. It includes tuning into your sensations (especially pleasurable ones), as well as noticing your posture, tension and any numbness, pain or discomfort. Expanding your pleasure potential requires you to be increasingly aware of what you enjoy and how your body responds to pleasure so you can saturate your awareness with sensation and amplify your responses. One reason solo sex is so important is because you can keep your awareness tuned in to your own experience without the distraction of another person's needs.

Anna Di Scala, *Erotic Desire*

Cultivating erotic awareness also includes noticing what's happening inside your head, especially thoughts and stories that arise during sensual and sexual play. When you become more aware of your thinking, you may notice negative thoughts or limiting beliefs. The negative tapes that you repeat frequently are the ones that most need to be transformed. When you hear yourself saying, "No, I can't," "I shouldn't" or "That's too sexy/slutty/naughty," note it without judgment. Remember, your mind believes itself, whether you're saying nice or negative things, so re-write your unconstructive programming by providing a new positive pattern. There's huge power in positive thoughts and affirmations. Every time you say, "Yes, I can," "Yes, I will" or "Yes, that's so wonderfully sexy/slutty/naughty," you're giving yourself permission to let go of inhibitions and explore new territory. The more you can say "Yes" to your freedom and your pleasure, the more of both you'll have.

## Three Positives

WE ALL HAVE A NEGATIVE interior soundtrack of criticism, nagging doubt and self-limitation, often and especially about sex. It can be re-written! Here's how:

1. FIRST, BRING IT INTO THE LIGHT of your awareness. Start to pay attention and really hear what your inner critic is dumping on you.

2. ANSWER THAT JUDGMENTAL VOICE, not by negating it but by expressing positive affirmations. Answer each self-sabotaging comment with a minimum of three clear, positive, self-affirming statements. Always give at least three responses as it takes that many messages to get past our internal negating gates.

3. BE PATIENT. It takes a while for the negative voices to become less intrusive. Repeat this practice often and you'll gradually reprogram yourself.

## Attention

Closely connected to awareness is attention, the process of selective concentration—it's how you allocate your very limited awareness resources. Attention is like the program or app that's running on top of the operating

> *The most precious gift we can offer anyone is our attention.*
>
> THICH NHAT HANH

system of your awareness.

Picture your attention as a bright silver screen in the unlit theatre of your mind. The darkness is a crammed warehouse containing the bits and pieces of your life experience. It's jammed with memories, stacked high with emotions and littered with unprocessed stimuli. It's a universe unto itself. Your attention can't possibly be on the entire warehouse—it's only on whatever happens to float up to the screen of your consciousness at any given moment.

You have some ability to adjust the size of your mind-screen. Your attention can be narrow, intensely spotlighting one particular little thing, or it can be wide with a big, broad focus. In general, during sexy situations, you want expanded focus. You want your screen to overflow with delightful sensations and steamy stories that will magnify your erotic enchantment.

We don't usually control what we attend to—stuff just shows up willy-nilly. Our attentional default tends to be set to random. To make matters worse, our inner projectionist has a way of playing material that's not useful. Ancient self-defeating stories, scratchy old recordings of 'should' and 'ought' and endless babbling about our faults, flaws and inadequacies are all-too-familiar fodder. The last thing you need is to have your screen cluttered up with fears, inhibitions and negative messages. You don't want to be distracted with internal chatter about whether your behavior is appropriate or if you're 'doing it right.' Thoughts like these keep you in your executive thinking brain or in anxiety mode, either of which can block you from going deeply into your arousal trance.

You don't have to let your undisciplined inner programmer run the show. You're in charge here—you can train the projectionist to play only material that serves you by enlarging your screen of attention and filling it with positive pleasure.

SOLO PLAY

### Awareness and Attention Practice

PRACTICE AWARENESS by noticing something and then focusing your attention on it. No need to be picky here: you can choose anything. Look at a plant, notice the clouds, pay attention to your breath, tune in to sensations. Focus on household chores like washing dishes or the particulars of an erotic encounter. Just pick something and play with keeping your attention there.

As you proceed through the course of your day, do an occasional awareness check-in. One day, focus on internal awareness. What's going on in your body-mind as you do this or that activity? What sensations, thoughts and feelings are arising? Another time, practice external awareness and notice what's happening all around you. If you want to, spend another day playing with flowing from internal to external and back again. See what happens!

In case you're wondering, yes, this is a form of meditation. You don't need to sit in a lotus position or chant "Om" to meditate, though. Once you cut through all the forms and practices, meditation is really very simple. It's about bringing attention to your awareness. You can do it anytime and anywhere—and the more you do it, the better you get at it.

### NATURALLY AGILE ATTENTION

Most of the time, our minds are like curious puppies, distractedly wandering without focus or discipline. Maybe we all have some level of attention deficit disorder because our attention certainly seems pre-programmed to wander. To reframe this tendency in a positive light, I prefer to think of us as having 'naturally agile attention.'

When it comes to, well, coming, training our attention to focus is immensely beneficial. We can train our gamboling attention much the same way we teach a puppy to stay—by repeatedly, gently bringing it back where we want it. When you're being sexual, that means paying total attention to the pleasure you're experiencing and staying present, positive and playful.

Most of us have had sexual experiences where our body was going through the motions but our mind was elsewhere—and when your attention strays, erotic energy and arousal tend to decrease. During solo sex, you may just roll along on automatic pilot, sort of like driving your car on the high-speed arousal straightaway. If

*Tell me to what you pay attention and I will tell you who you are.*

JOSE ORTEGA Y GASSET

you're with a partner, they may be doing things that usually get you off but nothing's working this time, much to everyone's baffled dismay. They may or may not realize that you're mentally wandering in and out of the encounter. Your entire arousal and orgasm journey may happen, but not in a way that's particularly satisfying. Why not? Because you weren't paying attention.

How do you deal with your wandering attention? By practicing awareness and paying attention to paying attention. Your attention is trainable. Like a muscle, it gets stronger with use. Most of us haven't gotten much experience in teaching our attention to stay focused, but we can all become more skilled at attending.

As you train yourself to attend, you'll get better at catching yourself quickly if you've gone walkabout. Kindly and firmly bring yourself back to your body and your immediate experience. Direct your focus to the sweet steamy stuff that's going on. Bring all those luscious sensations up into your brain and put them up on that screen in Technicolor. If you're in a duet, attend to your partner. Focus on the stimulating visuals or on the excitement of their turn-on. In subsequent chapters, I'll offer more sexcraft tools such as breath, sound and movement that you can also use to bring you back home.

We can become masters of mindfulness, artists of attention, connoisseurs of consciousness. The more you practice, the easier it becomes to choose where your attention goes and to keep it where you want—like on the entrancement of arousal.

## The Power of Intention

Your intention is your purpose or aim. It establishes goals and creates focus. It's your touchstone, your centering point, a way to orient yourself. Intentions clarify your desires and help make them happen.

Intentions can be conscious or unconscious. Our intentions are often vague and obscure even to ourselves. Not only might we be unaware of them, but they

Detail from the Sugimura Jihei Genre Handscroll

can also be negative towards others or ourselves. It's important to do the best we can to make our intentions positive, overt and clear.

There is a magic to intentionality—simply holding an intention can help your wishes come true. If you hold a healing intention, healing is likelier to happen. If you decide that your bed is a holy erotic temple, it'll be a lot holier—and hotter— than it would have been otherwise.

*We either live with intention or exist by default.*

KRISTIN ARMSTRONG

Positive intentions direct your energy. Simply having them can help you manifest whatever you wish to create.

Setting intentions is useful in all areas of our lives, not just the bedroom. There is great power in creating clear and positive intentions for the moment, your day and your relationships. And they can also make for spectacular sexual encounters.

### SETTING SEXY INTENTIONS

Think back to the last time you pleasured yourself. What were your intentions? Were they clear and positive? Different intentions generate very different experiences. Perhaps you were feeling stressed and simply wanted to relieve tension with an orgasmic release. Or you were tired and wanted a little orgasmic pick-me-up. Maybe you were feeling distracted by your erotic energy and wanted to get it out of the way. These intentions are fine, but if that's the whole range of your sexual purpose and aims, you're limiting the range of your amorous experiences.

To become more erotically adept, create intentions related to learning, practicing, expanding and experimenting, whether on your own or with partners. When you begin an erotic session, or play any of the games in this book, I invite you to create conscious intentions. Have them be clear, self-loving and pleasure-positive. Notice how that alters your experience. For starters, I recommend intentions related to developing your sexcraft skills, delighting in your body and exploring your pleasure potential. If you want to become more erotically skilled and empowered, start by intending it to happen.

SOLO PLAY

## Intentions—Setting Your Mind To It

COMPILE A LIST OF INTENTIONS related to loving yourself well and enhancing your sexuality. You may want to do it on an ad hoc basis or in a more structured way, for instance by maintaining a list. However you do it, here are two tips to bear in mind: State your intentions in positive terms and in the present tense.

Here are some suggestions:

- I AM MY OWN best lover.
- I SHOWER MYSELF with love and attention.
- I AM SKILLED at managing my arousal level.
- I SLOW DOWN and savor pleasure.
- I LOVE MY _____(fill in positive words here) _____(any body parts that need extra love).  Example: *I love my soft curvy belly.*
- I RELAX into my arousal.
- I AM GAINING SKILL at_____(fill in any particular skill).

### DOING IT INTENTIONALLY

START BY TAKING A FEW DEEP BREATHS. Repeat an intention to yourself several times as you breathe and center yourself. Give yourself time to envision and focus on your purpose. You may want to write out your intention, speak it aloud or create some sort of artifact that symbolizes your intent.

Once you feel really zoned in on your intention, proceed with your sex play. During your session, pause periodically to re-focus on your intentions. It's especially powerful if you can focus on your intentions as you orgasm. When you've finished, take a moment to notice how having clear and focused intentions altered your experience.

Try different intentions during subsequent solo-sex sessions and see what happens.

## Moving Attention With Intention (and Without Moving)

PUT YOUR HAND on an easily accessible body part, like your belly or thigh, or somewhere on your playmate's body. Without moving your hand, bring your awareness and attention to your palm. Notice your own skin, the size of the surface area and the sensations. Now, again without moving your hand, push your attention a millimeter out from your palm and bring your awareness to the body part beneath it. Tune in to what's under your hand. Notice the surface, the heat, the feel of it. Now bring your attention back in to the surface of your palm. Play with toggling your attention between your palm and the part that lies under it, all without any actual movement. The only thing that's moving is your attention and awareness—and what's moving it is your intention.

Isn't it interesting how you can shift your focus simply by shifting your intention?

## Presence

Quite simply, presence means being here now. Not dwelling in the past or imagining the future, but being in this moment, right now, with your attention focused on what's happening.

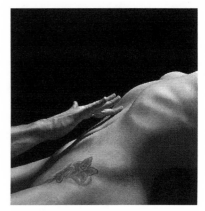

Remember how the process of perception works? A stimulus happens (belly stroke), travels through your wiring (nervous system) and passes up to your brain, where it lights up the corresponding section of your brain's body-map. Since only a small amount of information can occupy that limited space, what happens next depends on what goes onto the screen of your awareness. If you're running an old movie from the past or your screen is filled with

Doug Metzger, *Touch*

deprecating subtitles, you might not even notice the belly stroke. The more present you are for the experience, the more lit-up neurons you get.

If you aren't 'home,' if your awareness is elsewhere (or elsewhen), that belly caress may not even be noticed. It won't turn you on if you aren't there to be turned on by it. But tune into the luscious sensation and one simple touch of your belly can blaze across your awareness.

Presence is a highly pleasurable practice. And sexy, too.

## Authenticity

You are being authentic when you're acting in alignment with your real, essential nature. Being authentic takes practice, in no small measure because we tend to get blocked by culturally imposed ideas of who and how we should be. As children, most of us didn't get encouraged to check in with ourselves or to trust our inner wisdom, particularly with regard to just about everything, including our bodies, desires, feelings, pleasure and sexuality.

*Be yourself. Everyone else is taken.*

OSCAR WILDE

In this age of Internet porn, many of us are inundated with stories about who and how we should be sexually. Porn is entertainment, not education, but our poor susceptible brains don't know the difference. What starts off as external images often end up being internalized into beliefs about 'how sex is.'

We can reclaim that authentic aspect of ourselves, though—and the more we take the time to slow down and be present, the clearer the messages from our inner self will be.

Being authentic is especially important when it comes to sex. In order to connect to your own sexuality, you need to act in alignment with your true desires and needs. You need to be able to hear your own true voice.

If you pretend, you're not just feigning for others, you're betraying yourself. In relationships, if you can't tell the truth about who you are, what you need, and your boundaries, limits and desires, you aren't really being intimate—you're faking it. To actually be intimate requires honesty and that means knowing what's true for you. To empower your sexuality, you

*If you do not tell the truth about yourself, you cannot tell it about other people.*

VIRGINIA WOOLF

need to access and trust your inner wisdom, and be comfortable with your true erotic nature. Magnificent sex, be it solo or a duet, can only happen when you're connected to your authentic self and when you honor that connection.

---

PLAY & PRACTICE

SOLO PLAY

### Authentic Action

WHAT DO YOU DO when you're not sure what to do? Maybe you're considering whether to have sex with someone or confused about what boundaries would be best for you in an erotic encounter. Take a moment (or ten) and turn your gaze inward. Calm yourself and get centered. Ask yourself what you want, need or desire. Listen for the answer. Trust it. Act from that place. Notice how that feels and what happens when you act in alignment with your truth.

### Trance State of Consciousness

As noted previously, the brain has different channels, much like a television. As we go about our day, we flow through various states of consciousness, often rapidly flipping from one to another. The one that usually predominates is often referred to as ordinary reality. It's when your executive brain is in charge, busy analyzing, reasoning, remembering and planning.

When you're being sexual, you switch to the erotic trance station, where you have the power to go deep, deeper, all the way down. Let's look more closely at where the trance dance of sex can go.

*Everything we do is for the purpose of altering consciousness. We form friendships so that we can feel certain emotions, like love, and avoid others, like loneliness. We eat specific foods to enjoy their fleeting presence on our tongues. We read for the pleasure of thinking another person's thoughts.*

SAM HARRIS

Susan Singer, *Dancing with Hotei*

## Types of Sex Trance

There are basically three types of sex trance—solo, parallel and conjoined.

### Solo Trance

For most of you, your first forays into the altered state of arousal were by yourself. One way or another, you developed the ability to go into your *solo sex trance*. In this state, you're intensely focused on your own sensations and experience. To the extent that you're in relationship with anything other than yourself—like porn or fantasy—its sole purpose is to enhance your arousal. It's truly all about you.

The ability to enter your own arousal trance is foundational. You need to start here to be able to get to the other trance levels. It's your starter path and one you can always return to once you've established it.

### Parallel Trance

If you want to get turned on and have an orgasm when you're with another person, at a minimum you need to be able to engage in your solo trance alongside someone else. *Parallel trance* is when you're in your own solo arousal trance alongside a partner (who's probably in their own solo trance, too).

In partnered sex, playmates often take turns shifting focus and attention, alternating who's doing what to whom, and supporting each other's arousal level. Even if you're both actively pleasuring each other at the same time, your awareness frequently toggles from your own erotic trance to facilitating your partner's trance and back again. Often your playmate is doing the same in the opposite direction. Ideally this back-and-forthness takes you both up the arousal staircase. That way, you ascend more or less at the same pace.

The more deeply you're into your own trance, the easier it is to attend to your playmate's without a drop in your own erotic energy, achieving simultaneous parallel trances.

Skilled partner sex involves a playful improv that balances mutual awareness and alternating attention. There's nothing inherently wrong with taking turns to turn each other on. Being in parallel trances states is a fun way to play, but it can have some challenges.

The partners may intermittently tune each other out in order to focus on their private turn-on. While this can work for a while, ultimately it can lead to non-relational sex or very disparate arousal levels.

Conversely, you can focus too much attention on your partner's trance and tune yourself out. While you're concentrating on stimulating your partner, your own arousal level may drop. Even when you're simultaneously stimulating each other, you may get distracted from your own erotic trance while you focus on theirs. It can be hard to find the right balance and flow between each person's needs and desires so you both get to a similar arousal level. It can feel unfair and unbalanced if one person is getting lots more stimulation and arousal while the other gets left behind.

It's not uncommon for partners to find themselves at different and not especially compatible arousal levels. In a heterosexual coupling, the man may get totally aroused by being pleasured orally and want to proceed directly to intercourse. ("Do not pass go, do not warm her up.") Meanwhile, without concurrent stimulation and attention, her arousal may have dropped so she's not excited enough for penetration to feel fabulous. Being a considerate fellow, he turns his focus to arousing her and she gets all puffy and ready to receive him but alas, now his hard-on has wilted.

Timing, as they say, is everything.

There's an art to effective, alternating parallel play. You need excellent communication, timing and both self- and partner-awareness to make this dance work well.

## CONJOINED TRANCE

In *conjoined trance*, the partners share the same level and depth of altered state. Their mirror neurons are firing, causing their biorhythms to match up. Heartbeats harmonize, brain oscillations correspond, and breathing synchronizes.

This doesn't only happen during fabulous sex. Skilled musicians can get there during an inspired jam. Dance partners can get into a magical coordinated groove where their movements are in perfect connected flow. In any type of conjoined trance, the partners become supremely attuned to each other's energy. The connection feels telepathic, transcendent and sublime.

In this exquisite state of connection, the partners may not even know where one ends and the other begins. This is the ecstatic sexual state where ego boundaries dissolve and people experience Divine Union. Because we're so used to being separate from other people, being in a conjoined trance has a magical quality. At an experiential, embodied level, it reminds us, that we really are all connected—it's not just a woo-woo fantasy.

Alméry Lobel-Riche

In this state, we don't take turns doing each other. There is no 'other' to do unto. When we're pleasuring our partner, we're pleasuring our own self equally. The line between giving and receiving vanishes. You get as turned on by doing as by being done.

You gotta love those mirror neurons.

Shared trance is the trickiest trance state to get to. Some people haven't yet experienced this miraculous realm. Others may get there rarely and serendipitously. Perhaps you find yourselves in conjoined erotic trance in a hot new relationship, but can't get there when the falling-in-love (or lust) biochemical storm subsides.

We can maximize our chances of having this kind of telepathic divine-union sex by becoming practiced at entering and amplifying our solo erotic trance, skillfully juggling parallel arousal trance and using our sexcraft skills to enhance a shared trance. Going into conjoined trance is a learnable skill. By the time you've finished this book, you'll have all the tools you need to do it.

Eventually, if we play our parts right (and our partner's), we can dance among the trances.

## Imagine This

Your last, but by no means least, mind tool is your versatile, delectable imagination. It's your uniquely human ability to create, envision, conceive, dream, invent, and conjure pretty much anything you want. Your imagination is your multi-purpose mind tool, your mental Swiss Army knife—and a fantastic way to turn up your turn-on.

Your imagination is an inner movie where you write the script. Anything you want to happen, can. You can imagine possible futures. You can re-vision the past, only this time give it a happy ending (in whatever sense of the term you want). You can use your imagination to heal your sexuality, learn new skills, rehearse scenarios and explore your erotic landscape.

*The human erotic imagination is a vast wilderness of sexual possibilities.*

CHRIS MAXWELL ROSE

And, of course, to get really turned on.

Your brain circuitry responds to imaginary experiences as if they were actually happening. Whether it's dream sex or a hot movie scene, a romantic reverie or a lusty fantasy, we experience these mind stories as if they were real. When you combine your gullible brain with conscious intention and imagination, you create a powerful tool for transformation.

---

PLAY & PRACTICE

SOLO PLAY

### Using Your Imagination to Enhance Cross-Training

EARLIER, WE DISCUSSED the related techniques of switching and cross-training. You can use your imagination to amplify the effects of these training strategies. Here are three ways to do so.

1. IF YOU'D LIKE TO LEARN TO COME from having your nipples sucked, then while you or someone else is pleasuring your nether regions, also imagine a hot mouth suckling away on your nipples. As you orgasm, picture your nipple being ravenously ravished.

2. IMAGINE DOING SOMETHING SEXY to someone else, especially something that you want to learn to get off on. For example, if you'd like to learn how to come from giving oral sex, while your southern parts are being pleasured, imagine having your favorite type of genitals in your mouth simultaneously. Another option is to do this during partner sex. While you are actually giving oral pleasure, imagine someone else doing the same to you. This will help your brain learn to associate the two activities.

3. IF YOU'RE USING THE SWITCH TECHNIQUE where you intermittently discontinue one form of stimuli, imagine that it's continuing. For instance, if you're training yourself to be able to have hands-off orgasms, start with hands-on stimulation, then stop the manual action but imagine there's still a hand skillfully playing with your luscious bits.

---

### BROAD-SPECTRUM IMAGINATION

People's imaginations favor different senses. For some, imagination is a vividly visual experience while for others, the focus is more on sounds, words, movement or sensations. When you're running imaginary 'sexperiments,' start with the senses that come naturally for you. Then, embroider your story—the more imaginary senses you pack into your fantasy, the richer and more 'real' you make it. Visualize a sexy scene and that's hot. Imagine the accompanying sound track, textures and aromas and it gets sizzling.

*Virgin's Dream*
Anonymous illustration from the Musée des Familles, 1840

### FANTASTIC FANTASY

Your imagination is also your fantasy generator, be they make-believe erotic encounters or memorable moments recalled. Your personal mind-movies are especially effective because you custom-craft them to ignite and satisfy your unique desires.

Your fantasies can also be a rehearsal for a possibly anxiety-provoking future encounter. By previewing an upcoming date and visualizing it going smoothly, you can reduce any incipient nervousness.

---

PLAY & PRACTICE

SOLO PLAY

### Imaginary Rehearsal

HERE ARE SOME IDEAS to play with:

- RUN THROUGH that date you're about to have, envisioning it as comfortable and fun.

- IMAGINE a luscious seduction scene.

- PICTURE YOURSELF boldly flirting with a person you have a crush on—and getting an enthusiastically positive response.

- IMAGINE saying things you've been too shy to say aloud. Eventually you may find yourself able to say those hot and taboo things!

- FANTASIZE doing 'that thing'—that oh-so-naughty thing—that for years you've been longing to do.

---

Koryusai, woodblock print

Your imagination is prime territory for erotic experimentation and expansion. Your mind is a great (and safe) place

*Everything you can imagine is real.*

PABLO PICASSO

to explore new areas and push your edges. The wonderful thing about your imagination is that you're not obliged to act on it. You don't even need to share your imaginary sexual adventures: You can let your playmates in on your private fantasies or you can keep them as your secret stash of internal erotica. Your inner mind movies are yours to do with as you please.

## Your Personal Magic Movie

While you can always turn your imagination loose and let it freelance, you can also use it in a more structured way using a technique called *guided imagery* or *guided visualization*. In this process you create a story based on a conscious

*Your body hears everything your mind says.*

NAOMI JUDD

intention. You imagine a mental journey, then play it out in your head. You can follow someone else's story line or craft your own. Either way is fine, although once you get the hang of the process, creating your own scenario becomes

easier and also more effective because you can customize it to your specific needs.

For an extra-powerful practice, add guided visualization to your erotic play sessions. Erotic trance plus the power of imagination creates transformation.

## Sexy Guided Visualization

THIS EROTIC PRACTICE can be done with or without a hands-on-your-sexy-bits component.

FIRST, DECIDE ON THE THEME. If an actual script is involved, you might want to read it aloud into a tape recorder, then play it back while you just sit back and listen. Or read the script through a few times until you have the gist of it and can play it out in your mind.

CREATE AN ENVIRONMENT that makes it easy for you to relax and focus. Get comfortable. Turn off phones and create a space where you'll be undisturbed. Wear a blindfold if you choose. If you're combining your journey with sexual arousal, have what you'll need to get you going nearby. (Lube? Vibrator?)

BEGIN WITH DEEP SLOW BREATHING, to relax.

START YOUR IMAGINARY JOURNEY. Live into the script as deeply as you can. Try to embroider your imaginings by using all your senses—make it as vivid and real as possible.

IF YOU'RE USING EROTIC TRANCE to enhance your imaginary experience, pleasure yourself as you like, intermittently weaving it into your story.

GO ON YOUR JOURNEY. Allow the storyline to unfold. See what happens.

WHEN YOU'VE COMPLETED YOUR VISUALIZATION, take a few minutes to relax before re-entering the regular world.

IF YOU'RE JOURNALING, write down where you went and what happened. If you're making art, record images from your journey.

Here are a few examples of possible storylines for your guided visualization journeys:

- GO TO A SACRED sex temple and meet an erotic priest/ess

- HAVE A LESSON with a hands-on sex teacher

- EXPERIENCE a loving sexual-healing session

- OPEN A DOOR that reveals your hidden erotic desires.

---

*A good traveler is one who knows
how to travel with the mind.*

MICHAEL BASSEY JOHNSON

---

### THROW A CAST PARTY

Role play (or psychodrama) is another way to explore different aspects of yourself. Here, you do so by inhabiting one or more of your myriad personas and archetypes. Role play can provide you with invaluable insights. It also has enormous erotic and healing potential.

Doing role play in an erotic altered state is especially powerful because your arousal energy can transport you to previously unknown aspects of yourself. You can use role play and fantasy to explore your needs and desires and the broader landscape of your psyche.

*Imagination is better than a sharp instrument.*
*To pay attention, this is our endless and proper work.*

MARY OLIVER

You can do role play alone or with a partner. In long-term relationships, playing with personas can inject the novelty that keeps things exciting as we explore the never-ending cast of characters that lives inside us.

While the currently in-vogue options of dominant and submissive are fine roles to play with, they're not the only ones. Your inner cast includes a Hero/Heroine, Warrior, Temptress, Wild Man/Woman, Lover, God/Goddess, Pure Innocent, Sexual Teacher, Sacred Sexual Priest/ess and many more. Any of these archetypes makes fine material for exploring the mystery of yourself (and makes for a sizzling sexual playdate).

---

PLAY & PRACTICE

PARTNER PLAY

## Exploring Your Inner Cast of Characters

Invite your inner troupe out to play! Choose one of your personas or characters and spin an erotic story from their perspective. Give yourself, or rather your selves, permission to explore and experiment freely.

### EXPLORING FANTASY AND ROLE PLAY: LIONS AND TIGERS AND WOLVES—OH MY!

A simple way to explore role play is by pretending to be an animal. Not only can you select what animal you want to embody, you can also choose that

Lagrene, *Les Deux Amies*

creature's personality. Within the feline realm you can be a sex kitten, a cosseted house cat, a randy tom, a predatory puma or a powerful wild tigress. Going canine? You can be a friendly puppy, a service dog or a wild alpha wolf.

What happens when a wanton wolf meets a sex kitten? Go ahead and find out!

## Using Imagination to Free Yourself

What keeps you from expressing and exploring your full erotic spectrum? Most of us have preconceived notions about what's appropriate, acceptable or ideal behavior. Often we're blocked by fears related to the enormous power of sexual energy. Maybe you're afraid you might become sexually insatiable or behave unethically. Maybe you fear being judged or shamed by others or yourself.

Your imagination is a perfect place to practice personal liberation. You can overcome your fears and anxieties by making your mind a crime-free zone.

Felicien Rops, *Le Mannequin*

What goes on in there doesn't need to be politically correct, condoned by the authorities or approved of by anyone else. You are the sole owner of your mindspace and you get to decide what happens there.

Cultivate a "no mind-crime" policy and freely explore anything and everything that turns you on. Anything.

> *When authorities warn you of the sinfulness of sex, there is an important lesson to be learned. Do not have sex with the authorities.*
>
> MATT GROENING

### Just Sayin'

Needless to say (but I'll say it anyway), you need to maintain a clear boundary between inner imagination and outer action. Just because you can go wild in your imagination doesn't mean you can do so where other beings are involved. In the outer world, the laws of physics and consequences apply and your behavior needs to be responsible, respectful and consensual. Your inner world requires no boundaries, though. There, you can freely explore territory the socially appropriate part of you experiences as forbidden or taboo. Your mind is the perfect place to explore desires you'd never act on (as well as ones that, in the right circumstances, you might want to try). When you play in the imaginal realm, you have the opportunity to uncover erotic facets of yourself that you never knew existed. This can have personal growth value and it can also be totally sexy. The two are often linked: The fantasies that take you beyond your usual edge are especially likely to be super-hot because it's their taboo quality that makes them so arousing.

### It's Not A Shame

It takes courage to stretch past old limitations, even in the safe house of our mind. As long as you treat whatever is uncovered reverentially and without shame, your imagination will take you on a wonderful and totally positive voyage of discovery.

When you let your fantasies play out in your body-mind, you are giving yourself a precious gift. When you give free rein to your mind, you get more than heightened arousal and more sexual pleasure. You also receive invaluable information about what turns you on and what you yearn for. Your imagination is the place to run wild and free and to be shameless, authentic, bold and brave. It's where you can say an enthusiastic "yes" to the truth of who you are.

## Succulent Summary

### Your Mind Tools

- AWARENESS is your foundational mind tool. It's the state of perceiving and attending to your feelings and thoughts and being cognizant of your surroundings.

- ATTENTION is selective concentration. It's what makes it up onto the bright movie screen in your mind at any given moment.

- INTENTION is the mind tool you use to define and pursue your goals. Attention gives you focus; intention shapes and directs it. Intentions can be conscious or unconscious.

- PRESENCE is the ability all the great spiritual masters teach—how to be here now.

- AUTHENTICITY means being and acting in alignment with your essential core self.

- STATE OF CONSCIOUSNESS. While the body-mind has many states of being, our focus here is on trance states, where we turn off our chattering, thinking, worrying neocortical brain and enter the altered state of sexual arousal.

- IMAGINATION is your multi-purpose mind tool—your mental Swiss Army knife.

We tend to take our mind for granted. We often operate on erotic auto-pilot. Your multi-purpose mind is a terrible thing to waste. While we may not know exactly what consciousness is or even how the mind works, we can still make great use of its wondrous capacities. Your mind tools are a powerful way to magnify your pleasure, amplify arousal and explore your own erotic landscape. Utilize your sexy psyche and keep minding your mind!

Now, on to the tools and skills of your beautiful body.

# CHAPTER ELEVEN

# SOME BODY:
# BREATH, SOUND & MOVEMENT

*Here is my wish and my desire and my pledge as well:*
*that we remember our true nature . . . That we own and know*
*that we are more than our bodies and yet our bodies are*
*these sacred, beautiful, rhythmic houses for us.*

TRACEE ELLIS ROSS

## Your SexCraft Body Tools

THE NEXT BUCKET THAT WE'LL DIVE INTO ARE YOUR BODY TOOLS OF breath, sound, movement, vision, touch, smell and taste. In this chapter, I focus on the key three body tools of breath, sound and movement. In Chapter 12, I discuss the others.

When you consciously use your body tools, you're utilizing your voluntary nervous system to influence your involuntary one. You're tinkering with the machinery of your autonomic nervous system—you're shifting, by choice, your underlying state.

Sheri Winston, *The Body 1*

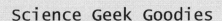

### science Geek Goodies

**Senses**

YOUR BODY TOOLS include your sensory equipment, your ability to move and your respiratory system. The traditional five senses are hearing, sight, touch, smell and taste, but they aren't the only senses we have. Movement combines other senses, including our kinesthetic sense (direction, acceleration), our sense of balance and postural equilibrium, and our ability to know where we are in space (proprioception). We'll go into detail about breath later in this chapter and talk about touch in Chapter 12.

# Science Geek Goodies

## Sensational Synesthesia

WHILE WE TEND TO THINK of each of our senses as distinct, we actually process them in an integrated manner—we combine the modalities neurologically. This is what enables us to make 'sense' of the world via our perceptions.

Everyone has multisensory integration to a degree, as evidenced by our language, with phrases like 'delicious touch,' 'warm look' and 'sweet sound.'

For some people, this ability goes further into a condition called synesthesia, an overlapping of the senses. They may see music, taste sounds or feel smells. For 'synesthesiacs,' this is natural, but can it be learned? Neuroscience suggests it can. Visually impaired people use the same parts of the brain to process stimuli such as sound and sensation that non-impaired people use for visual information. If they can train their brains—if they can learn to see with their fingertips—so can you!

*Blake said that the body was the soul's prison unless the five senses are fully developed and open. He considered the senses the 'windows of the soul.' When sex involves all the senses intensely, it can be like a mystical experience.*

JIM MORRISON

## Breath

### IN THE BEGINNING WAS THE BREATH

Breath. It's the foundation of life itself, one of the unchanging rhythms of existence. When you were born, the first thing you did was breathe—you 'inspired.' When you stop breathing, you die—you 'expire.'

*Breath is the bridge which connects life to consciousness, which unites your body to your thoughts. Whenever your mind becomes scattered, use your breath as the means to take hold of your mind again.*

THICH NHAT HANH

PLAY & PRACTICE

SOLO PLAY

### Do It Now

YOU CAN PRACTICE conscious active breathing at any moment. Try it right now. Inhale deeply and allow it to flow all the way out. Do three or four rounds. Notice how you feel before, during and after.

No one had to teach you how to breathe. The pattern of your respiration is determined by your actions, emotions and energy. If you're anxious, your breath tightens, becoming short and restrained. Panic makes it rapid, shallow and frantic. If you run fast, you breathe hard. As you relax, it lengthens into a regular sweeping flow. Most of the time, your emotional, mental and physical state are the engine of the train, pulling the car of your breath behind.

*I took a deep breath and listened to the old brag of my heart. I am, I am, I am.*

SYLVIA PLATH

But you don't have to breathe on auto-pilot. You can use your breath to alter your state. Your respiratory system is innervated by both your involuntary and voluntary nervous systems—it's the only system in your body with that overlap. It's where conscious choice intersects with unconscious programming. That means that your breath can become the 'engine,' pulling the 'train' of your state along behind. Anytime you want, you can become aware of your breath pattern and have it take the lead. While there are limits—you can't breathe once an hour or 300 times a minute—within those bookends, you have a great deal of flexibility. This is what has made breath the centerpiece of so many spiritual practices and mind-body disciplines and what makes it your most basic and flexible body tool.

## Science Geek Goodies

### Hyperventilation

WHEN YOU PLAY with your breathing, you can 'over-breathe' or hyperventilate, disturbing your body's critical balance of oxygen and carbon dioxide. If you're exhaling too much and not inhaling enough, you'll start to have symptoms of hyperventilation such as dizziness, tingling lips and fingers, and spasms of your hands, feet and face.

Anne Anderson
*Wind Blows*

## Hyperventilation Prevention and Treatment

Prevent hyperventilation with the following practices:

- Keep your inhale and exhale the same length.

- Alternate fast breathing practices with slow ones, or intersperse a few deep slow breaths with fast breathing.

- When breathing fast or doing long exhales, reinforce your breath with other tools, especially sound and traditional 'hands-on' stimulation. The more you use your whole toolkit to build your arousal, the less likely you are to hyperventilate no matter how wildly you breathe.

FEELING WOOZY AND TINGLY (and not in a good way)? To treat impending hyperventilation you can:

- Make your inhale long and slow, and do shorter exhales.

- Take a breath in, hold it for a count of three, then release slowly.

- Breathe into your cupped hands.

REMEMBER: Practice safe breathing!

You may not have thought about it this way, but you've probably already applied this concept. If you were anxious and took a few deep slow breaths to calm down, you were using your breathing to shift your state. It's that simple.

Now that you understand why breath is the bridge between states of consciousness, let's see how we can use this unique tool in our quest for erotic mastery.

## Transforming Anxiety into Excitement

Anxiety is just excitement without enough breath. This isn't just a pleasing aphorism—it's also true physiologically. The biochemical state of anxiety is literally the same as excitement, only with less oxygen.

Which gives us a straightforward antidote to anxiety. When you're feeling tense, simply deepen and slow your breathing. Use your whole chest and belly. Get some more energizing oxygen in there and you'll feel jazzed up and juicy instead of freaked out.

### Breath Awareness

BEGIN YOUR BREATH LESSONS with awareness. Notice what your breath is doing naturally. Don't do anything differently, just tune in and observe. Pay attention to your rhythm. Notice if you're using your nose or mouth. Check in to see what parts of your body are moving as you breathe.

Tune in to your breathing at different points of your day. Notice what's happening when you wake up, drive in traffic, are at work and while you eat.

*Breathing easily and fully is one of the basic pleasures of being alive.*

ALEXANDER LOWEN

Try doing a minute or two of breath awareness before doing any of the other practices. Do it again afterward. Notice any difference.

### THE BREATH OF SEX

The patterns of your breathing have a natural progression during sex—this happens without your thinking about it. As you get more turned on, your respiratory rate gets faster. If your arousal declines, your breath slows down. As orgasm surges, your breathing goes rolling through an ancient choreography of build-up and release. It's how we mammals are wired.

Doug Metzger, *Kiss*

As we've seen, arousal involves an interweaving of excitement and relaxation. You can use your breath to push your state in either direction. In general, breathing more slowly will help you:

- get present and centered

- relax and down-regulate (cool down)

- turn off your chattering front-brain and move into your animal arousal

- expand awareness and perception of sensations

- widen the steps (deepen your trance state at any level of arousal)

- stay on a particular step (including delaying orgasm)

- drop down the arousal staircase

- extend how long you're in orgasm.

Speeding up your respiratory rate can be used to:

- up-regulate and pump up the excitement (heat up)

- increase energy

- send you up the arousal staircase

- carry you across the threshold into orgasm.

**STEP BY STEP**

When you're using your breath to heighten arousal, just push it one step ahead of your state. Don't try to skip over any steps. If you're on step three on the arousal staircase and want to get more turned on, breathe as if you're on step four, not step nine—that's just faking it, which doesn't work. The key here is to just send your engine one step ahead of the train so that it pulls your arousal up along behind it. Take it one step at a time. Literally. Don't fake it till you make it—enhance it till you 'trance' it.

Orissan style Indian image from the *Koka Shastra*

## Breath Awareness on the Stairs

LEARN YOUR NATURAL erotic breath patterns. The next time you're being sexual, alone or with a partner, bring your attention and awareness to your breath at different phases of your erotic journey. Note how you breathe on each arousal step. What's the speed, the depth, the pattern? Do you ever hold your breath? What happens with your breathing as you move through your climax(es) and afterward?

You may want to try this more than once, in different erotic contexts. Make written or mental notes.

## Inspiring Eros

NOW THAT YOU'RE AWARE of your natural sexual breath patterns, you can play with enhancing your trance. During your next solo sexual exploration, use conscious breathing as the engine that pulls your erotic energy up. Don't fake anything or wildly exaggerate, just explore ways to enhance your natural patterns.

Play with yourself in your favorite fashion. As you journey through arousal, notice what step you're on, then shift your breathing one step further along. Don't try to send your breath many steps ahead of your actual state.

If you're on the ground floor, breathe as if you're on the first step. In early arousal that often means slowing down to tune into your body and sensations and relax. If you're at a five, breathe like you're at a six. When you're at mid or high-level arousal, going up a step will often involve ramping up the speed a bit.

Also notice how wide your step is—how deeply you're in your trance at any level. Then breathe to widen and deepen it. Usually, this will involve slowing your rate. You might be breathing pretty fast at a shallow eight and find that slowing your breath will allow you to drop deeper into your trance without becoming less aroused.

As you approach your orgasmic precipice, notice if you're holding your breath. If that's what you've been doing, experiment with keeping your breath moving. Run some experiments where you try slowing or speeding your breathing rate as you crest into your climax. During your orgasm, keep breathing and notice the effects.

When something gives you more pleasure, attunement and arousal, it's a winner, so practice doing it more!

## Breath Experiments

HERE ARE SOME breath experiments to try:

- Breathe a little faster, drawing your breath in deeply and letting it out a bit longer.

- Open your chest and belly more.

- Play with your inhale. Try inhaling through your mouth, then your nose.

- Use a three-count to inhale, then try four.

- Inhale by taking little sniffs. Or do a long inhale and then add an extra sniff at the end.

- Play with your exhale. Let it expand, long and languorous.

- Try to let your exhale fall out. Try to push your exhale out.

- Try a big inhale, hold your breath briefly and then exhale with a big sighing release.

*We live in an ocean of air like fish in a body of water. By our breathing we are attuned to our atmosphere. If we inhibit our breathing we isolate ourselves from the medium in which we exist.*

ALEXANDER LOWEN

## Pump It Up

To FIRE UP YOUR EROTIC ENERGY, you want to go fast but take your time getting there—in other words, get faster slowly. Start with slow deep breaths, pulling your breath all the way down into your belly, letting it expand. It may help to put a hand on your tummy so you can feel your belly swell with each inhale. Gradually increase the pace, each time pulling the breath all the way down into the belly. Keep getting faster until you're doing a deep rapid pant.

When you need to slow down, return to a deep, leisurely rhythm.

You can try this in cycles—accelerate to rapid breathing, then shift back to slow.

### Hot and Cool Breath

GET HOT AND FIRE UP some energy by breathing quickly and deeply for 30 breaths. Then cool down by taking three deep, long, slow breaths. Imagine you're drawing the energy up your central channel on the inhale and moving it down on the exhale. Do several cycles, alternating hot and cool breathing. Pay attention to how you feel in each phase and how you feel when you're done.

## OPEN EITHER END

Since you have an energetic and anatomical inner channel running from top to bottom, and what happens at one end is linked to what's happening at the other, you can use your breathing to open either end. Breathing through a loose open mouth and throat can fire up your southern regions and be a natural aphrodisiac.

### Dilating Breath

DO A DEEP, SLOW BREATH in and out through a loosely open mouth. Allow your lips to softly dilate, a little more with each exhale. Let all your facial muscles relax open. Keep your eyes softly focused. With each out-breath, release your jaw muscles so your chin drops a bit more with each. Rather then opening your mouth, allow it to relax and dilate. Allow the front of your mouth to expand, then the back of your mouth, then your throat. Let all the muscles of your whole face expand and open. Notice how you feel.

### Breathing Open the Tube

Connect your top and bottom with your breath (and a few mind tools to help).

Do the *Dilating Breath* and allow the opening to move further and further down your inner channel. Imagine your mouth and throat as one end of an unrestricted, relaxed tube that extends all the way through the center of your whole body, from mouth to crotch. Try to feel as if your entire internal channel is breathing freely. Let each breath expand your inner tube. (Breathing in through your nose is also okay, although try to keep using your opened mouth for the exhale.)

 *Come visit GetSexCrafty.com for more breath practices!*

## Bonding Breathing

Breath is as foundational to partner play as it is to solo activity. There are innumerable ways to use breathing to create and enhance connection. Solo breathing practices can be done with a partner, either simultaneously or in an opposite rhythm. Try variations by using different speeds and patterns. Making a soft but audible breath sound makes it easier to find a partnered rhythm that's right for you both. As with most partner play, experiment with different body positions. Try keeping your eyes closed or open with a soft or intense focus. Relax into the practices and see where you go together.

Peter Behrens, *Der Kuss* (*The Kiss*)

### PARTNER PLAY

### Breathing Together—Coordinated Breath

THE MOST BASIC partner practice is a *coordinated breath*, where you do the same pattern at the same time. It's a great way to connect at the start of a sensuous session or to re-establish connection if you've lost the thread. It's usually easiest to start by synchronizing on an inhale. Breathe in and out together. Find a rhythm that's comfortable for you both. Don't force it, just let it flow easily between you.

### Exchanging Breath—Complementary Breath

The *complementary breath* is the second basic partner breath. Central to this practice is the concept of breath exchange. You breathe out while your partner breathes in, then you inhale as they exhale. Keep your inhalation and exhalation equal.

> *Too much of a good thing can be wonderful.*
>
> MAE WEST

Imagine you're sending your breath into the other person and then receiving their breath into you. Visualize your air filling them and flowing back into you.

Complementary partner breathing is useful for connecting and especially good for pumping up the energy. You also each get to give and receive, balancing your yin and yang energy both internally and between you. It can create a very vibrant energy circuit.

# Sound

## What's Not to Love About Aural Sex?

Your next sexcraft tool is sound, a powerful and extraordinarily multipurpose instrument. It beautifully demonstrates the interconnectedness of your instru-

ments—to make sound, you have to be breathing and moving your mouth, diaphragm and vocal cords. Using it consciously requires awareness and intention.

Sound can rivet your attention. Your ears are part of your early warning system, always open, ever on the alert. You can close your eyes, but you can't close your ears!

Utagawa Hiroshige, *Shirasuga*

Since sound is so attention-grabbing, why not use it to your erotic advantage?

While sound can certainly include words, my focus here is on erotic sounds. Sexy talk is an invaluable communication tool during partner play and wanton words can up the arousal ante. But they can also activate the executive thinking part of your brain. Non-verbal sounds came long before words. They activate the ancient part of your brain that houses the most primal aspects of your sexuality. They speak directly to your deep erotic animal nature.

---

PLAY & PRACTICE

SOLO PLAY

### Breath Sounds

Try any of the breathing practices again, but this time add a sound to the exhale. Experiment with different sounds and notice if the sound makes it easier to do different breath patterns. I especially encourage you to accompany the Pump It Up and *Dilating Breaths* with sound.

Not sure where to start? Try 'ah,' 'oh' and 'ooo.'

---

## Sexy Sound Spectrum

You have an awesome capacity to create a spectrum of sexy sounds. You can play with timbre, intonation, volume and pitch. Sound can encourage and approve. It can orchestrate, modulate or syncopate. You can add rhythm, meter and cadence to the groove. In the land of Eros, your options include sweet sighs, melodic moans, wild wails, whispery whimpers, cries, croons and more.

SOLO PLAY

## Intend to Sound Sexy

How do you make sounds more erotic? It couldn't be easier: Simply add the intention that your sounds will be sexy and voilà, they will be. It's another amazing example of the power of intention.

William P. Gottlieb, *Portrait of Billie Holiday, 1947*

*In singing, there's a vibration that comes from deep down inside, literally from your sex. When you put out that vibration, people can feel it. Billie Holiday does it. Peggy Lee does it. It's very hot.*

ELIZABETH BERKLEY

## SOUND BENEFITS

The benefits of sexy sound are many. Let's take a look (and a listen!)

Sultry sighs and yummy 'ums' reassure your brain that you're safe, allowing it to relax its vigilance centers, be present and shift into early trance.

Sound focuses your distractible awareness, telling your brain "Pay attention, delicious sensations are happening right here, right now!"

Sensual sound silences your chattering, critical mind. When your brain is being distracted by the sound track of your pleasure, it can't also be reading negative subtitles. Your usual thoughts and worries get drowned out by your audible pleasure.

Sound illuminates more of your sensory brain map, literally amplifying sensations and increasing your pleasure. The sounds of arousal fire up more arousal in a delicious, super-positive internal and external feedback loop. You turn up your turn on with your own suggestive sounds.

Sound is a vibration and it oscillates through your body, harmonizing and synchronizing your biorhythms and energy fields, affecting your entire physiology in a positive way.

Last but not least, your erotic vocalizations are liberating and empowering— you're publicly claiming your pleasure in the face of potential societal disapproval. Sexy sound busts through inhibitions!

## The Sound Circuit

Sounds are a powerful partner connection tool.

Using sound is a potent way to ramp up your erotic energy circuits. It helps you align your body rhythms and vibrations so you can synchronize your states and get into a hot groove together.

Achille Devéria

Sounds are an exquisite feedback mechanism. They let your partners know where you are in your arousal trance, what you like and if something's getting you going. Sound helps you to be a responsibly responsive receiver when you narrate your arousal with accurate, clear and appreciative responses. Giving your partner positive signals is a gift to them. It lets them know what's turning you on and that they're doing a good job.

Of course, you know by now that making pleasure sounds will amplify your own perceptions and you'll feel more pleasure. But your playlist of pleasure sounds is also a potent turn-on for your lover. Your responsive sexy sounds are a way to give pleasure back to your partner, creating a win-win circuit. Then your playmate will be inspired to do more lovely things to you and shower you with even more erotic energy and attention.

Last but not least, your titillating sighs, moans and gasps are a way to encourage your partner to free their own sensuous soundtrack. Keep egging each other on with spicy sounds and at a certain point, the energy takes over and you're off on a wild energy ride together.

*When bodies talk, they speak to us all in quiet whispers, heart-to-heart, and soul-to-soul, in soundless conversations.*

STELLA PAYTON

## Energy Follows Sound

Sound can move—and as it does, it carries energy and awareness with it. When you make deep low sounds or ones that drop in pitch, your erotic energy will go down into your pelvis and genitals. A rising sound will send your energy up your body and tend to raise your arousal level. You can use the vibration and directionality of sound to open areas that are tight or blocked. Use sounds to orchestrate your energy circuits. You can actually use sound to send your erotic energy wherever you want!

## Narrate Your Pleasure

DON'T LIMIT YOUR aural pleasure to sex. Explore other ways to emphasize your enjoyment using pleasure sounds. It might be eating yummy food, taking a hot shower or getting a massage—anything that feels good. Notice how the pleasure of the experience intensifies when you allow your sounds to emerge.

## Partnered Sound Symphony

DO PARTNERED BREATHING, only this time with sound. Run through the various breath practices, only now make each exhale an opportunity for audible expression.

Try *Coordinated Breathing* with a big 'Ahhh' on the exhale. Then try it with an 'Ohhh.' Breathe together and make sounds in harmony. Turn off your brain and let the sound lead you. See what happens when you release your mutual sound.

Try playing with sound as you do *Complementary Breathing*, with one person sending sound with an exhale into their partner while the receiver opens to the sound, vibration and energy flowing in as they inhale. Then send the wave of sound and breath back into your lover as they open and receive.

### STARTING TO SING

Like any new thing, making sounds of pleasure can seem awkward, unnatural and embarrassing. Breaking free from pleasure-sound inhibition is challenging for many people. We've had a lot of training in being quiet, especially around anything that feels good. It's okay to yell if you hit your thumb with a hammer, but not if you hit a sweet genital hot spot. Take a moment and think about why we're so ashamed about letting the sounds of our erotic bliss emerge. It probably has something to do with the fact that it's about S-E-X! And that someone might know we're enjoying it. And then they'll know that we're _____ (fill in the blank with the first derogatory term that pops into your brain.)

Time for a different story, right?

If making erotic sound is difficult for you, I encourage you to embark on a campaign to free the inner soundtrack that orchestrates and amplifies your pleasure. You might start with the idea that your erotic overture is beautiful and that having pleasure and expressing it are gifts to be proud of.

At first you may have to push yourself to make sound, but over time you'll become comfortable giving voice to your bliss. Take it easy and play softly with the voluptuous voice of your pleasure. Maybe put on some sultry or ecstatic music—it's both an accompaniment and a way to cover your sounds. Begin with easy little sounds, like audible breaths, soft sighs and 'umms.' You don't have to raise the roof or scare the horses. As you get more turned on, don't hold back—let more sound out. Release it, liberate it, let 'er rip. Revel in your roars of pleasure!

The more sound you make, the easier it becomes to make more sound. At some point the sound will spontaneously emerge, freely expressing and encouraging your pleasure, and the observer in your head will be going, "Wow—listen to me! I sound spectacularly hot!"

Many people—especially guys—still their voice during the arousal journey. It's an old habit that limits the intensity of the experience. Another common pattern people have is to hold their breath and restrain their sound when they're coming. If you want your orgasm to continue for a minute, many minutes or more, keep your breath moving, let the sound roll out of your open mouth and your orgasmic wave will keep rolling, too!

Giving voice to your provocative, seductive and suggestive sounds creates an aural spotlight—communicating, narrating and expanding your pleasure. When you learn to truly free your sound, it will empower you in extraordinary ways.

---

PLAY & PRACTICE

SOLO PLAY

### Simple Starter Sounds

THERE'S NO LIMIT to the ways you can have fun playing with sounds. Try these out and see what happens:

- A simple and easy way to launch the shift from soundless to soundful is to make your breathing audible. Try turning up the volume and breathing loudly.

- Take a deep breath in and let it out with a soft sigh. Experiment with bigger, louder, deeper sighs. Try some 'flop on the couch after a long hard day' sighs.

- Play with changing the tone and timbre of the sounds. Experiment with sighs, moans, whimpers and 'umms.' Explore how different sounds affect you.

- Play with various vowel sounds. Try quiet, medium, and loud. Make them short or long. Repeat or vary the different vowels.

## Sound Play

NOT SURE WHAT SOUNDS TO MAKE? Here are a few suggestions:

- Make a soft loving 'ah.'
- Allow your lips to dilate as you make an 'ohh.'
- Feel the pleasure in your 'oooo.'
- Discover the yum in your 'umm.'
- Make like a pussycat and purr.
- Release your beast with a fierce 'grrr.'

## Movement

To be alive is to be in motion. Even when you're holding still, you're moving. Whether it's the micro world of molecular activity and your pulsing cells, or the macro movements of your relentless heartbeat and your dancing, walking, stretching body, you are always in motion.

*Sometimes it's only in the ecstasy of unrepressed movement that we may enter the stillness of our authentic selves.*

ALEXANDRA
KATEHAKIS

Conscious movement is another vital tool in your sexcraft repertoire, a key way to turn yourself on, conduct the symphony of sexual energy, guide and govern your attention and awareness, and amplify, well, just about everything.

William Blake, *Title* (detail)

### MOVING INTO DELIGHT

Certain movements are of particular interest to the budding erotic virtuoso. They include natural sexual motions such as shaking, spinal undulation, hip rocking and the more subtle pulsations of the pelvic floor muscles.

### MAKE LIKE A SNAKE AND UNDULATE

If you want to orchestrate your erotic energy, loosen up your spine and get it moving. The spine plays a major role in your arousal—remember that it's both an energetic channel and the central conduit of your nervous system, which means that it both literally and subtly connects everything, including your top and bottom. Free it up and it becomes a great pathway for waves of stimulating sensation.

Stuck on the ground floor, unable to turn off your brain and start turning on your body? Start to undulate gently. Add in some rhythmic breathing and soft sighs and that will usually be enough to

*The real dance is a spontaneous body movement that in harmony with the beats of the music in your heart.*

TOBA BETA

get you climbing your arousal stairs. It's also a great move if you're feeling caught on the stairs at any level. A serpentine spine can shift your stasis to sensation.

William-Adolphe
Bouguereau, *L'Aurore*

### ROCK THE CRADLE

The basic mammal mating motion is the pelvic rock. If you've ever watched a documentary about animals, you've surely seen this primitive reproductive rumba. This primal sexual movement taps into ancient sexual reflexes and activates archaic aspects of the brain. Even very small pelvic tilting motions trigger this basic sex reflex. Rocking your hips does more than spark the original plug—it fires up your nerves and rouses blood flow to your engorgeable genitals. (Yum, blood flow!) The old hip rock and roll instigates desire, incites excitement and impels arousal. As the energy builds, let it flow up your body naturally in waves, allowing your spine to ripple.

PLAY & PRACTICE

SOLO & PARTNER PLAY

## Do The Pelvic Rock

YOU CAN ROCK your pelvis in many positions.

To practice a standing pelvic rock, get centered over your feet about hip width apart with your knees loose and unlocked. Tilt your pelvis up and forward, mostly using your belly muscles to pull your pubic bone up while tucking in your tailbone. Then let your pubic bone move down, gently thrusting your butt out and using your lower back muscles to curl

Doug Metzger, *Skin to Skin*

your sacrum backwards. Allow your pelvis to gently rock back and forth.

The key here is to pivot where your thigh bones meet your hip joint. Let the movement be relaxed and small. You don't need to do big thrusts—a gentle rock is enough. Curl and uncurl your pelvis and get a loose and easy pelvic swing going.

### Lay It Down

THIS RECUMBENT pelvic rock strengthens your back muscles along with revving your erotic engine.

Lie on your back with your knees bent and feet flat on the floor. It's best not to have a pillow under your head.

Tilt your pelvis upward as you let your back flatten down to the floor. Then let your pelvis rock back down as you gently arch your back away from the floor. Feel like you're pivoting on your sacrum as you smoothly rock up and down. Keep the motions small, relaxed and fluid. It should feel fairly effortless. You can also let your knees gently open and close.

Try it with a continuous rocking motion, then a variation—hold your pelvis up for five seconds and gently arch your back while you let it roll back down.

## SHAKE IT UP

Vibration enlivens the body and opens the channels for ecstatic energy to run through you. It doesn't really matter where—it can be your feet, your shoulders or your booty. Any sort of vibration of any part of your body will shake it awake.

Try remembering a super-hot moment and let a shiver of pleasure run through you. Now just amplify that shiver to a shimmy and it's like magic—you get more pleasure!

It's also a great way to expand your orgasm. Play with the natural rhythmic oscillations of your orgasmic muscle spasms by consciously continuing to shudder and shake and you'll keep coming.

### Shake It Up

TO SEE WHAT VIBRATION can do for you, try this: Shake just one of your hands for 30-60 seconds, then stop. Hold both hands in front of you and compare them. What do you notice about the hand that you shook? What about the one you didn't? Now, just to even things out, shake your other hand.

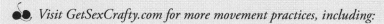

*Visit GetSexCrafty.com for more movement practices, including:*

- *Shake Your Booty*
- *Belly, Booty and Baby Dance*
- *Play with Pelvic Power*

## Pelvic Floor Play

You remember your pelvic floor from Chapter 7—the muscles that embrace your sassy swell-able genitals? Recall for a pleasurable moment how those muscles can squeeze, lift, push, pull, suck, expel, hold and generally fondle your own sweet sexy bits (and, should you be with a partner, someone else's).

Your inner trampoline is a major player in your own arousal orchestra. Train your inner muscles well and you'll be astonished at their skill, dexterity and capacity to enhance your erotic adventures.

> *My friends are so horny, they'll make love to anything that moves. But I never saw any reason to limit myself.*
>
> EMO PHILIPS

For your early experiments, use every part of your pelvic floor muscles (PFMs)—every layer, front to back, side-to-side. This includes the muscles that help you hold and release your urine, that let you hold in and push out poop and that surround and snugly hug your genitals. As you become more skilled, you can start to differentiate the movements of specific muscles and develop more precise muscle skills.

---

PLAY & PRACTICE

### HOT AND JUICY TIPS

### Am I Doing It Right?

To GET THE MOST from your pelvic floor muscle practices, get all your pelvic floor muscles involved. Here are a few tips to help you do that.

- Take a look at images of all the muscles so you can visualize them.
- Look at your crotch in a mirror and watch your genitals moving.
- Use your hands as external biofeedback devices by putting them on and/or in your body so you can feel the muscles moving.

And remember: There's no 'right way' to play.

---

## The Pleasure Pulse

To TONE AND TRAIN your pelvic pleasure muscles, simply tighten and release them. Start slowly and then go faster until you're going as fast as possible. When your pelvic floor muscles feel tired, take a short break, then repeat. Do a few short *Pleasure Pulse* sessions daily over a week or so and soon, you'll be able to go so fast it'll feel like you're fluttering them.

During orgasm, your pelvic floor muscles naturally go into a pattern of rapid highly pleasurable contractions. The *Pleasure Pulse* exercise builds muscle stamina so you can have longer, stronger orgasms. Not only that, but if you consciously flutter your PFMs while you're coming, you'll enhance the intensity and duration of your orgasm. Keep pulsing and you can keep coming! Think of it as sex muscle 'booty camp'!

## Pelvic Floor Pumps

Here's the basic *Pelvic Floor Pump.* Tighten the whole group of muscles by pulling them up, as if your bottom is an elevator going up while simultaneously squeezing them together like a drawstring. Then let the whole group relax down and release open. Repeat, repeat, repeat!

Suggestions:

- SQUEEZE AND RELEASE in a steady rhythm for a minute or two, then work your way up to going longer. See how many reps you can do comfortably. Try to do twenty to thirty squeezes, three times a day.

- EXPERIMENT with different speeds. Try practices where you see how slowly you can go from relaxed to tight and how slowly you can release. See how fast you can go.

- TRY PLAYING with patterns, like three super-slow squeezes followed by ten super-fast ones.

- PUT ON YOUR FAVORITE dance music and pulse your 'basement' muscles to the beat.

As with other practices, experiment with PF pumps when not aroused and at various stages in your erotic journey. PF pumps are especially useful if you want to bring more energy and attention to your genitals and ramp up your arousal level.

Let pleasure be your main guide and motivator.

> We should realize in a vivid and revolutionary sense that we are not in our bodies but our bodies are in us.
>
> RUTH ST. DENIS

## Going Up and Going Down (The Elevator)

Your pelvic floor muscles can do more than tighten and pull up—they can also push down and open out. In this exercise, you practice several sets of sexcraft skills. First, the ability to gain mastery in raising your PFMs and releasing them gradually and with control. Second, you'll work on connecting to their ability to open, push down and out, and thrust.

Imagine that your pelvic floor is an elevator in a building with three floors and a basement.

- Start on the first floor, neutral and relaxed.

- Partially draw the floor muscles up and together as if you were taking the elevator to the second floor. Hold there for a moment.

- Pull up to the third floor by drawing the muscles as far up and gathered together as possible. Hold for a moment.

- Let the elevator go back down to the second floor (partially contracted). Hold for a moment.

- Let the muscles go down to the relaxed neutral state of the first floor.

- Push down and out with your muscles as if the elevator were descending into the basement. Use your belly muscles as well as your PFMs (and it helps to let out a guttural 'Ugghh') to push your whole bottom open. (Yes, it's kind of like pooping, but with your whole pelvic floor, not just your anus.) Push down and out for the length of your exhale.

- Relax your bottom back to neutral.

- Repeat five or ten times. Check in and notice how you feel.

Once you master the three-story building, to gain greater discrimination and control of your floor muscles see if you can identify four, then five stories in your building. Work up (and down) to as many as you can.

*Go to SexCrafty.com and check out these webpages:*

- *Your Handy Dandy Personal Biofeedback Machine*
- *Hold It*
- *Softening and Releasing Your Pelvic Floor*
- *Rock, Roll & Resonate*

## Stillness

Now we come to the counterpoint of all the movement we've been discussing—stillness. This is a relative term. So long as we're alive, we're never actually still. No matter how hard you try not to move a muscle, you're still a big old mass of oscillating, vibrating protoplasm. Yet there is a place of stillness where we relax into the closest thing we can get to true stillness and simply let ourselves be.

As we've seen, sexual arousal is a dance between the two polarities of relaxation and excitement, the yin and yang of your nervous systems. Balancing and

Eric Gill, *Belle Sauvage III*

activating both aspects of your nervous system leads to relaxed excitement. When you're still, you're activating the down-regulating, relaxing parasympathetic part. Interweaving that with the up-regulating, hot fast fiery sympathetic aspect deepens your erotic trance. Remember, the more you dance between excitement and relaxation, the more you'll widen the stairs, deepening your absorption into erotic trance.

*Movement is the freedom of the body; stillness, of the mind.*

MARTY RUBIN

Stillness is as important as all the erotic moves that there are. In stillness, you can practice awareness. You replace striving with noticing. You can totally tune in. Being still allows your sexual energy to expand. In stillness, the erotic energy you've accumulated pulses, throbs and soars—and you have the space to really notice and experience it.

---

PLAY & PRACTICE      SOLO PLAY

### Stillness

EXPERIMENT with any of the breath and/or movement practices, adding periods of stillness punctuated by action. At the end of any practice, go into stillness. That's when the best noticing happens!

## Integrating the Key Three

When you play with your key three tools of breath, sound and movement together, the effects are synergistic—but integrating them can take some getting used to. Initially, coordinating your actions may feel awkward and complicated, but with practice it becomes easy. Your breath, sound and pelvic floor will be so connected that they'll always play nicely together. Anytime you take a big sounding breath, your inner muscles will naturally go along for the ride. You'll find yourself effortlessly weaving sound, breath, stillness and movement together.

Jean-Simon Berthélemy
*Reclining Bacchante Playing the Cymbals*

PLAY & PRACTICE

SOLO PLAY

### Pelvic Breath Pumps

LET'S PLAY WITH WAYS to combine your pelvic floor pumping with your breathing.

There are two basic patterns. Start by using whichever feels easier. Let your breath and bottom find their own natural groove. Then try the reverse pattern and play with that for a bit.

In the yin pattern, or *Flow Breath*, you tighten with your inhale and release with your exhale.

In the opposite yang pattern, the *Pump Breath*, you give a big squeeze of your inner muscles on the exhale and release with your inhale.

Try each pattern and tune in to notice how each one makes you feel. Try each pattern slowly, then at medium speed, then fast.

For most people, the yin *Flow Breath* (tighten PFMs with inhale) tends to be down-regulating, helping you go with the flow. It's great for getting grounded and present, relaxing into body awareness and shutting down your chattering mind.

Many people find that the yang *Pump Breath* (tighten PFMs with exhale) steps up erotic energy and is good for shifting from medium to high-level action.

Discover what's true for you as you run your own pelvic research station.

## Patterned Pelvic Pumps

### SOUNDING PUMP

LET'S PLAY WITH some sexcraft skill combinations to further expand our amorous abilities. Do the *Flow Breath* or *Pump Breath* (whichever you prefer) and add sound on the exhale. Use any sound you want. Not sure what sound to make? Try an 'Ah' or a sigh.

Do the opposite pattern, again experimenting with different sounds and noticing your response. Maybe try an 'Oh' this time. Be your own lab. See what happens.

### ROCKIN' SOUND

Try all the movement games again, making sound as you do them. Try each movement with a different sound and discover which combinations feel most fabulous. Not sure what sounds to make? Use your trusty vowel sounds like 'Ohs' and 'Ahs,' or try sighs, 'umms' and 'hums.'

### WORKING IT

LET'S COMBINE ALL THE TOOLS you've learned so far into a single experience.

Start with a pelvic rock, gently swaying your pelvis forward and backward. Next, coordinate your breath with your pelvic rock. Then add sound. Finally, add your internal pelvic floor muscles to the action.

Once you can do all these together, you're well on your way to enhancing every erotic experience you'll have for the rest of your life. Better still, the more you practice, the easier it gets! So pump your pleasure muscles in rhythm to your breath as you pivot your pelvis to your sexy soundtrack. Amazing pleasure awaits you!

Once you have these core skills nicely integrated, you can use them whenever you play with yourself or a partner. Get them on 'automatic' and they'll enhance everything sexual you do!

Take a deep breath and let it out with a sound as you pulse your pelvic floor.

That was good, wasn't it? Now let's explore the rest of your body's tasty toolkit.

CHAPTER TWELVE

# More Body: Vision, Touch, Taste & Smell

*The body is an instrument which can be tuned!*

AAIYN FOSTER

## Vision

WE HUMANS APPREHEND THE WORLD PRIMARILY THROUGH OUR EYES—
an astounding 80% of our perception is visual. Because attention follows our
senses, most of what we pay attention to is visual, too.

Just as your attention can be focused tightly or broadly, so can your sight.
You can contract your focus to attend to a tiny detail, or you can expand your
visual field and take in a broader scene. When you narrow your focus, you
activate your sympathetic excitement system and go into an alert, up-regulated
state. When you go broad and soft-focused, it takes you into a relaxed, down-
regulated place.

Another thing about vision, as we all know, is that you can look outward
or inward. Since the outer world is highly stimulating visually, if you want to
attend to your inner awareness it helps to close your eyes.

Of course, when the context is erotic, you don't want to always have your
eyes closed. There can be some great views nearby! To stay present when you
have your eyes open, try to focus on your immediate surroundings and the
exciting views connected to your physical experience. During partner play,
eye gazing and visually appreciating the delightful displays will enhance your
encounter rather than distract.

One extremely useful way to use your imagination is by visualizing the physical
changes that occur as your body gets turned on. This is one reason having an
accurate map of your anatomy can be useful: It enables you to picture what's
happening as your body parts swell and get juicy. When you visualize this process,
it creates a lovely feedback loop that creates more engorgement and arousal.

## More Ways to Use Vision to Enhance Arousal

**INNER:**

- LOOK AT ANATOMY illustrations and visualize what's happening to your body, especially your genitals, during arousal.

**OUTER:**

- LOOK IN A MIRROR at your genitals and see what your unique equipment looks like non-aroused and aroused.

- WATCH YOURSELF have solo sex.

- WATCH YOURSELVES have partner sex.

- LOOK AT YOUR PARTNER's genitals. Extra credit: Describe what you see.

*Thinking is more interesting than knowing,
but less interesting than looking.*

JOHANN WOLFGANG VON GOETHE

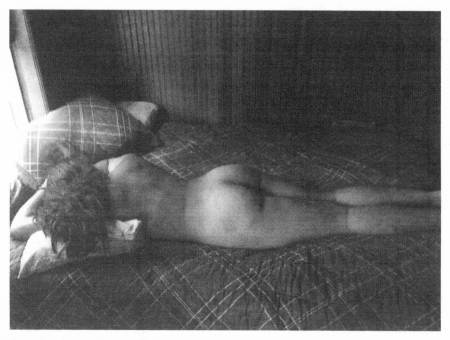

Ravin Baratheon, *Wanton Stillness*

## Seeing Sound

USE YOUR INNER VISION to expand what you can already do with your breath, movement and intention. You may find that connecting it to your sound is particularly powerful.

CLOSE YOUR EYES and take a few deep, centering breaths.

TAKE A FEW MORE BREATHS, releasing a sound as you exhale. Now, focus on your inner vision. What do you see?

YOU CAN TRY TO VISUALIZE the sound as a ball of moving light. Or, envision the sounds moving along your inner channel opening it to a glowing flow.

RUN A FEW EXPERIMENTS and search for sounds that expand your images.

AS YOU SLOWLY EXHALE, make sounds that fall in pitch. See a current of light following the sound down your inner conduit. As your sound gets lower, envision illumination filling the bowl of your pelvis. (For most people, very low, guttural, open-throated relaxed-mouth sounds will help the light permeate your pelvis.) Then let the light and sound spill out through your floor, opening your pelvic muscles as you do. Imagine the sound and light pouring out your whole bottom. Feel the pleasure and play with whatever enhances it.

NOW MAKE SOUNDS and images that ascend. Try short fast breaths and have the pitch go up on each exhalation. Visualize a fountain of light that rises higher as your sound does, or imagine your inner channel flowing upward in a stream that glows and brightens. Imagine your crown chakra and the top of your skull opening. Visualize the light, propelled by breath and sound, pouring up and out. Enjoy!

 *Check out GetSexCrafty.com for Seeing What's So*

---

*I don't have everything, but I have working eyes, ears, a mouth, a nose and can feel anything I touch and you know what? We take these simple things for granted too often. If you ever think you're having a bad day try to imagine a day without one of them—then adopt the spirit of gratitude.*

CALVERT JONES

---

## Chakra Vision

VISUALIZE THE LOCATION and color of each chakra in turn as you breathe and make sound. Try this with the 'traditional' chakra colors first. Also try it by breathing and sounding into each vortex and see whatever colors appear to you. You can play with one chakra per session or run through all the chakras, top to bottom or bottom to top.

As usual, start with a few deep, slow centering breaths. Imagine each chakra infused with light and color. Take your time to turn each one on.

Recommended: Do this while pulsing your PFMs.

## Seeing Into the Other

Eye-gazing is a powerful way to connect. Cliché though it is, the eyes really are our windows on the soul. They show our true feelings, vulnerabilities and desires. It's not always easy to eye-gaze, though. Looking deeply into another's eyes can be dauntingly intimate. You need courage to show up fully and stay present, to see and be seen.

*I believe I will never quite know.*
*Though I play at the edges of*
*knowing, truly I know our part*
*is not knowing, but looking, and*
*touching, and loving.*

MARY OLIVER

When we fall madly in love, we tend to gaze deeply into the eyes of our beloved, whether it's our brand-new baby or romantic partner. Wanting to eye-gaze comes naturally, but it tends to be limited to those times when our love hormones are in overdrive. As the years go by, most couples spend less and less time looking deeply into each other. The result is less intimacy and connection.

I encourage you to do more eye-gazing with your playmates, especially your long-term partners. And, while you're at it, see if you can fall in love with yourself a bit more by taking time to gaze lovingly into your own eyes.

## Eye-Gazing Galore

GET INTO A COMFORTABLE aligned position where you can easily look into each other's eyes. Make your gaze soft and relaxed. One particularly effective way to do this is by looking into each other's non-dominant eye (usually the left).

This is a great time to do coordinated breathing practice. Simply look, breathe and be. Relax into the experience.

## Sexual Breathing

TRY EITHER THE *Flow Breath* or the *Pump Breath* from the last chapter, now adding your inner vision and imagination. Sound is optional. Use whichever pattern is easiest for you. (And at some point, try the opposite one.)

After you get the breathing and pelvic floor muscle movement pattern established, add some visuals. You can envision your breath as a bright light moving in and out through your genitals, anus and perineum. Imagine that your air is literally flowing out and being sucked in through the floor of your body.

VARIATION: Add the image of your inner channel. Visualize the air rushing in and up as you draw it in, then flowing back down through the central conduit and rolling out your whole bottom.

You can also do sexual breathing with a partner. When you do it as a duo, you can synchronize with both of you doing the same pattern at the same time. Or you can counter-breathe, with one of you inhaling as the other exhales. Visualize a river of light flowing between you.

*Come check out the many exercises and practices at GetSexCrafty.com including a Guided Visualization on Connecting with Your Sexual Power.*

Giulio Romano, *Jupiter Seducing Olympias*

## Yin Wave Breath

THIS IS A SLOW RELAXING breath that helps your parasympathetic system down-regulate you.

Imagine a circular wave like the one that's created when a raindrop lands in a still pond. Envision this ripple rolling out from a central point in the middle of your diaphragm and/or solar plexus.

As you inhale and the barrel of your chest expands, imagine a circular wave rolling outward from your center. Exhale and as your chest contracts, see the circular wave flow back to your center. Use a natural tidal rhythm with no pause. Continue to breathe, envisioning circular waves rolling in and out in the ancient rhythm of the sea.

## Yang Fire Breath

THIS BREATH, which is a more or less standard feature in many erotic traditions, stokes you up by stimulating your sympathetic nervous system. Your breath is fiery, hot, fast. Visualize flames, glowing embers or flowing light. You're pumping up the energy and building erotic tension.

Although *Fire Breath* requires you to breathe rapidly, it's not a shallow pant. Keep your breaths deep. You can put a hand on your belly to remind you to breathe deeply, all the way down through your whole torso.

Close your eyes (or use a blindfold). Look up or let your eyes roll up into your head.

Breathe fast and deep. Imagine that you're building a fierce fire in your belly—and just like a real fire, more oxygen, more breath, will make it blaze more. See more and more of your body aglow. Envision intense colors. See fiery flames or a blazing ball of light.

Run this experiment breathing only through your nose, then just through your mouth. Play with taking deep sniffing breaths with your nose and exhaling them out your mouth. Try different images. Note how each feels and which works better for you.

Remember to take deep breaths! Otherwise you may hyperventilate and feel dizzy. If this happens, slow down and take deeper breaths.

## Fire and Water

START BY DOING A FEW MINUTES of *Wave Breath*, followed by a minute of *Fire Breath*, then another few minutes of *Wave*, followed by a minute of *Fire*. Do two or three rounds (or as many as you like). You will probably feel high afterward. Do not operate heavy machinery!

Seriously, just relax afterward and notice what you're experiencing. Enjoy!

*Your vision will become clear only when you can look into your own heart. Who looks outside, dreams; who looks inside, awakes.*

CARL JUNG

The *Wave* and *Fire Breaths* are great techniques to use by yourself. Use a *Wave Breath* to relax. Use *Fire Breath* to wake up and get energized. Alternate the two to play with natural highs.

They're also great ways to play with a partner (or partners). Share the visuals that you're using such as a glowing circuit, a fiery river or trails of pulsing light.

Start an erotic play session with five minutes of mutual *Wave Breath*. You can sit facing each other and eye-gaze. Or lie together with eyes closed, either spooning or in a heart-to-heart embrace, and get tranced out together on the Wave Breath. Eventually it may feel like you are no longer two separate breathing people, but a single breathing unit. This is a great way to launch an erotic session when one or both of you are feeling tense or distracted and unable to turn off your thinking brain.

Having a hard time getting all the way up the arousal stairs? Try sharing the *Fire Breath* practice and see if that causes blast off! Doing the *Fire* and *Water* combo will take you both deep into trance.

# Touch

## How Touching

Touch was your first sense, beginning while you still floated in your mama's womb feeling held, surrounded and safe. You were already touching your own body before you emerged.

Touch is so fundamental that without it, babies will wither and die. As grown-ups, we won't die from touch deprivation, but we won't be as happy and healthy as we would be if our minimum daily touch needs were met. Yet most of us are starved for this essential tactile nourishment.

> *A person could last a long while without touch, but once someone had experienced the comfort, joy, and sheer relief of another human body close, the desire to experience that again was hard to deny.*
>
> MARY JOHNSON

## In Touch

While touch (also called tactile perception) is considered one of the five traditional senses, it is actually derived from multiple senses and perceptions, including your ability to sense temperature, pressure and pain. Touch also includes what is called haptic perception—your ability to identify objects by touching them, also known as "seeing with your fingers"—and proprioception—your ability to know where your body is in space.

Martin van Maele, *Trilogie érotique*

Mirror neurons come into play here. They give us the bodily 'intelligence' that lets us know how it feels to someone else when we're touching them. They help us give pleasure with our touch and receive pleasure from it, too.

## Articulate Touch

Touch is a basic form of communication—we all speak this universal tongue. It's also one of our first languages of love, beginning with mother and infant.

At a subtle level, touch transmits intention, emotion, energy, relaxation or tension, and the rhythms of the body. If someone is touching you in a loving way with the intention of giving you pleasure, it feels very different than if they're touching you solely for their own enjoyment. Comfort, anxiety, caring, attention and distractedness are all transmitted through physical contact.

While touch is a language everyone shares, many people are tremendously confused about the purpose and value of touch, how to share it appropriately, and how to do it masterfully. Touch is complicated, delicate territory. It's easy to miscommunicate about it. And it's not always easy to touch with great skill and finesse.

Japanese Erotic Art Shunga

Whether or not a particular type of touch is pleasurable is completely subjective. For instance, the sensation of being tickled may be something you find dreadful or delightful. Personal preferences notwithstanding, when we fully activate our kinesthetic intelligence, we're most likely to touch our partner in a way they enjoy.

Remember, though, that no one is born knowing how someone else wants to be touched. Which is why we can't rely on touch alone. To give exquisite touch, even if we're totally attuned, it helps to add other modes of communication like sound ("Umm!" "Aah!"), words ("More pressure, please") and body language.

> *That's what it feels like when you touch me. Like millions of tiny universes being born and then dying in the space between your finger and my skin. Sometimes I forget.*
>
> IAIN THOMAS

## CONTACT COMMUNICATION

How can we communicate our desires and boundaries, our wants and needs when it comes to touch? It can be tricky, but we have words, sounds, gestures and body language at our fingertips, so to speak.

If we're using words, it's important to have a shared understanding of what we mean. With partners, you need to develop a terminology of touch, so your 'stroke' doesn't mean your partner's 'rub.' Sharing a wide touch vocabulary enables you both to communicate exquisitely about your tactile desires.

I also encourage you to arrive at a mutual awareness of what your sounds mean, so your "I love this, keep going" sound won't be confused with your "This is a little too intense, please take it down a notch" sound.

We also communicate with gestures and body language. Let your co-learning about touch include how to interpret your playmate's physical cues, signs and signals.

## SENSATIONAL TOUCH

One of the extraordinary things about touch is that you are always simultaneously giving and receiving. There's both a yin and yang quality to touch.

At the unbalanced yang extreme, you're imposing your will, un-attuned to the desires of the recipient. Purely yang touch is a way of taking. You're touching solely for your own pleasure, just to get what you want. It's more about having power over someone else than about their pleasure. (While consensual power play can be fun, it's not just about the top doing whatever they want to the bottom. The do-er needs to attend to the do-ee for it to work.)

We demonstrate true kinesthetic intelligence when we have a fluid balance of yin and yang in our touch. When our active yang 'doing' is balanced by yin receptivity, we're not just touching, we're also feeling. The 'eyes' in our fingers are open—we're receiving tactile information at the same time we're giving touch. We're getting as much pleasure as we give.

*So she thoroughly taught him that one cannot take pleasure without giving pleasure, and that every gesture, every caress, every touch, every glance, every last bit of the body has its secret, which brings happiness to the person who knows how to wake it.*

HERMANN HESSE

The consummate touch artist adds in additional layers of yin and yang with their intention and awareness. As you hold the yang intention to serve the other by giving pleasure, you juggle that with yin awareness of their response and your own delight in tactile sensations When your touch feels wonderful to you, your intention is to serve and delight your partner, and you're paying attention to your own and your partner's responses—that's when your touch will be brilliant.

SOLO AND PARTNER PLAY

### Touching and Feeling

PLAY THIS GAME in the dark or blindfolded. This will remove all other stimuli and help you focus solely on the sensations of touch.

Do your best to touch yourself with full attention and awareness. Use sound and breath to amplify the sensations and stay present. Alternate your

attention: Shift your awareness to the part being touched, then toggle back to the part doing the touching. Imagine that you're stroking velvet as you slide your fingertips along your skin. Run your fingers through your hair. Use the soft arch of your foot to stroke your other leg. Try to really focus on feeling yourself as you touch. Imagine that you are your own cat as you pet your fur.

Samuel Claiborne
*Touch*

### PARTNER PLAY

The two of you are blindfolded as you both focus on touching and feeling.

### THE FOUR LANGUAGES OF TOUCH

In order to better understand and communicate about our touch needs, it's useful to understand that there are four languages of touch—nurturing, healing, sensual and sexual. (We're talking only about positive touch here.)

The first and foundational level is nurturing touch, which transmits caring and acceptance. It's the kind of tender touch a loving parent gives their beloved child. It helps us feel loved, valued and worthy of being loved. Many of us did not receive enough loving touch as infants, or it was alternated with indifferent or negative touch. We need this kind of nurturing touch throughout our lives. Giving and getting loved that way is an important ingredient of healthy intimate connections.

*Touch has a memory.*

JOHN KEATS

Kinds of touching that feel nurturing include firm holding, rocking, rhythmic patting, soft dry (non-sexual) kisses, and hair and face-stroking.

The second language of touch is therapeutic touch—any form of contact that heals, eases stress, promotes well-being, repairs bodily damage, restores health or palliates pain. You can't do therapeutic touch without intending to heal, just as you can't do nurturing touch without intending to nurture.

Eric Gill, *Lovers*

Healing touch includes classic massage strokes like muscle kneading, vibration and passive stretching, as well as working acupressure or shiatsu points and energy healing.

The third language of touch is sensual touch—any form of contact designed to heighten the senses, amplify body awareness and magnify perception. Sensual touch is not explicitly erotic. While it might be a warm-up on the path to arousal and is often an excellent prelude to sexual touch, it's not designed to be a turn-on in and of itself. Think of it as turning on the senses, not the genitals. It's about waking up the whole body (and mind) with luscious sensation to enhance awareness and promote pleasure. Playing with the receiver's nervous system via sensation is a fun way to help them focus and expand their body awareness. Rhythmic, repeated motions can hush the receiver's chatterbox brain and lull them into a light trance.

A wide variety of sensation play can be included in the sensual touch category. Use your hands to give fluid strokes and teasing tickles or scratch lightly with your nails. You can use your own hot breath, wet mouth or silky hair. Sensation play can also make use of sex toys (like patting or pounding with paddles) or household items (like stroking with a piece of plush velvet).

Last but definitely not least, there is sexual touch—any contact that arouses and stimulates. Sexual touch entices your erotic energy to come out and play. It teases, titillates, ignites and (hopefully) satisfies your erotic desires.

Since one person's sensual touch can be another person's sexual touch, it really helps to communicate around touch styles using this framework.

We tend to think of the erotic virtuoso as someone who's skilled at sexual touch, but more than that is involved. Inspired touch uses awareness, attention and intention. A dexterous touch master can bring nurturing and healing to their contact to create connection, ease and safety. An erotic artiste can use sensual touch to take a person into trance and amplify sensation and then use sexual touch to give erotic delight.

The true touch master speaks all four languages fluently.

## Succulent Summary

### The Four Languages of Positive Touch

1. NURTURING: transmits love, caring, acceptance

2. THERAPEUTIC: healing touch

3. SENSUAL: delights and awakens the senses, entrancing

4. EROTIC: sexually stimulating and arousing

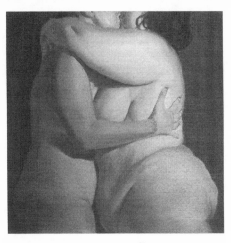

Susan Singer, *Susie Kissing Sally*

SUCCULENT SEX CRAFT

### Vocabulary Class

TEACH YOUR PARTNER what you mean by a particular touch word such as a rub, caress, or stroke. Show by doing it to them first, then having your partner do it to you.

Name a Move: Create names for types of touch and special moves. For example, I have a move called Spider Fingers, where I use each finger in turn in a rapid fluid touch.

Another useful communication strategy is to define which of the four languages different types of touch fall into for you. That way, it's easy to ask your playmates for what you want and to give them what they want.

## THE MODALITIES OF TOUCH

If you want to give and get exquisite touch, it's useful to differentiate its many modalities, such as tempo, pressure and pattern. Let's take a quick tour of some of the qualities and attributes of touch.

## Speed

The tempo of your touch can feed relaxation or excitement. Slower-paced moves generally down-regulate you and help you get entranced. Faster movements tend to be more energizing and stimulating. A gradually increasing pace builds tension and excitement. A well-timed shift to excruciating slowness can be very sensual and erotic. The primal animal rhythm of sexual climax is usually very fast.

Do you just have three speeds—slow, medium and fast—in your erotic gearbox? You can easily expand to a wider and more nuanced range.

### Speed Vocabulary

EXPAND YOUR OPTIONS. Do the same stroke at three speeds: Slow, medium, fast. Now repeat and use five speeds, then seven. Discuss. Is your 'super slow' the same as your partner's?

To simplify requests when you're playing sexually, try naming or numbering the different speeds. Super slow speed might be 'glacial.' Slow might be 'lazy' while very fast might be 'revved.' The specific names don't matter—what's important is that you and your partner speak the same touch language.

**Eight Levels of Contact**

Touch can go from very, very light (pre-touch, really) to very deep and penetrating. Here's a simple model of touch's levels of contact. Not coincidentally, these levels correlate with the tissue or layer of the body your touch is focused on and the amount of pressure you apply. Naturally, this is just a starter menu of options.

1. ENERGY FIELD: You can play with the energy envelope, also called the etheric layer, which extends 3-6 inches from the skin.

2. FEATHER: Here you stay just above the skin surface, either teasing the hairs or barely touching the skin. Beware (or be aware): This touch can tickle, which some people love and others abhor. Check-ins are strongly recommended in the tickle zone!

3. BRUSH: A light, delicate touch over the surface of the skin.

4. CARESS: A fluid touch that glides on the skin with a tiny bit of friction.

5. STROKE: Unlike the caress, with the stroke there's firm contact with the skin.

6. RUB: Goes below the skin surface and plays with the fascia and connective tissue underneath.

7. MASSAGE: Deep kneading and rubbing that gets into the muscles and joints.

8. ANCHOR: Holding the bones, firm, stable pressure on the bony prominences.

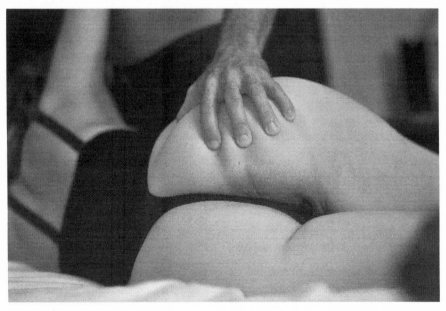

Vinette Perez, *Training Session*

## The Six P's of Touch

You can become a touch savant by playing with the six P's—presence, purpose, patience, precision, pattern and progression. When you do so, you get to the ultimate P—pleasure!

*It is in the imperceptible space between that which touches and that which is touched that one body can be felt, no matter how closely, to be different from another.*

DANIEL HELLER-ROAZEN

### Presence

When you are fully present and in the moment with your touch, it will be exquisite. Paying relaxed, soft-focused attention is a great way to let your kinesthetic intelligence emerge. If you're touching your partner's thigh, be present to the thigh. Don't think about where you're hoping to get to after that. Delight in the delicious now.

Use your own sexcraft skills to stay present. If you find yourself in a thinking or distracted place, slow down or better yet, get still. Get centered back into your own experience using breath, awareness, intention (or whatever your favorite centering tools are.) Then shift your awareness back to your partner.

### Purpose

Touch transmits intention. If someone is rubbing your back as a prelude to getting into your pants, you'll know it. If someone is intending to give you pleasure, their touch will transmit that, too.

I encourage you to create conscious intentions when you connect erotically with yourself and others. Focus on connection, pleasure and co-creating a great improvisational journey, not on getting or achieving.

### Patience

When I'm asked for one single bit of advice about how to have better sex, my answer is this—take your time. Quickies can be fun snacks, but extraordinary sex usually occurs when you slow down to enjoy the feast.

While I certainly recommend taking time to have leisurely encounters, I mean something else as well. Don't be in a hurry to get from point A to point B. Dogs (or should I say, core-yang people), this means not diving directly into your pussycat's nether regions. If you want to do some muff munching, consider starting at her toes, taking time with every digit, then traveling oh-so-slowly up her leg until she's desperate to have you dive into her glorious genitalia. Slow is good—it creates anticipation and builds arousal. The more patient you are, the hungrier your kitty will be and the more you'll be rewarded when you feed her (or feed on her).

## Precision

By precision, I mean touch that's discerning, accurate and exquisitely focused. It's one of the keys to touching masterfully instead of just "okay-fully."

It requires you to toggle your attention and awareness fluidly back and forth between yourself and your partner. As we get more turned on, it's easy to lose our focus and get wild and sloppy with our movements. As things up-regulate and your brain heads down toward the basement, do your best to pay extra attention to the importance of precision!

It also requires presence—you can't be precise without being present.

## Pattern

If you touch someone in the same way over and over again, it can get monotonous or irritating. If you deviate non-stop, it can feel incoherent and chaotic and keep the recipient from going into trance. There's a middle ground between chaotic and boring— pattern. Masterful touch is like

Alméry Lobel-Riche

music—it creates patterns with its combination of rhythm, repetition, harmony and syncopation. Repeating a move creates space for appreciation and feeds anticipation. It creates a pleasing expectation—a sort of touch security, as it were—and escalates entrancement.

Syncopation offers an accent note. It delivers the element of surprise, and it does so without taking the recipient out of the zone. Use motion and stillness, just as music works with sound and silence. Remember: Stillness is a 'move' just like motion is a move. Play with a beat, melody and cadence. Use repetition, surprise, rhythm, syncopation, tempos and motifs to create your very own symphony of touch.

You can also play with touch as if it were visual art. Pretend you're finger-painting, sculpting, outlining or shading. Here, too, use designs, motifs, recurring themes, and gradually changing patterns. Doodle with their body! There's a larger takeaway here: Touch is an art form—and mastery equals artistry.

## Progression

Pattern and progression are closely related. In fact, progression is how you get from Pattern A to Pattern B, or from Location A to Location B, without having it feel rushed, jumpy or chaotic. Let your touch have internal consistency, a sort of touch logic. Don't jump around randomly from one place on the body to another. Play with progressing coherently from place to place, or from one layer to another. Shift fluently between languages. Transition gradually between tempos or from broad strokes to detailed ones.

Generally, use smooth, gradual transitions (except when you want to delight with the surprise of an accent note). For instance, going from deeply therapeutic shoulder massage directly to genital stimulation might be disconcerting. However, if you move from deep kneading of the big back muscles down to the buttocks, shift to a lighter sensual rhythmic stroke down the thigh, followed with a teasing, feathery flit up the inner thigh, a quick brush past the crotch, to almost touching the genitals, and finally to landing there with a deliberate firm hand—well, that can be utterly delicious.

During all of this, of course, you'll want to practice another of the 'P's—patience. There's an art to finding the balance between taking your time and being too slow. Here, look for the receiver to give cues. As long as they're loving it, linger there. When they're not responding positively, it may be time to move on to something else.

Receivers, there's a message in this for you: Be actively responsive. Not only will this amplify your pleasure, you'll be letting your giver know how you love to be touched. And that's a positive pleasure circuit!

## Succulent Summary

### Six P's of Touch

1. PRESENCE: Be present. Touch here now.

2. PURPOSE: Hold a positive intention.

3. PATIENCE: Don't rush. Take your time.

4. PRECISION: Be accurate and focused.

5. PATTERN: Think musically and artistically—use rhythm, themes and motifs.

6. PROGRESSION: Keep it moving—and coherent.

 *Come to GetSexCrafty.com for a Guided Touch Meditation and more!*

## MORE TOUCH

I encourage you to actively seek out opportunities to spend more time touching and being touched.

As always, this starts with yourself. Look for easy ways to touch yourself more often and with increased awareness and attention. Take a two-minute break from work to give yourself a neck rub. When you get home, take off your shoes and give your feet a deep kneading. If you put on moisturizer, really tune in to how it feels on your skin. When you self-pleasure, start by stroking your whole body.

Now that you know the four languages of touch, it may be easier to create non-sexual, touch-buddy relationships. The languages aren't only explanatory—they also establish boundaries. With clear communication about what languages of touch you want and need, you can set up platonic cuddle sessions, massage exchanges or nurturing contact with your non-sexual friends.

With your erotic playmates, you can create more fulfilling connections by being sure to include all four languages in your touching. And, when touching and being touched, use your whole toolkit to enhance your trance and get lost in contact and connection.

## SMELL & TASTE

### Tasty Treats and Sexy Smell

I'm combining smell and taste in this short section because the two senses are so closely linked. Our taste buds have a limited palate: Sweet, salty, sour, bitter and umami (meaty or savory). All the other vast and varied flavors we 'taste' actually come from scent.

Smell happens when diffuse fragments of chemicals waft into your nose and the signals they arouse are transmitted to your old brain and your mammalian emotional centers. Unlike most of your other senses, the neuro-highway for scent connects directly to your most animal equipment.

John William Waterhouse
*The Soul of the Rose*

Since smell is such a powerful part of the mating dance, it makes sense that sex is a smelly business. How much we like, love or abhor the scent and taste of another's body is idiosyncratic. The taste of your lover's mouth, genitals and the various juices they produce are often acquired tastes (and a taste worth acquiring if it doesn't come naturally to you). However, I'm convinced that the more we run erotic energy with a person, the more we come to like their taste and odor.

How can we increase our desire for our partner's flavors? One trick is to spend time sharing hot, wet, sensual kisses. Saliva has molecules from all the glands and organs in the body, including sex and love hormones like oxytocin and testosterone. When we kiss and share our mouth fluids, we're also sharing those subtle sexy chemicals. It's arousing as well as bonding.

Our noses also pick up pheromones, chemicals that we don't consciously smell but that affect our state. No surprise, then, that scent is a primal path for sexual signals, whether we're aware of them or not. An interesting example is that while human females supposedly have hidden ovulation, they actually give off subtle olfactory clues about their fertility status. While they don't exhibit obvious signs of ovulation—many of our female animal relatives display a visibly engorged vulva by way of invitation—the waft of fertile female odors and pheromones unconsciously affects nearby males.

> *A good fragrance is really a powerful cocktail of memories and emotion.*
>
> JEFFREY STEPAKOFF

How can we consciously make use of our aroma-abilities? One way is by actually (and naturally) turning up your natural erotic aroma. I'm not suggesting that you use perfume or other external scents. You can do it internally and all-naturally by revving up your sexual engine. That's right, the more erotic energy you run and the more aroused you become, the sexier your personal perfume.

When we're in a sexual circuit with another person, we create an intoxicating scent and taste feedback loop. Increased deliciousness leads to more arousal and more desire to share, among other things, the flavor and aroma of our partner's body. It's why we want to smooch, lap up, sniff and nuzzle our lovers (and babies, too).

Not only is your sense of taste intermixed with your ability to smell (and get turned on by scent), but your mouth, lips and tongue are some of the most richly innervated areas of your body. That's why licking, kissing and nibbling are such significant erotic activities. You get the delicious combination of taste, aroma and tactile delight all rolled into one delicious ball.

---

> *Odors have a power of persuasion stronger than that of words, appearances, emotions, or will. The persuasive power of an odor cannot be fended off, it enters into us like breath into our lungs, it fills us up, imbues us totally. There is no remedy for it.*
>
> PATRICK SÜSKIND

---

## Yin Yang Partner Practice: Playing With Your Food

To develop your senses of smell and taste, play a delicious game. Feed each other blindfolded.

Start with a boundary check-in about what foods you want to receive. (Not to state the obvious here, but avoid allergens!) Gather an array of tasty tidbits.

Have one person be the giver, the other the receiver. The receiver gets blindfolded. The giver feeds playfully. Tease and tantalize, go slow, have fun and be creative.

Use your other instruments to enhance your aromatic and delectable experience: Smell, sound, feeling and movement as well as taste.

After you're complete, switch roles.

You've now gotten to play and practice with a panoply of mind and body instruments. You have more than enough to ratchet up your sex life, but why stop now? There are two additional domains to explore.

Next up, the heart and the magical power of love.

Johann Nepomuk Geiger

SUCCULENT SEX CRAFT

# CHAPTER THIRTEEN

# THE LOVE YOU MAKE

*Perhaps all the dragons in our lives are princesses who are*
*only waiting to see us act, just once, with beauty and courage.*
*Perhaps everything that frightens us is, in its deepest essence,*
*something helpless that wants our love.*

RAINER MARIA RILKE

## Sweet Heart

HOW DEEPLY WE YEARN TO LOVE AND BE LOVED! MORE THAN ANYTHING else, more than the desire for sex or fame or riches, we yearn to be loved unconditionally for who we truly are, imperfections and all. We long to be known, accepted and assured that we are lovable, not despite our faults, or because of them, but for our unique wholeness. The question that we are always asking, beneath every other utterance, is, "Do you love me?" We long for the big 'Yes!' and spend much of our lives looking for it, often in ways that are disguised or ineffectual. Sometimes we conflate sexual desire with love and make sexual choices that aren't self-loving.

While the desire to love and be loved comes naturally, loving well doesn't and neither does keeping the heart open in the face of the impulse to close it. These are learned skills.

If we're lucky—very lucky!—we grew up in an environment where we were seen, honored and respected. Some people had role models who showed them how to be compassionate, forgiving, generous and kind to themselves and to others. If you belong to this minority, you can probably love skillfully without having to think about it. Most of us didn't have these models, though. We need remedial love training if we want to get good at conscious loving.

Sheri Winston
*Heart*

239

SOLO & PARTNER PLAY

## Baby, Baby, Baby

**SOLO:**

IMAGINE THAT you are the most perfect parent a baby could ever have. Your love for your baby is evident in how you treat your beloved child.

What does that look like? How do you care for the baby? How do you create physical and emotional safety and security?

You pay attention, listen with awareness and respond compassionately. You hold, comfort and embrace the infant. In a multitude of ways, you let the baby know they are loved and worthy of love. You are open to the baby's expressing emotion and see those communications as important clues to the child's needs. When the baby has needs, you respond.

*You are your own baby.* That baby lives inside you. As you go about your day, check in with your inner infant. How is he/she doing? Notice if you're being a loving, attentive, responsive parent to yourself. Practice taking great care of your inner child.

**PARTNER:**

ENCOURAGE YOUR PARTNER to do this exercise by themselves. Then share with each other what you imagined and how it felt.

A great partner practice game is to set up a time and space to give the other's baby what they want. Use lots of nurturing touch and say the words they long to hear.

*The greatest happiness of life is the conviction that we are loved, loved for ourselves, or rather loved in spite of ourselves.*

VICTOR HUGO

Hans Baldung, *The Holy Virgin as Queen of the Heavens with the Christ Child*

## Let There Be (Self) Love

When I speak of the domain of the heart, I'm referring to our feeling center, to where our foundational emotional templates reside. Here, too, each of us has a set of tools and skills we can hone. While these are essential skills for intimate partner relationships, your focus here is on your level one heart skills: Your ability to love yourself.

Your solo love abilities include multiple skill sets. At the root is loving yourself in a general way. This includes integrating self-love into your solo sex. In addition, your self-love is what enables you to make sage, healthy and erotically satisfying choices about the 'who, when and how' of your sexual connections. These concepts are woven into the rest of the discussion in this chapter.

### SELF-LOVE SKILLS

When we think about 'loving well,' we usually think about loving others. As with so much else, though, loving well starts with ourselves. The first and most important place to practice your love skills is within yourself. Loving yourself can be especially difficult to do—after all, we know all about our flaws and faults. But practicing self-love is as important as it is challenging.

PLAY & PRACTICE

SOLO PLAY

### What's To Love?

TAKE SOME TIME for self-appreciation! Write down everything about yourself that's wonderful, lovable and positive. Keep adding to the list! Put it on your altar or refrigerator and refer to it when feeling less than fabulous about yourself.

French School, *La Petite Mort*

We have a cultural epidemic of low self-esteem, shame, bad self-image, and poor self-care. We struggle under mountains of self-criticism and negative self-judgment. Many of us believe we don't deserve to be loved. We often look to others to provide the compassion, care, honor and appreciation that we crave but cannot give ourselves. This is a losing strategy. If, at heart, we don't feel worthy of love, we can't fully receive it from others. You've gotta believe it to receive it.

Self-love is not selfish or self-indulgent. It's the basis for a healthy, happy relationship with yourself and ultimately with others.

SOLO & PARTNER PLAY

## Practicing Appreciation

**SOLO:**

MAKE AN INTENTION that today you will practice appreciating every little thing about yourself. Appreciate that you got up on time, made it to work, and handled that traffic jam without getting stressed. Appreciate that you made yourself a healthy meal, totally enjoyed eating that piece of chocolate and really listened to your upset friend. Find a way to notice and appreciate all the things you do for yourself and others.

**PARTNER:**

APPRECIATE EVERYTHING about your sweetie that you can. Actively communicate it with words, smiles and any form of pleasurable attention they love. Be specific. Thank your partner for taking out the garbage, walking the dog and washing the dishes. Thank them for their humor, perseverance, positive attitude, or whatever it is that you enjoy and admire about them.

You can even have an 'appreciation-off,' a fun game to out-appreciate the other. "I really appreciate your kindness." "No, I appreciate yours more!"

## The Heart of Your Emotions

In my formal education, I was taught that the heart is the mechanical pump of the circulatory system, an elegant, beautifully integrated, electro-chemical pulsating muscle. It is all that—and something else besides. Both literally and figuratively, the heart is home to our emotions.

This has been the view since time immemorial. I don't know of any indigenous people that doesn't take this as a given, and it's embedded in virtually every modern-day language, too. In

> And Love says, "I will,
> I will take care of you," to
> everything that is near.
>
> HAFIZ

tongue after tongue, people say their heart is full when they're feeling rich with love and that's it's broken when their love has been shattered. And it's not just positive feelings that the heart holds—it can also be hot with jealousy or rage.

Contemporary science is confirming this ancient and universal intuition about the heart-emotion link. It turns out that the heart is much more than a senseless hunk of living machine meat. It's an electrical energy generator, an emotional chemical factory, a highly responsive life support system, the basic soundtrack that helps coordinate your body's essential rhythms, and a generator of emotional energetic fields that affect ourselves and anyone around us.

Your heart is a producer of biochemicals that influence your consciousness and your feelings—thus it also acts as an emotional mediator. Let's say something scares you. Your fight-flight-freeze response kicks in, your heart starts to pound, and that drives you deeper into survival mode. Or you're sitting in a beautiful spot by the ocean, your heart lulled by the tidal sway into a slower beat, and you feel calm and contented.

At a biological level, the heart is a connection engine, too. It helps us bio-regulate with ourselves and others with its steady recurrent pattern and rhythm. Infants often have an immature system for keeping their heartbeat stable. Mom is a living, breathing pacemaker whose consistent heart rhythm helps her baby stay alive. Your heart tends to synchronize with nearby hearts that aren't your mama's or baby's—one more indication that we're wired to connect. Your heartbeat does the same for your own systems, helping coordinate and orchestrate your body's many rhythms.

When we use our sexcraft tools, we're leveraging our natural tendency to harmonize with ourselves and others. We're simply taking what is and making it conscious. When we think loving thoughts, act in caring ways and use other connection tools such as synchronizing our breath and sound with others, we're co-creating resonance. Whether it's with ourselves, our infant, our partner or our tribe, getting harmonic feels great.

Yanagawa Shigenobu, Illustrated shunga book, 1820

Our inner lives are awash in emotions. Complex and multi-faceted, they swirl about, stirred by the winds of our external experiences and shaped by the meanings we ascribe to those events. Learning to understand our emotions and manage them wisely is an ongoing challenge that most of us won't master in this lifetime. But we can make significant progress toward becoming a more emotionally intelligent and loving person.

Here's a straightforward way to understand all that complexity. This may be an over-simplification (or maybe it really is this simple?). Despite the many brain regions involved, your heart is the seat of your emotions and has two basic states. It's either open in love or it's closed, turned away from love. When it's open, you feel positive emotions like love, regard, respect, courage and passion. When it's closed, your mood is dominated by feelings like fear, shame, hurt and anger.

That's the basic choice we have in any given moment. Positive or negative. Love or fear. It's simple in principle to choose love, but not so easy in practice. And that's what staying open-hearted is—a practice! Choosing happiness, joy and positivity is a lifelong project.

I'm not suggesting you should never feel sadness, anger or grief. All feelings are valid and it's important to allow and acknowledge the full range of emotions.

Anonymous, *Lover's Dalliance*

Choosing to be open-hearted, toward yourself and others means consciously navigating towards being positive and loving. As a general principle, we can choose to have our inner gyroscope tilt towards joy. We can't always choose who we love, but we can choose to love.

## Sex, Love and Lust

Opening the heart is a life skill—and a bedroom skill, too. In saying this, I'm not suggesting you need to be in love with someone to have sex with them. There's nothing wrong with your being 'in like' or just 'in lust' with a sex partner so long as your choice is self-loving. So long as you're in alignment with your heart.

At the same time, the more you can open your heart to your partner and yourself, the better the sex will be. An ancient hard-wired pathway connects the heart and genitals. Whether it's a one-night fling or a life-time partnership, the best sex happens when your heart and genitals are connected and connecting.

As noted previously, production of oxytocin, the 'love hormone,' increases with high arousal and floods you as you orgasm. One reason why connected, open-hearted sex feels especially fulfilling emotionally and more delightful physically is that you're high on oxytocin. The hormone amplifies pleasure—and the more loving you're feeling, the more oxytocin you get.

You can have all kinds of erotic fun without a physical hard-on. But take the heart-on away and the experience will be diminished.

---

PLAY & PRACTICE

SOLO PLAY

### Self-Love Chakra Meditation

START WITH BREATHING, relaxing and centering.

If you're doing the practice without arousal, go right into the chakra meditation. If you're going for the erotic version, play with yourself first. Get moderately or very turned on.

When you begin the chakra meditation, you can start at the bottom with the root chakra and go up or vice versa.

Place one or both hands on each chakra. Breathe, sound and send love into each one until it feels filled with heart energy. Send loving thoughts, words and feelings into each center. Visualize the vortex getting brighter, larger and more open as you send love energy into it. Tune in to your sensations, vibrations and emotions. Take your time with each chakra, then move on to the next one.

If you're doing the sexual version, after all your chakras are buzzing with the vibration of love, return to self-pleasuring. Go for your orgasm(s) and envision a love wave moving through all your chakras.

In the non-sexual version, enjoy the sensations of having all of your energy centers open and pulsing with life and love energy.

### Mirror, Mirror On the Wall

Mirror play involves looking at yourself in a mirror while you do some sort of exercise. It sounds easy, but see what comes up when you actually do it.

There are innumerable ways to do mirror exercises. There is only one rule— no negativity allowed! Here's a simple way

*It is only with the heart that one can see rightly; what is essential is invisible to the eye.*

ANTOINE DE
SAINT-EXUPÉRY

to start. Look into your own eyes. Whisper sweet somethings to yourself. Send yourself love, admiration, appreciation, and more love. Notice what happens, how you feel and what you are longing to hear.

## The Seven Heartskills

The tools and skills of the heart in the Wholistic Sexuality model are loving intention, loving action, courage, forgiveness, witnessing, and giving and receiving.

### LOVING INTENTION

While being loving at every moment is a fine intention, if you're like most of us, you don't love anyone, including yourself, all the time and you never will. Even if you'll never completely reach that goal, you can still hold it as an intention. Being caring, respectful and honoring to yourself and others is a practice. The more you're able to remember your intention to love, the likelier it is that love will prevail, especially in situations where it doesn't come easily.

Having a general self-love intention includes things like choosing a positive station on the self-talk radio in your mind or looking at yourself in a mirror with love.

In the sexual realm, loving intention means that when you're having sex with yourself, you're doing so while holding a self-loving and self-pleasuring intention. You can have a small "this is a great way to de-stress" or a big "this is about healing my relationship with my sexuality" intention, but, at heart, it's about having a benevolent, positive, shame-free, self-caring foundation for your actions. It's about letting go of non-self-loving beliefs and stories.

Eric Gill
*Love*

---

SOLO & PARTNER PLAY

### Heart Meditation

YOU CAN DO THIS ALONE or with partners.

Begin your sex time with a simple heart meditation. Breathe into your heart. Imagine it filling with light and love. You can use words out loud or silently, such as, "I love me," "Love is all," "I open my heart" or "I love you." Feel your heart grow bigger, warmer and more open.

---

## LOVING ACTION

You practice loving action by choosing to act with care and respect toward all beings, including yourself. In the context of sex, love-in-action means loving yourself well by lavishing yourself with pleasure and positive attention. It means devoting adequate (ideally abundant) time and energy to your solo love practice. You can think of it as being a devotee to yourself.

Your self-love also includes making sexual choices that are right for you. If that includes having erotic partners, then loving conduct means interacting with them in ways that are respectful, caring and kind.

Don't ever do anything sexually that doesn't feel self-loving. This is your most important guidepost in the sometimes confusing land of erotic opportunity. When choosing who to share yourself with, what to do or not do, consider if your choice reflects a loving, caring attitude toward yourself. Ask yourself if your actions will increase or diminish your feelings of self-love. If it's the latter, then you're better off going solo.

Love-in-action also includes having an inner commitment to never having non-consensual sex: No violence, abuse or coercion and no taking advantage of anyone else. This includes not using others, no manipulating or lying to get sex, no 'scoring' and no revenge sex Let your erotic encounters always be about open-hearted connection, whatever else they may be.

PLAY & PRACTICE

SOLO & PARTNER PLAY

### Connecting Solo Sex and Love

START YOUR EROTIC SESSION by cupping your genitals in one hand and placing the other on your heart. Breathe into your hands, heart and sexy bits. Visualize a circuit or river of light filled with love energy and sex energy. Say

or think affirmations and positive intentions. During your solo-sex play sex, intermittently place one hand on your heart and repeat your intentions.

You can do this with partners, too.

Try variations!

Kunisada, *Untitled*

## Hot Loving Action

SOME WAYS TO PRACTICE self-love include:

- Begin your solo sex play with a heart meditation.
- Use all four languages of touch (nurturing, therapeutic, sensual, erotic).
- Set aside quality time for sex sessions.
- Make commitments to yourself regarding sexual self-care (example: committing to practicing safer sex with others).

PARTNER PLAY:

- All of the above.
- Share your desires with your partner.
- Say loving or appreciative words.

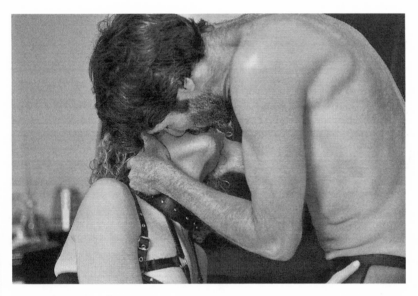

Vinette Perez, *Ascending*

> *Someday, after mastering the winds, the waves,*
> *the tides and gravity, we shall harness for God the*
> *energies of love, and then, for a second time in the*
> *history of the world, man will have discovered fire.*

PIERRE TEILHARD DE CHARDIN

## COURAGE

Courage doesn't mean you don't get scared. It doesn't mean you're foolhardy, either. Courage is the practice of choosing love over fear. When a firefighter runs into a burning building in order to save a baby, they're scared. They brave the flames anyway because someone needs to save the baby! You're being courageous when your love-in-action overrides your fears and anxieties and you do what needs to be done. When you act in the service of love.

*You gain strength, courage and confidence by every experience in which you really stop to look fear in the face. You must do the thing you think you cannot do.*

ELEANOR ROOSEVELT

Courage often isn't visible to others. Every day, we have opportunities to practice courage in ways no one else would notice. Every time you stretch your boundaries, experiment with new practices or push through your fear, you're being courageous.

Like your heart, your courage is a muscle. The more you use it, the stronger it gets and it becomes that much easier to use. Every time you do something brave, you're in service to your own growth and expansion—and you're arming yourself for the next battle.

Sexual courage doesn't mean doing things that are risky or foolish. It means having the courage to make responsible choices and to break free of scripts and

> **WORD NERD: COURAGE**
>
> THE ORIGIN of the word courage is related to the word for heart. From the Middle English *corage*, the Old French and the Latin *cor*, meaning heart.

beliefs that limit your self-expression and freedom. It takes courage to try new erotic activities, explore your desires and live into your sexual potential. For instance, if you don't currently have solo sex, be courageous and do it. If you do self-pleasure, break out of your habitual pattern and try something new. Perhaps you've never watched yourself. It takes courage to look in the mirror while you play with yourself but when you do, you'll learn things. Maybe you'll notice old postural habits that are limiting your flow of erotic energy. Perhaps you'll be surprised at how sexy your genitals look when engorged. Maybe you'll find that you don't get turned on by watching yourself. In many ways, it

*Courage is the most important of all the virtues, because without courage you can't practice any other virtue consistently.*

MAYA ANGELOU

doesn't matter exactly what you discover as you push through old limitations. The important thing is that you stretched your comfort zone. You were scared or anxious to try something new—and you did it anyway. Whether it's a new position or toy, exploring a previously forbidden body part or your darkest fantasy, your victory lies in having been courageous and not letting fear stop you.

## FORGIVENESS

It's not easy to be forgiving, whether toward ourselves or others. This is a difficult heart skill to practice. It's an important one, though. When you hold on to blame and other negative emotions, the only person you're really poisoning is yourself. You do yourself a service when you let go of blame and anger.

Forgiveness starts with oneself. Self-forgiveness and self-love are the first steps for us all. None of us is perfect. Accepting this about ourselves—letting go of unrealistic expectations, really—is an ongoing practice.

Titian, *Mary Magdalen Repentant*

When it comes to sex, most of us have made mistakes. (I know I have!) We may have regrets about what we did or who we did it with. We may have hurt or been hurt by others.

Sexual energy is a powerful force. Navigating it is like kayaking through class-four rapids. Since most of us didn't get good paddling lessons (or even a paddle), it's not surprising that our sexual past has included some floundering— or even foundering and crashing on the rocks. In the realm of sex, our mistakes can have serious consequences like unintended pregnancies, diseases, broken hearts, and betrayed trust. I'm not advocating bad behavior or irresponsibility here. Be responsible and respectful, and be careful. If you stay in integrity with your values and commitments (and practice safer sex and birth control), you'll be unlikely to have deep regrets.

*I am glad that I paid so little attention to good advice; had I abided by it I might have been saved from some of my most valuable mistakes.*

EDNA ST. VINCENT MILLAY

Whatever mistakes you may have made, start now to make amends where needed. Be compassionate to yourself and begin with self-forgiveness. See your past mistakes as opportunities to learn and practice compassion, and as your foundation for wise future choices.

Don't let past mistakes keep you from trying new things. Stick with your values, keep your commitments (especially to yourself), and your mistakes won't be disastrous. Learn to paddle in the shallow water so that, when you capsize (and you probably will), you'll get wet but not damaged.

The past is done. It's over. You don't have to forget it (in fact, you can't and shouldn't). But you can let go of negative stories and regret. Forgiveness opens the heart and enables us to love more skillfully, choose more wisely and feel more joy.

Susan Singer, *Che'*

## WITNESSING

To witness is to stand in open-hearted observation, suspending opinions, stories and judgments. In its biggest sense, witnessing means simply being present without feeling the need to do anything other than truly see what is. While for some, the term means to simply see and be present, for me, it includes doing so with an open, loving and compassionate heart.

First things first: When it comes to sex, witnessing does not mean watching! Witnessing is not about being a voyeur, it's a love skill involving empathetic, open-hearted, non-judgmental seeing. It includes not shaming anyone (yourself included) for their desires, fantasies and sexual choices. It means noting your erotic architecture without criticism or opinion.

As you go about your day, pause to be your own witness. When you pleasure yourself, let a part of you step back and watch without critique. If you notice old self- disparaging opinions or sex-negative stories arising, just notice what they are, without judgment. Let them go by stepping into the place of the compassionate observer. Being your own self-loving witness can help you re-format outdated programming and change your brain-station from 'Radio Fuck You' to a station of acceptance and love.

SOLO PLAY

### Witnessing and Forgiveness

START WITH A FEW DEEP centering breaths. Recall an instance from your sexual past where you feel regret, anger, blame, shame or other 'closed-heart' emotions about your behavior or choice. Notice any judgments and stories that arise. Take a mental step away into neutral territory and be your own witness. Remind yourself that what's done is done, that everyone makes mistakes and let it go. Use a *Wave Breath* to wash the pain away, allowing each ripple to expand your heart and release negative emotions. Invite your heart to open, imagine it swelling with love and compassion for who you were then. Grant yourself forgiveness.

THE LOVE YOU MAKE

## GIVING AND RECEIVING

Giving and receiving are heart skills you can cultivate. Many people are better at one than the other. Generosity, giving and serving are yang skills while being open-hearted and receiving are yin abilities. You want to be able to practice both, sometimes simultaneously. In fact, your solo sex is the perfect opportunity to be both. How much pleasure can you give yourself? How much can you receive? The best solo sex happens when you do both abundantly.

*Feeling gratitude and not expressing it is like wrapping a present and not giving it.*

WILLIAM A. WARD

In addition, the best partner sex happens when everyone is generously giving and receiving. Pleasure your playmates profusely! Erotic generosity includes lots of active touch, enthusiastically doing the other person, and giving your lover lots of what they like best.

*The greatest thing you'll ever learn is just to love and be loved in return.*

EDEN AHBEZ

There's a flip side to this: Receive pleasure generously. Give enthusiastic feedback using sound and movement to clearly demonstrate how much pleasure your partner is giving you.

'T'is better to give and to receive!

---

## Succulent Summary

### Your Heart Tools

- LOVING INTENTION: Holding the intention to be loving, respectful and honoring is a foundational attitude and ongoing practice.

- LOVING ACTION: Acting on your loving intention. Behavior in service of love.

- COURAGE: Consciously choosing love over fear.

- FORGIVENESS: Living the adage that "To err is human, to forgive divine."

- WITNESSING: Observing. Suspending judgment in a context of compassion.

- GIVING AND RECEIVING: The capacity to be balanced in our yang and yin aspects. Letting open-heartedness flow in both directions.

Michael Fingesten, *Improvisations on the Theme of Love*

## Integrating Self-Love and Sex

It's totally possibly to have sex without love, but for sex to be good it has to be, at a minimum, respectful and caring. Of others, yes, but most of all it has to be loving of yourself. When you're sexual from an underpinning of strong self-love, you'll make wise choices about partners and boundaries. You'll be empowering yourself to grow into your full erotic potential.

As far as partner sex goes, there's nothing wrong with having sex solely for the pleasure of the encounter, just as there's nothing wrong with choosing to only share your sexual energy within the bonds of a committed relationship. Whether you prefer to be sexual only with a life-mate, with a network of intimated committed partners, or with less committed or short-term playmates, I encourage you to make all your connections heart-centered.

When you're sexual with another person, you're sharing intense primal forces. Just because we live in a culture that plasters shallow erotic imagery over every surface doesn't mean we need to succumb to a model of disconnected sex. In my book (my life book, not this volume), sex is about connection. You do that by choosing to be loving, even if that doesn't mean love in the romantic soul-mate sense.

Be committed to loving yourself and self-honoring, self-loving choices will naturally follow. Respect yourself and you'll only choose partners who respect themselves and you.

However you decide to 'do it,' do it with an open heart.

SOLO & PARTNER PLAY

## Having a Love-gasm

DURING YOUR SEX PLAY, consciously bring your arousal into your heart. Use your favorite tools (such as breath, sound, intention, imagination) to move your erotic energy to your heart chakra. It may help to put your hand there. If you're with a partner, put your hands on each other's hearts. Think loving thoughts. Focus on the word love. Imagine your heart filling and swelling with love-light. As you tip into orgasm, visualize the orgasmic energy pulsing through your heart. Enjoy your love-gasm!

*Visit GetSexCrafty.com for more practices such as:*
- *The "I Love You" Game*
- *Positivity Day*
- *Partner Nurture Time*
- *Your Perfect Lover Inventory*
- *Discovering Your Perfect lover*

Doug Metzger, *Skin to Skin*

In many ways, the heart is a yin organ. You can't force it to open nor can you make love happen. But you can choose your intention and your actions. When you intend to be loving, you have a compass for your ship that makes it easier to steer towards love, especially when you're feeling challenged by difficult emotions.

You cannot rule your heart, which ultimately loves as it will. But you can consciously make the choice between love and fear by asking yourself questions like, "What's the most loving way to be right now? Is this self-loving? Is this in service to the people/person I'm in relationship with?"

*And when you get down to it… that's the only purpose grand enough for a human life, not just to love—but to persist in love.*

SUE MONK KIDD

When you practice your love skills and strengthen your heart tools, it makes it easier to choose love—to make the simple yet difficult choice, over and over, that changes everything.

# CHAPTER FOURTEEN

# SPIRIT MATTERS

*We are not human beings having a spiritual experience.*
*We are spiritual beings having a human experience.*

PIERRE TEILHARD DE CHARDIN

## Spirit Matters

ALL PRIMAL CULTURES RECOGNIZED THE SACREDNESS OF SEX.
After all, sex makes life, so how could it be anything other than sacred? In
cultures that especially revered sexuality, Eros was considered a path to connect
to the gods and goddesses, to the Divine. Sex was considered a prayer and the
fertility that often resulted a blessing.

Many of these cultures used similar practices and techniques to draw on
the power of Eros in service to the sacred. The approaches I lay out in these
pages are drawn from paths cultures
throughout time have taken to honor the
spiritual in matters of the body and the
bedroom. These techniques and tools are
designed to utilize erotic energy for sacred
purposes, including
blessings, manifestation and enlightenment. And, not
least of all, when your sex is integrated with your spirit,
it can lead to not just transcendent mind-blowing sex,
but a personal experience of the Divine.

> *The degree and kind of a man's*
> *sexuality reach up into the*
> *ultimate pinnacle of his spirit.*
>
> FRIEDRICH NIETZSCHE

Writing about spirit and spirituality is in some
ways the trickiest challenge in this book. I want this
information to be accessible and useful to everyone,
no matter what their beliefs. So, let me start with
this invitation. If my approach to understanding
spirit and sacredness doesn't work for you,
please feel free to translate it into terms that do.

Sheri Winston, *Spirit*

If you don't relate to these concepts, simply think of sacredness as what makes things special, cherished and unique. Or, if the notion of spirit doesn't resonate for you at all, then disregard this domain entirely.

For me, spirit is real and something to be celebrated. When I refer to spirit, I'm not talking about religion or even spirituality. Perhaps because of my decades as a practicing midwife, I think of spirit as life's incorporeal aspect, as the part of you that entered your body-mind when you took your first breath. It's the magic spark that animates you beyond the mechanistic physical plane. But it's not just in you—it's in everything. When I write about connecting to spirit, I mean connecting to the sanctity of life, the holiness of all beings, and the sacred fire within you. It's the Divine not as a separate, superior being, but as the mysterious force that's manifest in everything.

Spirit is what the Native American Lakota people call Wakan Tanka, the 'Great Mysterious Power' or the 'sacredness that resides in everything.' It's the ineffable energy that, among other things, connects the carnal erotic to the mystery beyond matter.

*The first peace, which is the most important, is that which comes within the souls of people when they realize their relationship, their oneness with the universe and all its powers, and when they realize at the center of the universe dwells the Great Spirit, and that its center is really everywhere, it is within each of us.*

NICHOLAS BLACK ELK

We use our sexcraft spirit tools to honor spirit incarnate and to sacralize sex (or to remind ourselves of its inherent divine dimension). Your spirit tools are sacred intention, sacred sound, meditation, manifestation, ritual and ceremony.

Mughal style miniature

## Sacred Intention

Holding the intention to make something sacred is your most basic spirit tool. You can use your other spiritual tools to make your intention more concrete (which often helps), but the essential skill is to intend your practice to be sacred.

As we've seen, intention is a mind tool. Here we use it in the service of spiritual purposes. Simply hold the intention for something to be spiritual or sacred, and that's what it becomes. It's a simple yet profound (and almost miraculous-seeming) practice. Use sacred intention whenever you have sex, be it solo or partnered, a quick snack or a prolonged feast. Define a sacred purpose for your pleasure, create a consecrated container, touch on your sacred intention during your erotic activities, appreciate and affirm the holiness of your erotic actions—and it can be transformative.

You can dedicate your erotic energy and your orgasms to a spiritual purpose such as enlightenment, blessing or healing.

If this path appeals to you, try using your spirit tools and see what happens. The choice to create sacred ground for your sex is yours.

> *"Sacred space" is another way of saying "with intention."*
>
> S. KELLEY HARRELL

DIVINE PLEASURE

## Using Sacred Intention to Make Sex Divine

BEFORE YOUR NEXT SEXUAL ENCOUNTER, take a few moments and create a spiritual intention for your experience. Here are a few suggestions:

- Simply repeat silently in your mind, "Sex is sacred, my body is sacred, my genitals are sacred."

- Think, say or write sexual spiritual intentions. Examples:

  *All the pleasure and love created here is in service of the sacred.*

  *I am open to the Divine.*

  *I feel all the sacred pleasure I'm capable of.*

  *I'm connected with the life force.*

  *Whatever happens inside this sacred space is holy.*

Kunisada shunga

## Creating Sacred Ground

- CREATE A SACRED sex space by drawing an imaginary boundary around your room or bed. Sit in the center and use your finger to draw an imaginary circle.

- WALK IN A CIRCLE around your space while speaking or thinking your intention.

- CREATE A SACRED SPACE by making a real boundary. Paint a circle on your floor, or use a special rug or specially designated mattress as a sacred space. Consecrate this space and dedicate it to your spiritual practices, including sexual ones.

- IF YOU DON'T RESONATE with the idea of sacredness and spirit, make your space special by using it only for erotic practices and experiments.

- ENGAGE YOUR SENSE of smell by burning incense, sage or sweetgrass in your room. If smoke is not for you, try aromatherapy spritzers. Hold a spiritual intention as you scent your space. Examples: "This scent is clearing negativity," "This smoke welcomes in spirit."

---

*"All acts of love and pleasure are her rituals."*

*From a chant attributed to* DOREEN VALIENTE

---

## Sacred Sound

Sacred sound is any sound used in the service of spirit. Many traditional spiritual practices use spoken prayer, chants, toning and instruments like drums, rattles or flutes. While any sound can be sacred if you intend it to be, certain sound vibrations are particularly potent such as the full-body resonance of singing bowls and the ethereal sound of chimes.

Bijou Xochi, *Yab Yum*

SUCCULENT SEX CRAFT

DIVINE PLEASURE

## Making Sacred Sound

- TAKE A FEW MOMENTS and say a prayer for your erotic experience.

- CHANT a sacred chant.

- TONE. Try the traditional Tantric sounds for each chakra (see page 168-169). Or create and explore your own versions.

- SING A SONG that speaks to you of the sacredness of your body, your sex play, your divinity and that of others.*

- FIND MUSIC that feels sacred to you and play it during luscious lovemaking sessions. I'm a big fan of Qawwali, the ecstatic devotional music of the Sufis. Play music that carries you away.*

- USE SACRED SILENCE. Silence provides the space for greater awareness and expansion of the erotic energy.

*See our online resources at SucculentSexCraft.com for suggestions. Feel free to add your favorites.*

*"Help, Thanks, Wow: The Three Essential Prayers"* Book title by ANNE LAMOTT

## Meditation

The term 'meditation' means different things to different people. As used here, it means any practice you use to create an altered state of reality, that gets you into trance. Since you now know that arousal is a trance state, it's totally reasonable to treat your arousal experience as a meditation practice.

While many people think of meditation as a quiet and still practice, you can also do active moving meditations, sound meditations—and arousal and orgasmic ones. You can use your arousal energy for secular meditation purposes such as getting centered, clear and present, becoming more embodied, relieving stress, promoting relaxation and alleviating anxiety. You can also use it as a spiritual practice to connect to the Divine, to the life force, to your own sacredness and that of your partners. Meditation can also help you open your heart and become more loving and compassionate—powerful practices that can enhance your erotic life.

You can also practice *medibation**, sexual self-pleasure dedicated to getting deeply entranced. Of course you can share sacred erotic trance with others, too.

---

* This term was coined by former porn actress and 'sexecologist' Annie Sprinkle to describe the combination of meditation and masturbation.

## Arousal Meditation

DO THIS AS A HANDS-OFF PRACTICE or get aroused the old-fashioned way. Orgasms are optional, as always. Try it both with and without climaxes. Men, try it with and without ejaculating.

Go to your sacred space or set the intention to be in sacred space. Choose a sacred intention to focus on.

Get comfortable, close your eyes and get centered.

START BY ACTIVATING YOUR IMAGINATION. Imagine a current, recent, distant or imaginary fantasy scene that involves the hottest sex you've ever had or can dream up. Use all your senses. Take the time to see the details, feel the textures and temperatures, and to taste, smell and hear everything. Let yourself become absorbed in the scene. If you're doing this hands-on, go all out with your self-pleasuring. Involve your whole body as well as your most sexy bits. Remind yourself that this is sacred.

Take the arousal that you're generating and visualize it. See a red light ball of pulsing sexual energy that nestles in your pelvis. Feel the throbbing heat. Relax into your arousal. Intermittently repeat your sacred intention.

Use your favorite breathing, sounding and pelvic floor muscle-pulsing arousal techniques. Use your tools to expand the energy ball. Play with it while focusing on your intention.

Bring your awareness to your belly, expanding the energy ball. See it rising up to fill your belly, then up to your chest, flooding your heart, your head and up beyond the top of your head. Imagine your erotic energy connecting to the disembodied Divine energy of the universe. Send it down, expanding it to include your legs and feet and then down into the ground. Visualize your light ball connecting to the embodied Divine energy of the earth, rooted into matter and tapping into planetary power. Remind yourself that you're experiencing holiness.

Run the energy up and down your whole body, from the earth to the sky and back again. Feel it connecting you to the pulse of all life, to the Divine Spark.

Play with yourself in whatever way expands the pleasure. If you're including orgasms, go for it. Dedicate your orgasmic energy to healing, empowerment or cosmic love.

CLOSE BY ALLOWING THE ENERGY to come down from a boil to a simmer, slowly calming and quieting the breath. Repeat your sacred intentions.

When you're done, lie quietly. Just notice and feel blessed.

## Manifestation

This word, too, has many definitions. For me, manifestation is the art of creating the physical embodiment of something intangible. The simplest way to make magic manifest is to visualize your goal. Another manifestation strategy is to create a concrete representation of your aim or intention. Either way, the practice is to focus your attention and intention on manifesting your desire.

One way to practice manifestation in service to your divine sexuality is by creating an altar that's a physical representation of your sacred erotic intentions and desires. Another is to create a temple space, an area especially dedicated to sexual spiritual practice. Try doing any of the practices in this book (or any you create) in front of your altar or in your temple space. It will feel different and have more power to transform.

*"you're a divine animal and you're beautiful*
*the divine is not separate from the beast;*
*it is the total creature that transcends itself"*

LENORE KANDEL

Alméry Lobel-Riche

## Your Altar to Eros

FIND A SPACE IN YOUR HOME for an altar dedicated to Eros. If it's something you don't want to leave up all the time, use a tray as your altar base so you can move it. Take it out when you want to use it and store it away when you wish.

What do you want to manifest? You may immediately know what you want to focus your magic on. If not, get still, close your eyes, do some deep slow breathing, quiet your chattering brain, and explore what you want to work on. Ask yourself questions such as 'What do I want to focus on?,' 'What do I want to heal?,' 'Where do I want to change?,' or 'How do I want to grow?'

Areas you may want to play with include connecting sex and spirit, reducing your sexual inhibitions, loving your genitals/body, loving your whole self, seeing the Divine in all or the sacredness of your sexuality. After you have an answer, create an altar or a special spot with items that call your intention and aim to mind.

*Every desire of your body is holy;*
*Every desire of your body is Holy.*

HAFIZ

Let's say you decide you want to heal your relationship with your genitals and see them as beautiful and divine. You might start by laying down a plush piece of burgundy velvet fabric to represent your delicious blood-filled flesh. Next you might add a seashell if you have a yoni, or an oblong rock or crystal if you have a lingam. Add a red candle to represent the heat and light of your sexual parts. Fill a crystal glass with clear water to represent your sexual fluids and 'going with the flow.' Bring beautiful flowers (real ones or a picture)—the sexual parts of plants are a great reminder of the beauty of your own sexy parts.

What else? Whatever works for you. Perhaps a poem or written affirmations. How about a mirror? Can you draw, paint or otherwise create a lovely image of your luscious loins? You can always add to, subtract from or change your altar. In fact, I recommend doing so—it's a great way to keep it a living representation of how you're changing and growing.

Now that you have your altar, use it. Pause there before your sex sessions. Light your candle. Chant a love song to your lovely bits. Meditate on your gorgeous engorgeable genitals. Go back to your altar again after you're done doing. Shower yourself with gratitude for having a body with such exquisite pleasure parts.

What else can you do? Whatever you want. Whatever you desire to manifest. Whatever magic you want to play with, you have the power to create.

## Your Sacred Sexy Temple

Perhaps you have a space in your home that you can dedicate to pleasure and beauty. If so, great! If you don't you can create a pop-up temple space. Here are some ideas for both kinds of temples.

### A PERMANENT TEMPLE SPACE

How fun is it to have a space just for pleasure? Way fun! Paint the walls a warm sexy hue. Magentas, pinks and purples are sensuous colors. Hang luscious fabrics. Put up erotic art. Make sure there are no electronics in your temple. This is a television, computer and phone-free space!

Create a soft yet firm play space. Put a futon on the floor or have a big, very firm bed with luxury linens. Add lots of pillows—big, little, soft, firm. Special sex cushions are more than a nice touch—they add tremendous options for positions and activities! Make space for beautiful altars—candles, flowers, feathers, seashells, artwork. Don't forget to include a way to have music in your pleasure temple.

### A TRANSIENT TEMPLE SPACE

With ingenuity, you can quickly and easily transform a space into a temporary temple. The key is to make it easy to transition the space to temple and then back again. Make a 'Temple in a Box' by putting all your special things in a bin so you can quickly set up your sacred space and then hide it away.

Here are some ways to easily change a bedroom or den into a magical sex temple.

Drapes can be strategically placed, so with a whisk of fabric you close off the parts that don't belong in your sanctuary. Curtain off your desk, the TV, the laundry or anything mundane that could distract you from being present to bliss. Folding screens can deliver the same effect. Toss decorative fabrics over everything that doesn't belong in your temple so your work,

Anonymous 18th century print

the kid's toys, the computer or the pile of mail are hidden from sight.

*continued on next page*

*continued from previous page*

YOU'LL NEED A PLAYGROUND. Consider a futon couch or sofa bed to quickly shift a living room into a playroom. A floor mat especially designed for sex can be rolled out. A blow-up mattress is an option and even cushy exercise mats can work. If you're using your bed, have a special coverlet that you only use for temple time. Use your imagination and see if you can create a comfy nest to play and relax in.

Candlelight can't be beat for its beautiful energy (and everyone looks better in the glow of flames). Create safe candle spots so you don't have to worry about knocking them over. Practice safe illumination! Can't manage that? Use flameless candles. Also have your lights on dimmer switches, or have a lamp or two with colored bulbs that only get turned on when you do. Add a salt lamp or two for the warm glow and enlivening negative ions.

Now that you've set up the visuals, add elements that enhance the pleasures of your other senses. Not strategically located by a burbling stream or waterfall? Buy or make a fountain and add the energy and

Anonymous 18th century print

sounds of the splashing flow. The wafting scent of incense or naturally scented candles instantly transforms the energy of a room. Turn on the music and enjoy the power that sound has to shift the ordinary into the special. Or leave the music off and enjoy your personal sounds of pleasure.

Gather your sacred and sensual playthings in bins and baskets or on trays. Sex toys. Feathers, fur and other sensual toys. A silk blindfold, bondage tape, massage oil . . . you get the idea.

When you're almost ready to go, set out a tray of tasty snacks like fruit and nuts (and chocolate). Have plenty of water (don't forget the bendy straws—hydration is so important!) and perhaps a glass of wine or fruit juice.

Now you're ready to go. And come!

---

*How do we remain faithful to our own spiritual imagination and not betray what we know in our own bodies? The world is holy. We are holy. All life is holy.*

TERRY TEMPEST WILLIAMS

---

## More Erotic Altar Ideas

PLACE THINGS on your Eros altar that represent:

- THE FOUR ELEMENTS (a candle, a feather, a stone and a bowl of water)

- ANIMALS that you feel a deep connection with

- Representations of your ANCESTORS—pictures, a drawing or their name

- DEITIES, SACRED BEINGS, SPIRIT GUIDES

- RELIGIOUS SYMBOLS

- NOURISHMENT—food like a perfect peach or luscious chocolate. Seeds. An image of food.

- NATURE—flowers, crystals, rocks, shells

- PERSONAL MEMENTOS

- EROTIC ART

- JOURNAL AND PEN

- DRAWING PAD AND ART MATERIALS

## Ritual and Ceremony

All human cultures throughout time have used ritual and ceremony to induce altered states of consciousness, create group resonance and establish a sense of collective identity. The terms ceremony and ritual are related and sometimes used interchangeably, but they're different. Ritual is more about the container. It's a process, practice or pattern of behaviors and actions with a sacred purpose. Ceremony is more about the formalized and traditional aspects of worship, reverence or propitiation.

> *Ritual itself is not sacred, but it allows the sacred to emerge.*
>
> NINA HARTLEY

Repetitive chanting, drumming, and dancing, along with fasting, symbolic actions and other techniques are among the many tools communities use to create a collective trance state.

Unfortunately, over time these rituals sometimes become entrenched traditions governed by inflexible rules, defined by authorities and requiring unconditional obedience.

Ritual and ceremony have a potent impact on the human psyche. If we go beyond prescribed behavior, we can extract the power of ritual without being constrained by strictures and sanctions.

We can create our own rituals and ceremonies and use them to serve our own desires. In the sexual context, this means using these time-honored processes to create a sense of purpose and imbue our erotic activities with sacredness.

The power isn't in the tradition. It's in the practice.

---

DIVINE PLEASURE

## Transition Ritual

It's often difficult to shift from regular life to sex life. Simple rituals can make it easy. Here are a few suggestions:

- Take a luxurious shower or a long, soaking, dimly-lit bath. Make it a ritual cleansing. Imagine the water washing your worries and cares away and preparing you for pleasure.

- Do whatever works for you to shift your state: Meditate, chant, do mind-body practices, dance.

- Spritz with aroma. (If you're prepping for partner play, make sure it's one they love).

- Light special candles (naturally scented ones, perhaps).

- Light incense or burn sage or sweet grass.

- Put on sultry, lush music

- Dress for the occasion. How will you adorn yourself? A silk robe and velvet stockings? A simple loosely-draped sarong? Latex or leather?

- Ritually undress for the occasion.

- Close the doors to your temple space.

---

*Spiritualizing sex is actually a movement of energy—feeling and emotion—that rises within you and moves into your sexual physicality as an alive, tender, erotic, or passionate expression.*

ALEXANDRA KATEHAKIS

## Sex Rite

IF YOU'VE CREATED AN ALTAR, use it every day or every time you have sex (alone or partnered). Do your ritual in a similar way as repetition over time imbues your actions with power.

While there is no one right way to do ritual, here's a sequence you might follow, with some suggestions for each segment.

- CREATE A CONTAINER. Set energetic and physical boundaries. Light candles in the four corners of the room. Walk in a circle around your sacred space with a stick of burning incense. Use a piece of yarn and lay out a circle. Draw an imaginary circle with your finger. Create an altar that represents your intentions.

- OPENING. Sit and take centering breaths. Light a candle on the central altar and put the incense stick in a holder there. Open your heart, mind, body and spirit.

- CALLING IN: Call in the four directions, the earth and sky, the ancestors, your spirit guides, or sacred powers.

- CONNECTING. Connect to the powers you've invited in. Talk to them, sing to them, send them love.

- GETTING ALTERED. Use any of your sexcraft tools to get entranced. Sing, breathe, visualize—do whatever does it for you.

- RELEASING. Let go of blocks, old negative stories and useless inhibitions using your mind and body tools of breath, sound, movement, intention and imagination. Use your breath to let go by breathing out what you want to release and drawing in what you want to replace it with. Use manifestation by writing what you want to release on a piece of paper and then burning it.

- MAKING MAGIC. While self-pleasuring or sharing partner pleasuring practices, think or speak your sacred intentions. Intermittently bring your awareness to your altar to focus your intentions. Dedicate your orgasm(s) to manifesting your intention.

- THANKING. Say words of gratitude—to your body, for your life, to your partner, to the world.

- CLOSING. Thank and release the directions, the earth and sky, the ancestors and the other beings.

- OPENING BOUNDARIES. Blow out your altar candle, snuff your incense. Walk in a reverse circle, blowing out the candles as you go. Pick up your yarn or unwind your imaginary boundary.

DIVINE PLEASURE

## Finding Your Inner Erotic Priest/ess

**SOLO PLAY:**

THIS GAME IS MUCH LIKE your hot date with yourself, only the emphasis and intention are slightly different. This time, you're calling forth your own inner sexual priest/ess. Imagine that a sacred sexuality priestess or priest will be coming over to enact an erotic ritual. How would you prepare yourself and your space for this sacred sexual encounter? How much time would you dedicate?

Here is an example—feel free to create your own version.

BEGIN BY SETTING UP YOUR SEXUAL SANCTUARY SPACE. Next, prepare yourself. See *Creating Your Erotic Temple* and *Transition Rituals*, earlier in this chapter.

SET A CONSCIOUS INTENTION. Have it reflect the sacred nature of your play. Use that as a mantra—a phrase or idea to repeatedly focus on throughout your solo sex ritual.

INVITE YOUR INNER PRIEST/PRIESTESS to emerge. Begin with simple breathing and being present. Cue up your soundtrack and dance or move in some way.

As you continue your erotic encounter with yourself, move more fully into an improvisation of breath, sound, movement and opening to the sexual energy. Play with yourself in a leisurely fashion, honoring and celebrating your pleasure. Frequently remind yourself of your intention, your divinity and your connection to yourself and Spirit.

If you're orgasmic, move into your orgasmic eruption(s), dedicate your pleasure to yourself and then to the All. If not, relax into your pleasure and just ride the wave of delight. End in gratitude.

I ENCOURAGE YOU to make this a regular practice in your life. Vary the ritual—or not as you see fit.

**PARTNER PLAY:**

In this version of the ritual, each partner plays the role of the priest/ ess for the other. You create shared intentions and then breathe, play and dance together

William Bouguereau
*Faun and Bacchante* (detail)

## Finding the Divine Lover Within

THERE ANY MANY WAYS to use guided imagery. One option is to go on imagined interior journeys of discovery. Here's one that can bring you into contact and connection with your inner Divine Lover.

BEGIN WITH YOUR BREATH, allowing yourself to get centered and relax. Take your time.

On your inner movie screen, see yourself walking on a path. Notice the setting. Appreciate the details as you move along the trail.

You come to a doorway. Take the time to note the details of your door. What does it look like? What's it made of?

When you open the door, you'll see a stairway. Again, take the time to tune in to the details. Does it go up or down?

With each of the next ten breaths, ascend or descend your stairs. Breath one, the first step. Breath two, the next. Slowly move along your staircase, breathing your way up or down.

With the tenth step, you arrive in your beautiful, perfect, safe and sacred space.

Susan Singer, *The Bliss of It All!*

It's the ideal place for lovemaking. Is it indoors or out? Notice the setting. Appreciate the details. Delight in your special inner temple. Get comfortable.

You notice that you're not alone! There's someone else there. Your Divine Lover. A Deity/God/Goddess/Beautiful One is there with you. Imagine this being in whatever form works for you. (Multiples count, too!) He, she or they come to you, smiling and full of love. They sit in front of you. Take their divine being in, appreciating all the details.

Ask them anything you want. Listen for their answer. Repeat. Continue until you feel complete.

If you choose, you can engage with them more actively. You can embrace, be nurtured, be stimulated, be worshiped …whatever you need, they're there to give you. Take your time. Imagine the sensations and feelings. Enter into the experience as you engage with your personal erotic deity.

*continued on next page*

*continued from previous page*

WHEN YOU FEEL COMPLETE, give them a gift that communicates your gratitude. Open your hand and receive their gift in return. Thank them.

IT'S TIME TO RETURN TO THE WORLD, but know that you can come back any time.

WALK BACK OUT OF YOUR SPECIAL PLACE, back to the stairs. Take a breath with each step. At the top or bottom, go back through the doorway, closing it behind you. Your inner temple is safe and secure.

WALK BACK DOWN YOUR PATH.

TAKE A FEW MORE DEEP BREATHS, bringing yourself back into your body and into the room. Take your time. When you're ready, wiggle your fingers and toes, then gently stretch. Uncover and open your eyes.

You may want to write or do artwork about your journey, your temple and the Divine Lover you met there.

*Humans are amphibians…half spirit and half animal…as spirits they belong to the eternal world, but as animals they inhabit time. This means that while their spirit can be directed to an eternal object, their bodies, passions, and imaginations are in continual change, for to be in time, means to change. Their nearest approach to constancy, therefore, is undulation—the repeated return to a level from which they repeatedly fall back, a series of troughs and peaks.*

C.S. LEWIS

PLAY & PRACTICE

DIVINE PLEASURE

## Partner Play: Genitals Need Love, Too!

Everyone wants to be loved. Genitals especially need love, care and tenderness after all the flak they've gotten for millennia.

Make a ritual around adoring your partner's pleasure parts. Gaze at it lovingly. Shower it with flower petals. Anoint it with sweet sensuous oils. Give it little kisses. Share a shower or bath and wash every speck of their special parts. Say out loud how beautiful their sexy parts are, how sacred and divine! Give your sweetie the gift of showing and telling them how much you enjoy, appreciate and desire their genitalia.

## Healing the Pelvic Temple

SACRED RITUAL CAN BE USED in the service of holy healing.

Create your healing space. Get comfortable. Close your eyes or put on your blindfold.

Begin by taking deep, slow breaths. Let your breathing center you in your body.

Bring your awareness to your breath. Watch as it flows in and out. Feel the ebb and flow as it enters and leaves your body. Gradually calm your breathing, allowing it to deepen and slow. Each in-breath draws in life energy and vitalizing oxygen. Allow energized

Shunga, *Genital Love*

relaxation to flow in. Each exhale releases tension, allowing your muscles to get soft, heavy and loose. Let your exhale carry away all your thoughts.

As you continue your deep, rhythmic breathing, begin to imagine a stream of light pouring through you, flowing in and out, filling you with warm vibration. Send it up and then down. Imagine that the stream is pooling in the warm dark center of your pelvis. Breathe it into the bowl of your bones.

Tune in and feel sensations. Notice how the energy shows up for you. Is there light or dark? Is it hot or cool? Is there a color? How does it feel? Play with the sensations of the energy flow.

Imagine it spiraling around your pelvic bowl. Breathe. Visualize the movement. Notice the sensations. Inhale pleasure and healing energy. Exhale pain and stress. Inhale freedom and flow. Release blockages, inhibitions and fears.

When you're ready, start to move the energy back up your body, feeling it move with your breath, spiraling up through your belly, your chest and back to your throat, and then in and out through your mouth and nose.

Linger as long as you like. When you're ready to re-enter the world, wiggle your fingers and toes. Stretch gently and then more vigorously. Slowly sit up, remove your blindfold and open your eyes.

You may want to journal or draw about your experience.

A variation on this theme is to add sexual arousal with optional orgasm(s) to your healing practice. To do so, after you've filled your pelvic bowl with lovely flowing energy, self-pleasure (or enjoy partner play). During your arousal, hold the healing intention. If you include orgasm, imagine that the orgasmic energy is bathing your pelvis with healing power.

# Succulent Summary

## Your Spiritual Tools

- SACRED INTENTION: Holding an attitude of sacredness or having a sacred purpose. Choosing to make a place or activity sacred or spiritual.

- SACRED SOUND: Sound in the service of spirit. Examples include spoken prayer, chanting and toning.

- MEDITATION: A practice used to enter an altered state of non-mundane reality.

- MANIFESTATION: Concrete representation of sacred intention, e.g., creating an altar. Utilizing intention to create reality.

- RITUAL: A practice or pattern of actions with a sacred purpose.

- CEREMONY: A formal or traditional rite, an established or customary religious or spiritual observance.

Your sexcraft spirit tools offer many gifts. They help you connect with your own holy self, forge profound bonds with others, enter into a felt sense of unity with the pulse of the planet, and experience divine union. When you imbue your sexuality with sacredness, you support both spiritual and embodied healing. Sacred sex provides a portal to enter a delightful domain of magic and wonder. And, oh yes—it can make for not just enhanced erotic experiences, but encounters that are awe-inspiring and transcendent.

Erotic Persian
Miniature (detail)

# CHAPTER FIFTEEN

# How To Be a Sexcraft Virtuoso

*Tell me, what else should I have done?*
*Doesn't everything die at last, and too soon?*
*Tell me, what is it you plan to do*
*with your one wild and precious life?*

MARY OLIVER

## On the Path To Becoming an Erotic Virtuoso

AS WE APPROACH THE END OF THIS BOOK, WE'VE COVERED ALL THE tools in your sexcraft toolkit. Now it's time to look at integrating them.

There are a number of levels of integration. The first involves getting to the point where you become fluent—you can automatically call on whichever skill you need at any given moment. Another level is about integrating your various tools with each other so you gain the synergies that come with playing multiple instruments simultaneously. In the first part of the chapter I'll provide an overview of the best way to 'hold' your practice and integrate your sexcraft tools.

The second part of the chapter lays out some advanced skills that require a sophisticated level of integration. These are the kind of thing a lifelong student of the erotic arts will want to explore. After all, even a master musician wants to go on learning new material.

The highest level of integration entails the ongoing process of integrating your sex life with the rest of your life. I'll touch on that at the end.

Girl Crimson, *Revolution*

# Mastering the Inner Game

Here's how to make it happen, knowing what you now know.

## BE A MAD SCIENTIST

To become a sexual virtuoso, all you really need to do is make up experiments and run them. Lots of them. Be in discovery as you explore your abilities. Be an 'inner-naut'—investigate who you are and what you're capable of. The most important question to keep asking yourself is, "What would happen if I do it this way or try it that way?" You are your own laboratory and perpetual researcher into your capacity for pleasure.

*If we knew what it was we were doing, it would not be called research, would it?*

ALBERT EINSTEIN

## NO RIGHT, NO WRONG

There is one thing I can't say enough, so I'll say it one more time. There is no right way to do anything. You can't do it wrong because there is no wrong—there are just things that help you connect to yourself and your sexual energy. Or don't. Your assignment is to discover what works for you.

*Flying is learning how to throw yourself at the ground and miss.*

DOUGLAS ADAMS

Be in inquiry. Know that if something doesn't work one time, it may work if you try it another time. If you don't have success with one approach, try something else.

Be patient and self-loving as you research the myriad ways you can connect to your own erotic energy. Hold the intention to become continually more skilled at expanding your ability to plug into your inner pleasure circuits.

## IT'S SEX *PLAY*

They call it sex play for a reason! The suggestions I make are only that—suggestions to use as fodder for your own creativity. Your mission is to play and practice, with pleasure as your trusty guide. Let your sexual improvisations be delightful, spontaneous frolics. Whatever the mood, be it racy or romantic, sacred or silly, loving or lascivious, do what delights you and brings you bliss. Focus on fun!

Shunga, *Women Putting Lubricant on Their Dildo*

## INTEGRATE, INTEGRATE, INTEGRATE

Try including more and more of your toolkit in your practice sessions. Add different tools as you go, starting with the ones that come most easily to you.

Take small steps and celebrate your successes. Add one new tool at a time until all (or at least many) of them become effortless to access. Keep experimenting and creating your own brilliant combinations of instruments. Keep at it and eventually you'll become fluent across a wide range of skills.

### GETTING THERE—FROM NOVICE TO ADEPT TO VIRTUOSO

How do you get better at a practice? That's right, by practicing. To achieve erotic mastery, you don't have to quit your day job—and you don't have to practice for eight hours a day, either (although that would be fun!). Yes, you have a life outside of sex. Yet it's also the case that the more you practice, the quicker you tend to learn.

Be creative in finding the time for play and discovery sessions. Sprinkle mini-practices throughout your day. Add an extra 15 minutes to your coffee break and make it a mini-orgasm break. Regularly set aside a generous time slot for more serious practice. Find ways to find time. Prioritize your pleasure!

### THINGS COME UP (AND NOT IN A GOOD WAY)

There will probably be times during your erotic learning journey when you'll find yourself facing challenges. You may discover places in your body where your energy feels blocked. You may have areas of numbness or pain. You may be trapped inside negative stories that distract you from being present

*The only journey is the one within.*

RAINER MARIA RILKE

and feeling your pleasure. All this is normal—and surmountable. If you discover blocks or unconstructive beliefs, create a plan for dealing with it. Perhaps a series of erotic healing meditations or sexual rewiring rituals. You may want to write intentions related to integrating your heart and your sexuality—and then read them daily or before your erotic experiences. Consider adopting an energy practice like qigong. Therapy may be your answer, or connecting with partners who are skilled at loving and listening. Just remember—challenges are a normal part of the journey.

Ditto for mistakes and disappointments.

Use obstacles, mistakes and challenges as teachers and opportunities—don't let them derail you. Be unstoppable! Sexual transformation is a journey, not a destination.

Nor is a journey towards erotic empowerment something you have to do. It's a choice . . . an ongoing series of choices, actually. It's about choosing, again and again, to be open to discovery and to act in service to love.

Especially and foundationally, self-love.

## IT'S ABOUT THE EROTIC ENERGY

All your sexcraft techniques and tools are in service to a higher goal—becoming adept at managing and moving sexual energy. Erotic energy follows intention, imagination, breath, sound, blood flow, awareness and motion. You use your instruments to orchestrate the energy. If you play the piano, after you're finished you don't want someone saying that your playing only "showed good technique." You also want them to feel moved and inspired by your music. While technique is important, it's just the foundation for being able to create magical erotic-energy improvs.

Every time you play and practice, remember—you're getting more skilled at spontaneously and joyfully dancing with your sexual energy.

---

## *Succulent Summary*

### How To Become A Sexual Virtuoso

THE STEPS ARE FAIRLY SIMPLE, although it may take some time for you to get from where you are now to full virtuosity.

- TELL NEW STORIES. Identify your old stories about sex, figure out which ones don't serve you and replace them with ones that do.

- DISCOVER YOUR SEXCRAFT TOOLKIT. All the instruments are already there inside you.

- LEARN TO USE YOUR SKILLS. Remember, you are both the musician and your instrument. You have the capacity to make exquisite erotic music, to become fluent in the language of sexual energy.

- PRACTICE AND PLAY! As with any skill, to get better you'll need to practice, which in this case also means play. (Such a happy coincidence!) On the whole, what you do is less important than doing something, anything, that will help you learn. And remember—you don't need a partner to practice! The more you the practice—the more you play—the more skilled you become.

---

## A Short Course in Advanced Play and Practice

There are a virtually infinite number of ways to combine and integrate your sexcraft tools to create amazing sexual experiences. In the pages that follow, you'll find examples of ways to integrate your instruments along with some advanced practices that call on your more sophisticated sexual skills. As always, these are just serving suggestions!

## Turning It On, Turning It Up

HERE'S AN OUTLINE for a basic solo erotic session that incorporates many of your sexcraft tools into a single pleasure practice.

### CREATE A CONTAINER

Use ritual, altars and other sexcraft spirit tools to create a sacred space.

### CREATE CONSCIOUS INTENTION

Set your intention for the session. Some suggestions:

- *I am practicing techniques for turning my arousal energy on and then up.*
- *I am exploring my extraordinary pleasure potential.*
- *I am cultivating my sexual energy.*
- *I'm practicing self-love.*

### PLAY WITH PRACTICE

Start by focusing on your breath. Use your awareness to tune in. Begin in silence, then expand your exhale with pleasure sounds. Next, let your pelvis gently rock in rhythm. Then pulse your pelvic floor muscles, synchronizing them with your sounding breaths.

### USE 'VISION PLUS'

Close your eyes or put on a blindfold to turn your vision inward. Explore different images to see what helps you connect with your erotic energy. Among the options:

- Imagine your inner channel. Feel it expand as you breathe, sound, vibrate and see it opening wider.
- Visualize energy as light streaming through your body with each breath. See it get brighter, change color and fill you with illumination.
- Imagine liquid flowing up from your pelvic floor, surging through a channel in the center of your body up into your head. Then let it pour back down.
- Pulse your pelvic muscles. Notice that as you're squeezing, you're also pumping and plumping your pleasure parts.
- Imagine blood flowing into your genitals, expanding and engorging them. See them opening like a flower or puffing and plumping up.
- Imagine a string, like on a stand-up bass, that runs through your center channel. Visualize each breath and sound vibrating the cord.
- Use fantasy and erotic imagery to get turned on.

*continued on next page*

*continued from previous page*

### TAKE TIME TO TOUCH

Once you have the breath/sound/movement/ vision instruments playing, begin to slowly touch yourself. Start with the non-sexual areas of your body. Rub your belly, stroke your legs, hold your feet, fondle your arms, caress your face. Maintain the basic practices of breathing, sounding, seeing and feeling while you do this. Whatever you touch, send your breath there. Bring your inner vision to that specific part of you. Imagine energy flowing there. Send love, acceptance and care to all your parts (especially the ones you struggle to love and accept). Feel your whole body becoming more alive. Pay attention! Notice how it feels. Take as much time as you want to really touch yourself. Awaken your whole body.

Arthur Hacker
*The Cloud* (detail)

### TURN IT *ON*!

When your whole body feels alive and awake, you're ready to move to the more sexual areas of your body. Play with your breasts (if you have them) and nipples. Run your hands over the surface of your genitals. Keep breathing, making pleasure sounds and rocking, pumping and pulsing your bottom. Keep your vision focused inward. Continue to send your erotic energy into each precious part of you.

### GENITAL JOY

As you proceed to playing directly with your genitals, practice beginner's mind. Pretend you've never touched them before. Explore them as if they were a brand-new toy. Try touching them in new ways. Keep noticing how delightful it feels. Practice paying attention. Experiment. Play with your different sexcraft skills and tools as you self-pleasure and notice what happens. Keep using them as you build your arousal.

- Pay attention to how it feels when you send your breath into your genitals. Notice what happens as you draw that breath up your spine.

- As you breathe into your pelvis and genitals, you may start to see or feel heat and light pulsing. Envision them aglow, incandescent with light.

- You may feel increasing vibrations. Enhance that with sound and movement.

- Play with different sounds in tune with different hand strokes.

### OPTIONAL ORGASM

Have orgasm(s) or not, as you desire.

## EROTIC MEDITATION PRACTICES

Erotic meditations are practices that incorporate awareness and intention to take your sexual altered state out beyond your individual boundaries, beyond the limits of your self. Whether focusing on arousal or orgasm, these erotic meditation practices are for more than pleasure. They're about using erotic energy in transformative ways.

There are all kinds of reasons to do them. You can use them to cultivate health and vitality, or inner peace. Sexual meditations can connect your erotic energy with your heart, or help you develop love skills such as open-heartedness, compassion and forgiveness. You can play with integrating the four quadrants of mind, body,

*The human body and mind are tremendous forces that are continually amazing scientists and society. Therefore, we have no choice but to keep an open mind as to what the human being can achieve.*

EVELYN GLENNIE

heart and spirit. Your arousal energy can be channeled in the yin direction to help you relax into your arousal; it can take you deep into the yang polarity to intensify your excitement; or you can toggle between the surrender of yin and the tension of yang.

You might want to do an orgasmic meditation to get into a highly mindful turned-on state. You can use your erotic energy to practice being exquisitely aware of and present to your pleasure, which can amplify your pleasure to extraordinary dimensions.

Last but not least, you can use erotic meditations to have body-rocking, cataclysmic orgasms. The choice is yours!

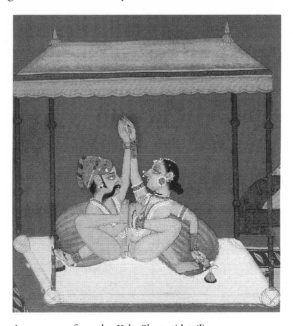

Anonymous, from the *Koka Shastra* (detail)

## Sexual Energy Cultivation

SO NOW YOU'VE BUILT UP all this sexual energy. You can release it in orgasm, but that's not your only option. You can direct that energy toward useful purposes that don't involve orgasm.

Here's one possible approach to cultivating sexual energy.

Begin as in *Turning It On, Turning It Up.*

Now set your intention. What do you want to use your sexual energy for? Ask yourself questions if the answer doesn't leap out at you. Do you feel tired and want some zest? Are you worried and tense and need to relax? Does something hurt? Do you feel emotionally or physically blocked somewhere and want to open it up? Identify what you want to focus on and concentrate for a moment on that intention.

Self-pleasure, using your favorite sexcraft tools to create juicy sexual energy. Play with your parts as you please.

Once you've reached moderate- or high-level arousal, start to focus your sexual energy on your intention. If something hurts, send the energy into that painful place to ease the pain. If an area feels tight or blocked, swirl the energy around to open the area. Move the energy to your solar plexus if you need vitality. Spiral the energy up your spine and swish it around inside your head to relax or be inspired. Roll the energy round your heart to practice self-love. Play with the energy as you please for as long as you like.

Once you feel complete, you can re-focus on directing your arousal towards having an orgasm or you can skip the climax and gradually let the energy settle and subside. Take some time to bask in your own glow.

Ideally, you'll repeat this practice often following whatever intention shows up for you at the moment.

## TO COME OR NOT TO COME

Having an orgasm when you do erotic meditation is entirely optional. Personally, I recommend giving non-orgasmic erotic meditation a place on your menu. Run some experiments and find out what happens when you go into your turn-on trance without taking it to its logical orgasmic conclusion.

That said, orgasm itself can also be used as a meditation practice. Getting ecstatic is a fine way to meditate. Here, you're going for the orgasmic crescendo and using its powerful primal energy for manifestation, renewal, health-promotion or a sense of communion. You can discover many dimensions of orgasm, including expanded ones where you stay in a bliss state for an extended period of time. (For men, this usually requires having non-ejaculatory orgasms.) Prolonged orgasmic states are intensely healing, vitalizing experiences—and they can also be intensely transformative.

If you want to manifest something, focus on your intention while rolling in orgasmic bliss. Or just experience the rapture without any goal or thought—just be intensely alive and overflowing with euphoria.

With or without orgasm, it's important to remember that erotic energy is very powerful. It can be transformative and, in this specific sense, magical. Use it to heal, grow and love.

AROUSAL MEDITATION

## Relaxing Into Excitement

START BY USING either your hands-on or hands-off sexcraft skills to get to low-level arousal. With slow breathing, relaxing sighs and gentle stretches, relax into your arousal.

Now fire up your erotic energy in any way you like. Bring your arousal up to mid-level. See if you can relax into your arousal by slowing your respiratory rate, doing deep sighs, and moving slowly.

Explore stillness by keeping your hand motionless on your genitals and refraining from rocking and pulsing. Get quiet. Go soft. Focus your awareness on pleasure and sensations. Allow thoughts and goals to drift away.

Next, rev up again, using whatever works to get you to high-level arousal (ideally including fast deep breathing, hot sexy sounds and sensual movements). Get near your almost-coming place, but don't go all the way there. (Guys, for you that means stopping just before you reach ejaculatory inevitability.) Once again, relax into your arousal by slowing your breathing, slowing or stopping your motions and tuning in to sensation and pleasure. Let your sounds get quieter or silent. Let go of any sense of urgency, performance anxiety or pressure to make something happen. Allow yourself to drift into bliss. Let the erotic energy move through you as it will.

Karoly Brocky
*Sleeping Bacchante*

You may want to do three rounds of this practice, revving your energy up, then relaxing into your arousal.

You can end by coming or not, as you prefer. If you choose not to climax, close by visualizing the erotic energy moving into your solar plexus or belly. This will transmute the energy into vitality.

# Going Further—Advanced Arousal and Orgasm Skills

When you've mastered your sexcraft skills, you can get into ecstatic states that seem implausible.

### Non-Ejaculatory Orgasm for Men

For men, orgasm and ejaculation are usually so entwined that it can be difficult to believe they aren't a single event. They are,

*Start where you are. Use what you have. Do what you can.*

ARTHUR ASHE

in fact, two separate processes. The first involves the events that propel sperm from the testes along the 'sperm trail' and ultimately out through the penis. This begins with a set of contractions that sends sperm out of the testicles. A separate prostatic event then sends those little swimmers out the penis. The squirting part is ejaculation. The second (and separate) process is the orgasm part—the waves of ecstatic pleasure that wash through your body.

Guys, you can learn to have the orgasm without the ejaculation. You'll feel the bliss waves throughout your whole body—and they can go on and on. In this amazingly pleasurable experience, you don't have an orgasm, you become it. You know how women can have multiple orgasms? This is the male equivalent.

Guys, I know you love to ejaculate, so don't get me wrong here. Ejaculating is a fine thing—and having ejaculatory choice is even better.

Choice means you can channel your orgasmic energy where you want it. You can send it inward to cycle instead of spill, or you can send it outward, either just energetically or with an ejaculatory release.

One obvious benefit is more pleasure. Why come for twenty seconds when you can come for twenty minutes?

Another benefit of bypassing or delaying ejaculation is longer sex sessions with a more sustained erotic charge. When most men ejaculate, they deflate (energetically and anatomically). What follows is called 'down time' for a reason! If you circulate that orgasmic energy instead of squirting it out, the fun doesn't have to stop.

Many Taoists believe that practicing non-ejaculatory orgasm is great for your health. They view all that sexual energy running through your body as vitalizing and rejuvenating, while ejaculation spills and depletes your chi. Western science is currently weighing in on the side that says it's healthier to ejaculate—although what they're comparing is men who don't squirt (and are probably not running energy) to men who do ejaculate. I don't know what's true here, although it's pretty clear to me that total celibacy—simply letting your sex energy stagnate in your pelvis—is probably unhealthy. Run your own experiments to see how you feel and go with what works for you.

## Non-Ejaculatory Orgasms

I ENCOURAGE YOU to start your ejaculatory experiments with solo pleasuring, so you can focus on yourself, practice self-awareness and apply your sexcraft skills without distraction. It's a lot simpler than partnered sex and you'll learn faster.

THERE ARE TWO BASIC STRATEGIES. One is to channel the orgasmic energy up your body instead of out your penis. The other is to let the orgasmic wave move out through your cock, flowing around your prostate, bypassing the semen ejaculation part of the process.

Either way, your first step is to develop your ability to identify the moment immediately before you reach the point of no return. It may take some practice to discover that precise pre-inevitability moment. That's okay—keep practicing!

Self-pleasure as usual. Stop stimulating yourself just before you reach the point when ejaculation would be inevitable. Squeeze and hold your pelvic

Giovanni Lanfranco, *Boy With Cat*

floor muscles for a count of ten. Keep breathing! Relax for a few moments, than resume self-pleasuring. Bring yourself back to the edge. Repeat several times.

When you're ready, go for a non-ejaculatory orgasm. Continue to self-pleasure, attending to the beginning of your orgasm sensations. As soon as you notice the little fluttering contractions that begin your orgasm, squeeze the PFMs around your prostate, relax everything else and stop self-stimulating. Try to hold the ejaculate back while simultaneously releasing the waves of orgasmic pleasure. Use breath and sound to relax into your pleasure while holding tight to your prostate with your pelvic floor muscles. Use breath, sound and visualization to channel the energy away from your genitals. Draw it up your body—up your spine, into your heart or out the crown of your head. Or, send the energy out your cock by imagining the erotic rush bypassing and flowing around your prostate.

You can end your session with an ejaculation or not, as you wish.

If you choose to squirt, go for it with gusto, pulsing your pelvic floor muscles and using breath, sound and movement to increase the length and intensity of your explosion.

*continued on next page*

*continued from previous page*

If you decide not to ejaculate, your sexual energy and engorgement will slowly subside over the next 30 to 60 minutes. You can relieve any continuing congestion by gently massaging your testicles and pulsing your pelvic floor muscles.

Most men need to play with these techniques for a while to become adept. You'll probably have the occasional "oops!" ejaculation. If that happens, don't fret about it. It's not like having an ejaculatory orgasm is a bad thing!

If you have a partner, at some point you'll want to add these techniques to your shared play. Communicate clearly so your partner shares your expectations and can support your non-ejaculatory goals. Your lover can help by stopping or decreasing stimulation as you approach your point of no return. They can also help you re-direct your energy by stroking upward from your lingam to your heart or up your spine.

When you've developed mastery, you'll be able to enjoy multiple non-ejaculatory orgasms and ongoing orgasmic waves. If your partner has comparable abilities, you can ride the waves together. Yum!

## HANDS-OFF, FULL-ON ENERGY ORGASMS

Is it possible to come without any genital touching, or for that matter any touching at all? It is! Sometimes called energy orgasms or 'thinking off,' it's not only possible, it's learnable.

You can learn to turn up your own arousal energy at will. You can open up your internal sexual energy channels and direct that luscious energy where you want it. When you can do that, you become much less dependent on your partners' technique. With practice (and play), you can get to the point where you can get aroused and even climax without needing direct stimulation.

*You have brains in your head.*
*You have feet in your shoes.*
*You can steer yourself in any*
*direction you choose.*

DR. SEUSS

This is doubly useful. It enables you to circulate ecstatic energy without physical stimulation and it's also a great a way to enhance your more usual manual, oral and genital erotic activities. The key is to find the inner paths that connect you to your erotic energy. You now have everything you need to discover them. Give yourself permission and go for it! (By the way, this is for both men and women.)

Here are some exercises for learning how to do this.

## Turn Up The Volume—Hot Energy Practice

HERE'S A PRACTICE to develop your erotic energy skills.

Get yourself to a high level of arousal by playing with yourself in your favorite ways. Hopefully you're now using your sexcraft toolkit fairly effortlessly as you play. When you reach high arousal, enhance your breath, release more sound and pump your PFMs. Rock your pelvis and undulate your spine. Tune in to your vibrations. Turn your vision inside and notice what you see. Imagine your nicely plumped-up genitals filled with hot light and pulsing with color. As you breathe in, visualize the light flowing up your body. As you exhale, see the light as a powerful wave pouring down you. Play with moving your arousal energy up and down.

You can alternate hands-on stimulation with hands-off energy play or do them simultaneously.

There's no need to have an orgasmic agenda here. Just play with the energy, notice what happens, and experiment to find out what amplifies it. You may have an energy orgasm or you may not.

As you become more adept with your erotic energy skills, run some more experiments:

• Start your play session without hands-on contact. Use only your hands-off tools. See how far you can go in your arousal. At some point, add your usual physical stimulation techniques.

• Reverse the experiment by starting with your regular stimulation techniques along with your favorite sexcraft skills to get to high-level arousal. Then shift to just your hands-off tools. In subsequent experiments, try making the shift at different levels of arousal.

Shunga
*Fish Penises*

## Crescendo Breath

IN THIS PRACTICE, you incorporate sound and breath, movement, intention and imagery to orchestrate your erotic energy to bring it an orgasmic crescendo. You pull your erotic energy up your body, spiral it inside your head, then surf the energy wave back down, sending it out your whole bottom in an orgasmic release.

Use this practice with or without genital stimulation. Try it at different levels of turn-on, or just before or during a physically stimulated orgasm.

Start with slow deep breaths, making a low full sound on the exhale. Pulse your pelvic floor muscles in rhythm with your breathing. Gradually accelerate. Keep sounding as you exhale, letting your sounds be super-sexy. As you breathe faster, allow your sound to rise in pitch until you're breathing fast and making short, high sounds. (Remember to keep the back of your throat open!) It should sound like you're about to have an orgasm, with an increase of tension, shorter breaths and rising sounds.

At the same time, imagine your erotic energy surging up your spine or inner tube until it reaches your head. At this point, you'll be doing deep, rapid breaths accompanied by high-pitched sounds. Pull your breath up as high as you can—visualize yourself pulling a bowstring taut. At the top, tighten your pelvic floor and belly muscles. Hold them and take a big slow inhale. Hold your breath and imagine the energy spiraling around inside your head. Allow the pressure to build until you can't stand it anymore.

Let your breath out slowly with a big, open, descending sound as you imagine the energy rolling down your body in a big wave and pouring out your crotch. Allow your sound to get deep and guttural so it sounds really juicy and orgasmic—you can do this by keeping your mouth and throat expanded and your face dilated. Your inner pelvic muscles will open as your breath and sound drop—your entire bottom will be dilated wide and the energy will flood out. Let the wave undulate through your whole body. Give yourself permission to be orgasmic.

Repeat the rising, holding and falling pattern three more times. Check out what you're experiencing—the pleasure wave will probably build more with each repetition.

*Nothing has ever been achieved by the person who says, 'It can't be done.'*

ELEANOR ROOSEVELT

SUCCULENT SEX CRAFT

## Where Are the Hot Tips for Female Ejaculation?

WHAT ABOUT ORGASMS with ejaculation for women, you may be asking. My answer: Been there, gushed about that! For more information about

learning to have female ejaculatory orgasms, check out my first book, *Woman's Anatomy of Arousal: Secret Maps to Buried Pleasure*, or *Secrets of the Sex Masters* (edited by Carl Frankel), another Mango Garden Press book.

Shunga, *White Moon Flower Medicine*

### MEGA-ORGASMIC STATES

How long can you come? When you've achieved orgasmic mastery, you can come for many minutes . . . even hours. Like a surfer finding that perfectly balanced sweet spot on an endless wave, you can find your orgasmic sweet spot and let your ecstasy wave carry you for a long time.

These orgasmic states aren't just prolonged, they're also expanded. Your orgasmic realm becomes vast and even more blissful.

*The most radical thing we can do in this world is be joyful.*

PATCH ADAMS

It's easiest to get to an ongoing orgasmic state when you've built up lots of erotic energy and have gone very deep into your sexual trance. To get into that deeply altered state usually requires prolonged warm-up with lots of roller-coastering up and down the arousal ladder along with plenty of relaxed excitation. With this prelude, when you start coming, you can keep going. Think of it like pushing someone on a swing—once you really get them going, it just takes a little well-timed tap to keep them swinging. You can play with your orgasm the same way. Once you're in this space, when you start to come, you can use your sexcraft tools to keep 'pushing the swing.' One finger, so to speak, can be enough to do it!

The amount of direct genital stimulation you'll need to keep going (and coming) will depend on many things, including how you're wired sexually and your emotional and energetic state. You may need lots of direct stimulation, you may need it intermittently or you may need it not at all. Only you will know. If you're going solo, you can provide that exact stimulation. If a partner's doing the doing, it helps to have some simple signals for 'steady on,' 'more' and 'less.' You may just need them to play with your energy field, offer encouraging sounds and words ("Keep coming, don't stop"), or send their energy into you.

HOT TIPS: SOLO OR PARTNERED

## Expanding Your Orgasm

Use a variety of sexcraft skills to surf your orgasmic wave:

- HOLD THE INTENTION to keep coming.

- KEEP YOUR BREATH and sound moving.

- VISUALIZE THE ENERGY continuing to flow.

- USE INTENTION AND MOVEMENT to roll the energy down your body and out through your genitals.

- SPIRAL IT AROUND your pelvis and roll it out your bottom, or send it up your spine and out the top of your head.

- KEEP RUNNING orgasmic breathing patterns.

- ROCK your hips.

- PULSE your pelvic floor pump.

- LET THE ENERGY VIBRATE and ripple through your body.

- ALLOW IT to keep going.

- GIVE YOURSELF PERMISSION to stay in your rapture.

- SURRENDER to it and stay with it.

Shunga
*Woman Reading*

*Do not let what you cannot do
interfere with what you can do.*

JOHN WOODEN

## A Rousing Seven Chakra Orgasm Meditation

BEFORE BEGINNING, review the seven-chakra system (see page168–169).

You can do this practice standing, sitting or lying down. If you're standing, have your feet shoulder-width apart and your knees slightly bent or unlocked. If you sit, be in a position where your spine is straight and you can rock your pelvis. If you lie on your back, have your knees up and feet flat on the floor.

In the version of the practice I describe here, you're using hands-off arousal and orgasm techniques without direct genital stimulation. If you want to do a variation where you self-pleasure (or have a friend assist), that's fine, too.

START WITH SOME DEEP, SLOW BREATHS, using a loose mouth with an open throat. Tighten your PFMs with each inhale and release with your exhale. As you pull in with your muscles and your breath, imagine that you're drawing energy in. As you exhale and release your bottom muscles, envision that you are opening and releasing energy out.

Next, draw energy into your first chakra by breathing slowly and directly into the perineum. Breathe your root chakra full of hot light. Exhale and let the root chakra open. With each new round of breathing, expand the energy. Pump up your breath, getting faster and more intense. See the light get brighter, and feel the heat grow or the color intensify. Continue until the chakra feels full and charged.

Using the same basic pattern, charge your second chakra. Start with slow, deep breaths and work up to deep, rapid ones. As you do this, imagine your sex chakra filling with heat, light and pulsation. Keep going until that chakra also feels charged up.

Do each chakra in turn, taking enough time with each to get it pumped up and fully activated.

Now do some *Crescendo Breaths*. Ride the wave of expansion, imagining your orgasmic energy surging through all your chakras. Pull the energy up from your root to your crown, then surf the wave back down to your root and out your whole bottom.

Finish by leaving the whole channel open and charged, or by moving the energy to one specific area that you wish to vitalize.

🍒 *Visit the GetSexCrafty.com webpages for more practices such as:*

* *Fire Breath Orgasm Meditation.*
* *Feast of the Senses Ritual for Partners*
* *The Solo Sensual Self-Pleasure Ritual.*

# Succulent Summary

## New Narratives

### Your Sexuality is:

A BEAUTIFUL, SACRED part of you that is all the more compelling because it connects you to yourself, others and everything.

THE FLAME THAT FUELS your existence. When you feel connected to your erotic power, you can tap more easily into your vital force.

A GIFT—and your pleasure is your birthright.

### Sex and Pleasure

SEX INCLUDES the whole range of consensual erotic activities.

A HEALTHY RELATIONSHIP to pleasure is a valuable and trustworthy guide, not our enemy tempting us to sin. When we're in balance with our relationship to pleasure, it's a reliable voice illuminating wise, self-loving, empowering life choices.

PLEASURE IS AN EVOLUTIONARY strategy for surviving and thriving. You need only to think of a newborn, ecstatic at their mother's breast. We desire to connect, to be nourished, to be loved, safe and warm—and that is all good.

PLEASURE IS A HEALTHY positive force. Erotic pleasure is healing and health-enhancing.

### Erotic Skills

YOU CAN DEVELOP your erotic skills like a musician develops theirs, becoming more and more adept and over time attaining mastery of your sexual abilities and erotic energy.

YOUR SEXUALITY DEVELOPS, grows and matures throughout your life.

YOU ARE ON A LIFELONG journey that's an ongoing process of discovery and learning.

YOU CAN LEARN TO NAVIGATE the powerful currents of erotic desire with skill and finesse.

### Connection

BEING IN CONNECTION with your sexual power enables you to achieve a loving relationship with yourself and others. At its best, your sexuality can be a profound and deeply meaningful part of a healthy, happy life that empowers you to live with more energy, clarity, confidence and consciousness.

A HEALTHY RELATIONSHIP with our own sexuality frees us to have nourishing erotic relationships with others that are responsible, respectful, honorable and caring. Our own self-loving provides the foundation for satisfying, joyful, healthy and pleasurable connections.

## Juicy Blessings

This book hasn't only been about using your sexcraft tools to achieve sexual mastery. It's also about the ultimate practice of integrating your sexuality and sex life with your entire life. It's about becoming a whole—and wholly integrated—person.

Anonymous, *Untold Stories in Japanese Mythology*

"Tell me, what is it you plan to do with your one wild and precious life?," the poet Mary Oliver asks. Here's my answer to this wonderful question. Begin with your primary relationship—the one you have with yourself and connect to your pleasure and your power. A new story is emerging that celebrates your right to pursue erotic fulfillment and be authentic and responsible sexual beings. This new understanding can catalyze powerful changes that go far beyond the bedroom to how we see ourselves and the choices we make about how we live our lives.

> *In the depth of winter,*
> *I finally learned that*
> *within me there lay an*
> *invincible summer.*
>
> ALBERT CAMUS

I've given you a variety of maps you can use to navigate your personal journey through the land of Eros. The next steps are up to you. A map does you no good if you don't go out and use it.

I hope you'll let these maps guide you in your explorations. Ideally, you've come out of this book feeling inspired to develop your sexcraft skills, discover your inner connections, integrate the power of pleasure into your life and have empowering sexual adventures (definitely by yourself and optionally with others).

Based on my decades of teaching this material, I'm confident that your new skills will enable you to experience radical, dramatic, positive changes in your sexuality, body image, self-esteem and relationships. If you haven't already, I want you to discover how magnificent, transcendent, hot, and just plain fun sex can be. My hope is that you'll be a life-long explorer of your erotic potential.

Pleasure is your birthright. I trust this book will help you claim it!

We've come to the end of our journey into the wonders of sexcraft.

It's not really the end, though.

*It's the beginning.*

# VISIT GetSexCrafty.com

WE'VE CREATED SPECIAL WEBPAGES JUST FOR YOU, THE READERS of this book. It's easy to join and costs nothing.

At GetSexCrafty.com, you'll have access to material we couldn't find space for in this book. We'll also be expanding the content regularly. It's all part of our plan to create an ongoing Wholistic Sexuality learning community. We hope you'll avail yourself of all this additional information and participate!

Come to GetSexCrafty.com:

- For more information, resources, practices and exercises.
- For a bibliography and suggested reading list.
- For a list of our Kickstarter supporters and more contributing artist info.
- To post your responses to the exercises that invited your input.

PLANNED:

- Community web pages where you can share with other SexCrafters.
- Video segments and more!

# CONTRIBUTING ARTISTS

WE ARE VERY GRATEFUL TO THE FOLLOWING ARTISTS who generously shared their work to help illuminate this book. Thank you! Please go visit their websites and check out more of their work. Gratitude as well to everyone who sent in their work for consideration.

ABIGAIL EKUE, www.photos.abigailekue.com

ANNA DI SCALA, www.annadiscala.vpweb.co.uk

BIJOU XOCHI, www.bijouxochi.com

CYNTHIA WILSON, cinza@aol.com

DOUG A. METZGER, www.dam-photography.com

GIRL CRIMSON, www.girlcrimson.com

GRACE GELDER, www.gracegelder.co.uk

JESSICA PRENTICE, www.jprenticeart.com

KATHLEEN MANDEVILLE, www.ignivox.net

KSENIYA VLASOVA, www.ptika.com

RAVIN BARATHEON

SAMUEL CLAIBORNE, www.samuelclaiborne.com

SARAH NICHOLSON, www.sarahsphotographs.com

SUSAN SINGER, www.susansinger.com

VINETTE PEREZ, vperez10128@gmail.com

# ACKNOWLEDGMENTS

I WANT TO THANK ALL MY MANY SUPPORTERS WHO HAVE PATIENTLY sustained me through the elephantine pregnancy that ultimately resulted in the birth of this book.

To start, let me thank my Beloved, Carl Frankel—my life, business and writing partner, sweetie, co-conspirator and creative playmate. Without your editing wisdom, this book would not be what it is. In fact, your contributions were so significant that I felt you deserved to be credited, so I'm publicly acknowledging your wonderful and wise input by having 'with Carl Frankel' on the cover. I love to share living and learning with you.

Tilman Reitzle, book formatting genius, deity of patience and perfection—thank you for sharing my vision of this book and making it into reality!

For the Intimate Arts team: Bryan, Fatima, YS, Ryan, Val, Zac: You are the wind under my office wings, the supporters of spreadsheets, doers of details, the packers of endless workshop gear … you are the folks who make things happen so I don't have to. You all ROCK! I am so grateful for your support and lucky to have you on the team!

Huge thanks to all of the artists that shared their work. You have made this book immeasurably better.

To be comprehensive in my expressions of gratitude, I'd need to go back to my earliest teachers about sexuality. Thank you to the women whose births I attended, and to birth itself—you were a powerful and profound teacher of what sexuality really is and how one can develop skills to manage and celebrate life energy, whether it's laboring, birthing, getting turned-on or having orgasms. I have also learned from my thousands of students, clients and patients over my many decades of practice and teaching.

I have been privileged to study with a multitude of wise teachers whose insight, genius, knowledge and wisdom have been enlightening and inspiring. I can only teach about sexuality the way I do because I had you all to learn from. Thank you, one and all.

I am indebted to my 219 Kickstarter backers for offering me not just financial support but the power of your belief in me and my work and the desire to help get it out there into the world. Adrienne, Alexandra Tait, Alida Engel, Amanda & John Giles, Amanda Painter, Amy, Amy Goldin, Amy McAllister,

Ann Garvin, Annette Hunner, Arnim, Becky M, Belkis Rodriguez, Bill Softky, Bruna & Andrew, Bucklawrence, Carolyn, Cary Kittner, Catherine, charlie and abby, Chelsea S., Christine VanCoughnett, Clare Stevenson, Claudia, Cynthia Entringer, Daniel Winterhalter, Dara Frohman, Dave Brower, David Karlson-Weimann, Deb Grace, Deirdre, Diana, Donna Lomp, Duck Dodgers, Elizabeth, Ellen All, Eric Wagoner, Fred, Heidi, henry glenn, J. Patrick Walker, Jacki, Jeff Bogusz, Jennifer and Sebastian Posada, Joan Shanley, Jodiah, Joe Potato, Joella Autorino, Joyce Shotwell, Judith Eldredge, Jussi, Kabuki O'Neil, Kaitlin Strong, Kathryn, Ken, Kerstin, Klara Tyman, Ky, Laura Covello, Lily, Lily Hockley, Lorna Gale, Mantz and Mitchell Radio Show, Mare Simone, Mary C Campbell, Mary Cameron, Matlin Zeitler, matthew gorman, Melinda F. Brown, Michele & Sean Andersen, Michelle Huber, Mimi Gelb, Nancy Garnhart, Nekole Shapiro, Noel, Oceana LeBlanc, Oliver Peltier, Paul Nosko, Paula, Peggy Starnes, Peter, Peter, Randie Cartman, Rhea K., Richard, Roberta Lemes, Robyn Vogel, Ron Barker, Ruth Barron and Jeff Ommundsen, Ruth Pine, Sabannah, Sam, Samara, Sarah H., Sayaka Adachi, SG Pipes, Sheila Kamara Hay, Tanya Bezreh, Tara Dawn, Tatiana Pechenik, Tek, Teresa Vaughan, Ward McCary, Warren, Yolanda Capel and all my other backers who wished to remain anonymous. Thank you, Kickstarters!

Thank you, Cory for choosing me as your mom. I've grown more from being your mom than I could have ever imagined, including how to love better. I will love you forever and for always.

All kinds of gratitude to my family, which views me and my work as wonderful (and not at all weird or embarrassing). Lucky me!

And, of course, big juicy thanks to my friends, sweeties, honeys, compadres, dance buddies, sisters, creative instigators, visionaries, silly sausages, co-creators and allies. You fill up my life with frolic, fun, meaning, sharing, support and connection!

*If you ask me why I came to this Earth,*
*I will tell you: I came to live out loud.*

EMILE ZOLA

# INDEX

# Check out these other great titles from Mango Garden Press!

*Books about Sexuality, Relationships and the Intimate Arts*

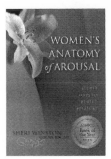

## Women's Anatomy of Arousal
### *Secret Maps to Buried Pleasure*

### Sheri Winston CNM RN LMT

2010 Book of the Year
American Association of Sex Educators, Counselors & Therapists

A guide to female anatomy and sexuality—a roadmap to amazing sexual pleasure.
For women and the men who love to love them.

*"The most comprehensive, user-friendly, practical and uplifting book on women's sexuality I've ever read. It's the gold standard!"*
— Dr. Christiane Northrup

## Secrets of the Sex Masters
### Edited by Carl Frankel

Sixteen of the world's greatest sex teachers share their specialized knowledge to enable you to have the same incredible sex they do. Topics include Tantra, non-ejaculatory orgasm for men, expanded orgasm for women, female ejaculation and much more.

## Love and the More Perfect Union
### *Six Keys to Relationship Bliss*

### Carl Frankel

A short, immensely useful guide to navigating your intimate relationship.

*"Eloquently describes the universal sticking points for all couples and charts a course of action for creating domestic tranquility with 'day trips' to paradise. Creatively combines established principles of relationship happiness with an original and useful map."*
— Dr. Jamie Turndorff

## MangoGardenPress.com

Mango Garden Press is the publishing arm of The Center for the Intimate Arts.
Discover *empowering erotic education* at IntimateArtsCenter.com.

Made in the USA
Lexington, KY
15 September 2014